MEDICINE IN ART

A Cultural History

CONTENTS

Preface
> by Louis Pasteur Vallery-Radot,
> the Acadèmie Française

Introduction
> by A. V. J. Martin

Introduction to the American Edition
> by Albert C. Santy, M.D.

From Prehistory to the End of the Fifteenth Century
> by Hans Schadewaldt, Professor of the
> History of Medicine, University of Dusseldorf

From the Renaissance to Our Times
> by Leon Binet, Member of the Academy of
> Medicine, Paris, and Charles Maillant, former
> Head of Clinic of the School of Medicine, Paris

The Far East and the Middle East
> by Ilza Veith, Professor of the History
> of Medicine, University of California

MEDICINE IN ART

A Cultural History

Jean Rousselot, General Editor

McGRAW - HILL BOOK COMPANY
New York · Toronto · London · Sydney

Library of Congress Catalog Card Number: 66-24885
54103

Printed in Italy

Preface

"Medicine in art"... But what does the word Art mean?

Art is originally the depiction of Beauty.

For those of Greek and Latin culture, this depiction was identical with that of the gods, the demi-gods, and the heroes of Mount Olympus, or else the God of the Trinity, the Virgin Mother, and the saints of the Christian heaven. Olympus, heaven... This is where the artists sought beauty. They never even dreamt that it might be found anywhere else.

Of course, certain "abnormal" ones occasionally hazarded a step into the profane world, but they were exceptions: art always returned to an ideal, that is to say, divine notion of Beauty, and thereby to a spiritual conception of the function of art.

For a long time, art was limited to the celestial: the viewer gave free rein to his dreams before a bas-relief of Aphrodite or a Botticelli Virgin.

Gradually, however, there developed the idea that everything involving life, sickness, death can enter the domain of art by way of intelligence and sensitivity; that there is beauty in everything that exists, provided we look at it with new eyes; that our here-and-now can be just as "ideal," if the the artist approaches it with a felicitous arrangement of forms, a harmony of colors, the projection of a poetic play of light.

At last, men understood that one can seek Beauty not only on Mount Olympus or in the Christian heaven; that Beauty exists in everyday life, in the street, in the movements of crowds, in the objects that make up the framework of our life and in the faces of the beings who surround us.

Sick people, degenerates, lunatics, even corpses—and more generally, all aspects of medicine and surgery—can become "objects of beauty." Rembrandt's *Anatomy Lesson,* Velásquez's *Las Meninas,* Gérard Dou's *Dropsical Woman,* Teniers' *Village Doctor,* Brueghel's *Parable of the Blind,* Goya's *Insane Asylum,* David's *Pain* are among the most beautiful works of art.

An old dictionary contends that art is a talent for, a skill in, doing some sort of work, and obtaining some sort of "result."

But this definition applies more to artisanry than art.

Art is something else.

Art is not a mere depiction of the world. Art presupposes a transposition, which in turn can be achieved by an extremely sensitive "stage director," an artist capable of showing us things and living beings in a new light. In this sense a raw, unformed vision of nature is perhaps not art.

On the other hand, Boudin, Renoir, Monet transformed our vision of the world. We no longer see skies, ponds, interiors, female bodies as we used to, because these painters modified forms, colors, and light.

And what about medicine? In the chapter on the sixteenth century the reader will arrive at a better understanding of how dependent the evolution of the concept of Beauty is on the art of Aesculapius, which in the course of its own development increased our knowledge of man and his relationship to nature.

In that period, not only did Europe set out, intoxicated and enthusiastic, to discover the earth; Leonardo da Vinci, a prodigious genius capable of analyzing and understanding anything, a scientist, anatomist, and inspired painter, explored the human body to fathom organic mysteries and spiritual secrets.

A volume such as this one would have to be abundantly illustrated. And so it is. It contains a literary and pictorial wealth, which for the first time helps us measure the considerable contribution made by medicine to art throughout the ages.

LOUIS PASTEUR VALLERY-RADOT
of the Académie Française

Introduction

No matter how far back we go in the history of human-ity, there is abundant proof of man's constant desire to improve his lot, which Pascal called that of a "disposses-sed king." In the course of long, dark centuries, man gradually developed the idea of his dignity and his pre-eminence over the other species, an idea which gave rise to his ambition of taking fullest advantage of all his means and faculties to dominate the world and use it to his own profit.

Man's greatest and most decisive advance was his in-crease of knowledge about himself, which permitted his powerful intellect to utilize the full extent of physical resources.

And thus, from the dawn of time, medicine has been of essential significance in all its forms and, together with the growing awareness and development of humanity, has been evolving constantly towards adapting itself to social concepts and objectives, which are unremittingly trans-formed according to the acquired results.

Medicine is man's prime and most powerful encroach-ment upon his vulnerable but perfectible condition, and art is his prime and most powerful means of expressing this very condition, that is, defining the relationship to adversity, which he intends to yield to or struggle against, resorting either to exorcism or revolt.

Inevitably, an extremely close and fruitful rapport was established at the very beginning between medicine and art. Both primitive medicine and the very first works of art, namely the ritual depictions in pre-historic caves, were products of magic. Now, after hundreds of centuries, can we be so sure that this relationship has undergone much of a change?

In point of fact, it remains the same, even if it has

become far more complex and subtle—after all, we have evolved, and so have art and medicine. But if we make a comparative study of Freudianism and certain psychological paintings, either Surrealist or non-figurative, symbolist or anecdotal, it becomes obvious that the links between art and medicine, far from slackening, have grown even stronger.

Observation, diagnosis, treatment: these three phases of medicine correspond to three phases of the artistic process. Greek statues, the cripples of medieval sculpture, the anatomy lessons of the seventeenth century, Hogarth's caricatural dissection of the eighteenth century, the operating rooms that inspired so many American and European painters in the nineteenth century—one could maintain that a good part of this artistic production, of which the principal subject is man, touches on medicine of the mind and the body.

First of all, observation. Can we not say that in front of a human being in good or bad health, the artist and the physician both work "on the motif"? The field spreading out before them is equally immense for both of them.

The diagnosis that ensues from the observations is no less important for the artist than for the doctor. Thus a work of art, whether it depicts a patient alone or in the presence of a physician (thereby approaching a picture of customs and manners) can take on the character of a diagnosis. Sickness and suffering are the potent acids that penetrate the human heart and lay bare its most secret corners. On the level of ontological knowledge, this makes for the enormous value of such works of art which would never have come into being had the subject matter not been furnished by some illness and the practice of the art of medicine.

The diagnosing physician was a particularly good subject for artistic depiction of great expressive intensity; and the artist, for his part, following the doctor to the bedside of the patient, found a whole repertoire of details which, with the historical and social context, establish the correlations that are indispensable for the understanding of any work. With the treatment, the third phase of the medical act, we come to therapy and the world of hospitals.

It is a strange, disconcerting, almost closed world, which has its own rites, traditions, and atmosphere. Though neither society nor heaven are forgotten, one seems to see them in a distorting mirror. Society, in these alternately pathetic, grotesque, and chimerical surroundings, often resembles its own caricature. But what is a caricature if not a hyper-lucid depiction of the truth?

To these briefly sketched correspondences between art and medicine, we can add many others, beginning with the psychologists who find in spontaneous or supervised artistic activity of the mentally ill a supplementary field of clinical observation, nay, a new means of therapy. The present foreword must limit itself to this brief allusion.

The domain of the relationship between art and medicine is indeed vast. Thus, such connections, which go back to the origin of the species and can be found in the farthest depths of the human personality, are so numerous and complex that it might seems foolhardy to undertake a thorough analysis, or even a simple enumeration. Yet this is the task the authors of this work have set for themselves, and we must offer them our heartfelt congratulations for having been successful in their hazardous undertaking.

A. V. J. Martin

8

Introduction
to the
American Edition

The Country Doctor
After a drawing by A. R. Waud, 1869

Medicine as a subject in American art appears relatively late; it wasn't until about 1800 that we began to see what could be called "medical" scenes. One of the very earliest examples was a colored etching by William Birch (1755-1834), a miniaturist and engraver. In his twenty-eight plate series *Philadelphia Views* (1800), the one called *Philadelphia Hospital in Pine Street, Philadelphia* shows the exterior of the building (considered to be the oldest independent hospital in America) very much as it is today and a sick man being carried in a chair.

Very little more medical art appeared until about 1850, when Army Captain Seth Eastman (1808-1875) became interested in the North American Indian during his service on the frontier. While at Fort Snelling, he made many sketches of Indian life which were used to illustrate his wife's books about the frontier. He was a most accurate observer, and *Medicine Man Curing a Patient*, his best work, is a detailed lithograph showing the Indians' approach to disease.

It was also in the 1850's, when the lithograph and the steel engraving came into popularity, that the illustrated magazine developed. *Harper's Weekly* (1850), *Putnam's* (1853), *Atlantic Monthly* (1856), and *The Century* (1870) were the best known. Many of the men whose works appeared in these magazines later became famous artists, and many of their pictures were of medical interest. A. R. Waud's *Country Doctor* reproduces the spirit of frontier life as it existed in many parts of America at that time and the difficult conditions under which those early doctors practiced. The doctor pictured on horseback was later replaced by the doctor in a buggy and even later by the doctor in a " flivver." Winslow Homer (1836-1900), one of the most famous innovators of the closing

9

WINSLOW HOMER
Playing Old Soldier

decade of the nineteenth century, first appeared in these magazines. His Civil War engraving *Surgeon at Work During an Engagement* came out in *Harper's Weekly*. His *Surgeon's Story* and his *Playing Old Soldier* portrayed the organization and practices of the Army Medical Corps during the Civil War, and they can be compared to practices in modern warfare. In 1874 Homer did a watercolor called *Sick Children*.

Perhaps the most famous of nineteenth-century American artists was Thomas Eakins (1844-1916). A student of Gérôme, from whom he learned his taut, disciplined naturalism, he was an ardent disciple of Rembrandt, from whom he learned the value of luminosity and monumental simplicity. Eakins studied anatomy at the Jefferson Medical College, and his scientific interest ultimately

resulted in the *Gross Clinic* of 1875, which represented the outstanding surgeon of the day lecturing to a class during an operation. It might be said that *Gross Clinic* is in the direct line of Calcar, Vesalius, DeGheym's *Anatomy Lesson* (1616), and Rembrandt's *Anatomy Lesson of Dr. Tulp* (1632). The similarity between Rembrandt's and Eakins' paintings indicates the relationship. Although *Gross Clinic* is perhaps Eakins' greatest medical painting and one of the greatest in all of American art, his *Agnew Clinic* (1889) is also important, even if it is not as powerful nor as ambitious as the earlier painting.

In the twentieth century, medical subjects as such were often subordinated to the portrayal of social problems. Artists developed great interest in showing the conditions surrounding the poor which affected their health and nutrition. The pathbreaking group called " The Eight " veered away from all earlier directions followed by American artists and wished to depict life that was specifically American, to be American painters rather than painters in America. From "The Eight," the *Anatomy Lesson* by John Sloan (1871-1951) is the only painting representative of any direct medical interest. It shows a lecture by Thomas Anshutz, the painter who succeeded Eakins at the Pennsylvania Academy.

George Bellows (1882-1925), who comes from the same tradition, liked the strong, hearty, pungent flavors of life, the prizefights, the religious revivals, the swarming streets of New York, and the drama of the great rivers around Manhattan. His lithographs were some of the best in that art: *The Drunk* (1924) showed the dissolute life, *Business Men's Class* stressed physical fitness, and *Dempsey and Firpo* showed the male body, anatomically, at the peak of fitness. In 1917 he did a lithograph stemming from a similar work by Goya, *Dance in a Mad House* (also done in oil, see p. 266), in which his approach is essentially romantic, its emphasis being on the melodrama, the picturesqueness of the scene, and not necessarily on the character of mental derangement as such.

A second wave of interest in scenes from everyday life and the problems of the poor occurred during the 1930's as part of the American reaction to the effects of the Depression. Social content played an enormously important role in all phases of American art, and during the late thirties and early forties it became identified with social protest. In the Depression many young artists had begun to crusade with pictures of the American dispossessed, the unwanted and exploited. Artists such as the Soyer brothers, Jack Levine, George Biddle, and many others have given us pictorially interesting and often quite moving portrayals in this genre. Ben Shahn, with an idealism controlled by a sense of irony, painted many fine pieces, among them *Death of a Miner* (1949), which poignantly shows the sufferings of the miners and their families during the Depression. Jack Levine (1915-), a painter of great force, whose satire is the major element in all his paintings, ostensibly has depicted little more than an interesting facet of charlatanistic medicine in his *Medicine Show*. Yet, this is more than merely the representation of a traveling faker — the purveyor of snake oil and elaborate nostrums concocted for the ignorant — it is a protest against the practice of modern pharmaceutical fakery and questionable medical practice. In a period which offered abundant opportunity for satire, painters like Levine and Joseph Hirsch took it upon themselves to comment on every aspect of American life. Even more directly than "The Eight," the painters of the Depression showed great concern with the social implications of twentieth-century life.

Medical art in the United States received a considerable boost during the Depression years through the activities of the Federal Art Project, which encouraged the placement of mural paintings in hospitals, schools, libraries, and other public buildings. Necessarily those paintings done for hospital exhibition dealt with medical subjects, as evidenced by William C. Palmer's *Controlled Medicine*, which shows the practice of preventive medicine. We see a doctor with his stethoscope, interns, oxygen tanks, sterilizers, operating room lights, X-Ray machines and leaded aprons to protect the technicians from the lethal rays, and a child being vaccinated. This is indeed a far cry from the orderly and precise *Gross Clinic* of Eakins! Palmer had worked on many WPA projects, and from the ideas gained he painted *Functions of a Hospital* (1936) and fourteen panels depicting the development of medicine. His father was a physician, and his paintings show the effect of his descent from an ancestry of clergymen and men of medicine.

During World War II, the government itself became a great patron of the arts, and many artists were sent to the various fronts to record the works and the days of the American serviceman at war. Many pictures necessarily dealt with the wounded and the activities of the branches of the Medical Corps in treating their wounds. Important artists were often assigned to these duties, and a number of very significant documents have come from that period, notably Joseph Hirsch's series.

This quick sampling of medical subject matter in American art is necessarily little more than a shadow of what is to be found in the following pages in other areas and from earlier days. For by the time American wilderness was settled comfortably enough to permit a turn to the pleasures of art, Western civilization and

JACK LEVINE
Medicine Show

THE METROPOLITAN MUSEUM OF ART, NEW YORK
Gift of Hugo Dastor, 1956

science had already removed much of the "magic", miracle, and mystery from the treatment of human ills. Hence, the sophisticated American artist was less often drawn to medical subjects than his early European ancestor, whose innocence, superstition, and lack of knowledge led to a richness and variety of approach which we see so amply illustrated in the rest of this book.

ALBERT C. SANTY

11

HANS SCHADEWALDT

FROM PREHISTORY TO THE END OF THE FIFTEENTH CENTURY

Prehistory

The great German thinker Friedrich Wilhelm Schelling (1775-1854), whose natural philosophy marked the high point of the Romantic period and whose philosophy consciously or unconsciously influenced the famous French paleontologist and Jesuit Pierre Teilhard de Chardin (1881-1955) in arriving at his much-debated new and complex world view, was convinced that there are two ways of attaining an understanding of the world: "One of these wonderful languages is spoken only by God.

The Venus of Laussel

With her wide hips, her voluminous bosom, the cornucopia in her hands, this Venus is a symbol of fertility.

MUSÉE PRÉHISTORIQUE DES EYZIES, DORDOGNE, FRANCE

The other is spoken only by a chosen few among human beings, whom God has made His favorites. I mean nature and art."

In fact, it is mainly these two means of communication that permit us to fathom the intellectual world of prehistoric man. Discoveries of fossils and tools—so-called "direct remains" of artistic representations—which appear long before the invention of any kind of writing and which were for the most part an expression of differing religious concepts, make it possible for the anthropologist, ethnologist, and paleontologist as well as the medical historian to transmit a rather vivid picture of those early epochs of mankind.

For, in the words of Gerhard Hauptmann (1862-1946), "The oldest holy language of mankind is art." The legendary "Magus from the north," Johann Georg Hamann (1730-1788), clearly perceived that instinct and intuition stood at the beginning of mankind's journey when he wrote the aphorism: "The heart beats earlier than the head thinks." Prehistoric man, however, who developed

13

The Venus of Sireuil

The emphatic arch of the hips, the protuberant abdomen, the massive fusion of the buttocks and the enormous thighs are elements of relative grace.

DORDOGNE

from the anthropoids of the Tertiary Age, from the Hominids of the Pliocene, from the Australopithecus Africanus, Pithecanthropus, and Sinanthropus to Homo Heidelbergensis between one million and 150,000 B.C., was certainly a "Homo empiricus" in his first phase of consciousness. The discovery of fossils makes it clear that early medicine may have grown from instinctive cures and the dressing of wounds with medicinal leaves, the licking of injuries and infections and the covering of them with impermeable substances similar to those encountered in Jesus' miracle cures in the New Testament. The setting of fractures and dislocations was practiced as a nursing measure, without being simultaneously connected with magico-religious or even etiological concepts. The accidental success of these methods and cures proclaimed them above and beyond self-help; and as specific individuals took over these practices, the profession of "medical helpers" arose. In contrast to the Utopian concepts of Jean-Jacques Rousseau (1712-1778) concerning the prehistoric Eden enjoyed by natural man, one is now convinced that his life expectancy was excessively short and his existence constantly menaced by sickness and injury. Not only the arthritic symptoms of "cave gout," or the discovery of very different micro-organisms in remains of prehistoric times, but also osteomyelitic deformations and pseudoarthrosis bear witness to this fact. Prehistoric man was not yet capable of giving artistic expression to these difficulties in his life although he had learned to form working tools from unwieldy stones.

With the appearance of Neanderthal Man, a new era begins in the history of mankind—an era that can be located in the period between 150,000 and 50,000 B.C. and that can be distinguished from that of the much wider differentiated Cro-Magnon Man of 30,000 to 10,000 B.C. The intellectual conquest and penetration of the world now begins; now the first artistic objects of mankind appear and the medical historian no longer has to rely solely on the meager direct sources of fossil and tool finds which can only illuminate the pragmatic-empirical level. On the basis of these so-called "secondary sources," he can imagine an infinitely more subtle picture of prehistoric man's conflict between body and mind, between health and sickness. From then on art is faithful mentor to the medical historian who must steadily draw on it in order to gain a completely valid picture of the doctor and patient as well as the concepts of disease in a given period. Often art is the only means of answering questions about which the literary or special disciplines often remain silent.

With the consolidation of smaller and larger groupings, prehistoric man enters into the stage of the "primitive races." For the Greeks these were all "barbarians"—a term

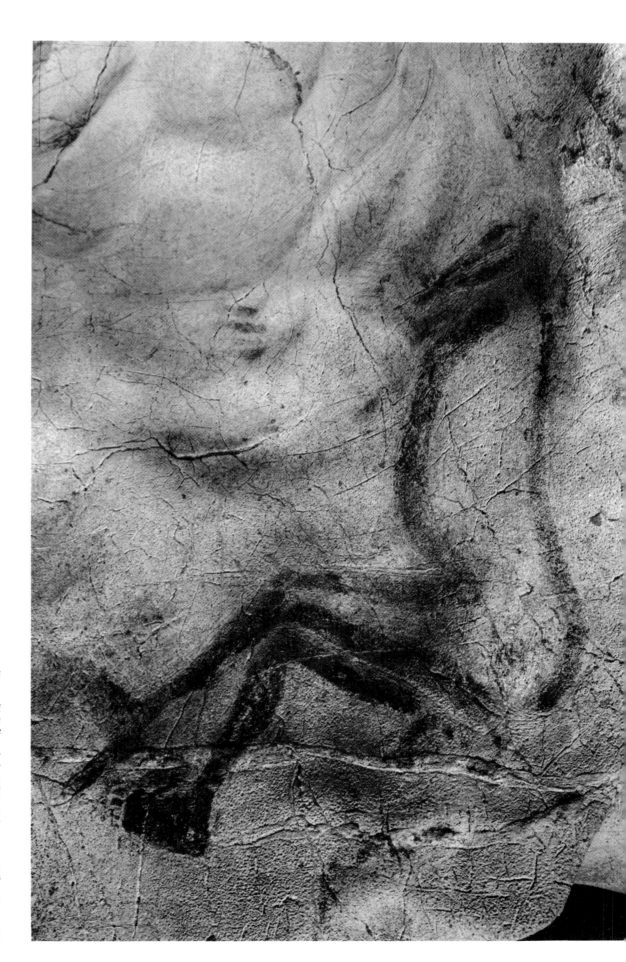

The Sorcerer of the Grotto of Trois Frères

This is the first extant depiction of a witch doctor. Dating from the Magdalenian period, it is some fifteen thousand years old. To obtain this photograph, it was necessary to organize a veritable speleo-photographic expedition, because the drawing is five yards above the corbelling of a chimney forming the roof of a grotto—the so-called Grotto of Trois Frères—difficult to approach.

The drawing shows a man wearing a deer mask and a bushy tail. This picture is a precise characterization of the sorcerer who is both doctor and priest, as in many primitive societies, notably in Africa.

MONTESQUIEU-AVANTÉS-ARIÈGE, FRANCE

including all people not familiar with the Greek tongue. The connection between culture and one's own language was so strict in antiquity that the idea of relativity was foreign to the Greeks. The Humanists were the first to designate as *indigena* (natives, savages) all those who were, by and large, dependent on nature, who showed only little of merely local political organization, and who were almost totally unfamiliar with writing or the sense of history, and in most cases enslaved to concepts of magic and demonology. This passage from empiricism and pragmatism to demonology was in fact a decisive step toward the self-knowledge of mankind. It is here that reflective thinking and an attempt to establish Homo sapiens in the cosmos began. Concepts similar to those held by prehistoric man may have been held by the primitive races of later times, so that it seems legitimate to deduce by analogy—on the basis of the behavior of primitive tribes still in existence today—the intellectual-cultural situation of prehistoric times As early as the end of the last century, the former naval doctor and subsequent founder of the Berlin Museum of Natural History, Adolph Bastian (1826-1905), had in this connection formulated the thesis of "elemental thought." According to this thesis it is assumed that all nations in the world demonstrate comparable developmental stages based on cultural and psychological factors reflecting universally human motives. The German medical historian Paul Diepgen (1878-1966) also carried this theory over into medical history. We ourselves believe that this is, in fact, a possible explanation for the extraordinarily similar, in some cases even analogous, notions of health, sickness, and medical treatment to be found among the most different primitive races which certainly could not have come into contact with one another. An example would be the anatomical concepts of ideal feminine beauty. It is interesting to note that the oldest preserved portrayals of the female human form are idols of a peculiarly adipose nature, in which the secondary sexual characteristics are exaggerated. The artist placed great value on the molding of breasts, pelvis, belly, and thighs but, by and large, neglected the face. The famous so-called "Venus of Willendorf," unearthed in 1908 in a tiny lower Austrian village and presently housed in the Vienna Museum of Natural History, exhibits such an exaggeration of the feminine sexual attributes. An individualistic face, however, is not to be seen; the forehead and the back of the head are hidden by an abundant, neatly waved hairdo. The "Venus of Laussel," excavated in the same year as the one from Willendorf, is represented in a similar fashion. She belongs to the same period as the Aurignacian Man, but is, in terms of locale, far removed from the other sculpture which originated in the Dordogne. Here too the same exaggeration of the breasts, the

The Venus of Willendorf

Primitive man does not aim at beauty but at the symbol. Thus, with the exaggeration of her female attributes, this Venus expresses prehistoric man's very precise conception of the distaff role: to give birth, feed, and perpetuate the species.

MUSEUM OF NATURAL HISTORY, VIENNA

16

broad hips, and the overflowing thighs are prominent features of this female form, holding a bison horn in her right hand and shaped from a *relief en face;* so is the anonymity of the largely disfigured face beneath the undulating hairdo. The famous cliff and cave drawings of the Franco-Cantabrian area, placed at 15,000 to 5,000 B.C. or by some dated even further back than 40,000 B.C., show—in contrast to the narrow-hipped shepherds and hunters who wear an odd loincloth like that worn until recently by the naked tribes of Central Africa—voluminous females with expansive buttocks. This is a typical steatopygy, visible also on the Egyptian fresco at Deir-el-Bahari which pictures the queen of Punt forced to pay tribute to the Egyptian pharaohs and hints at certain dietary rites, i.e., the daily intake of many liters of camel's milk, as is still the custom in Mauretania. This early ideal of beauty is likewise found in the post-Christian Arab culture. Moreover, the exaggeration of the sexual organs is a perfect symbol of fecundity and is still manifest in many African fetishes. In this phase individuality yielded completely to typing by sex.

In this second magico-demonological phase of human development, other personalities come to the fore. The magician and medicine man now distinguishes himself from the group and he becomes the object of special attention and respect. Originally disease was understood as a "substance" which penetrated the body from the outside, e.g., an impacted thorn or an enemy arrow, but also worms and other parasites that had to be removed from the body. Later every sickness was viewed as following an ontogenetic law and every disease deduced as coming from a foreign body that penetrated the organism from the outside. Thus the first medical theory was founded—the "foreign body theory." Since every cause of sickness could not be determined, one believed in invisibly introduced, almost independent pathogenic impulses which lodged in the sick body. "Animism" was born. Closely connected with the development of this new theory was the concept of the soul. For if the seat of life had long been assumed to reside, for example, in the mammoth's heart, as in the famous drawing from the mountain cave of Pindal in Asturias, it was only after man had begun to reflect upon himself that he could arrive at the concept of "homo" as a dualistic being with a body and soul. On the other hand, thought of man's spiritual environment only occurred in the sense of Lucien Levy-Bruhl's (1857-1939) *participation mystique.* Wish fulfillment, ego, and the reality of the environment were not differentiated. Everything was tangible, including carriers of disease, which were given the proportions of demons, or else were dispatched by them. To remove them or to keep them away from the human body could only be achieved by persons possessing equal or stronger magical powers. Just as the prehistoric

Sorcerer

Rock painting of Matalen-Amazar in Tassili.

ALGERIAN SAHARA

magicians sought with the aid of animal skins, antlers, etc., to exorcise the demons that were to be captured, attempting to change into demons themselves in order to share in the *participation mystique,* so the medicine men sought to achieve these special powers with the aid of fetishes and special gestures or curative songs. For this they often had to resemble externally the very demons they were fighting, or through conspicuous behavior, incantations, etc., attempt to draw the attention of these demons away from the sick or those in danger, and on to themselves. In one such scene the Stone Age artist portrayed the medicine man in what is perhaps the earliest representation of its kind in the history of the world. This is in the famous Trois Frères Grotto north of the Pyrenees, and is of the Magdalenian period about 15,000 B.C. The scene shows several magicians in their animal costumes dancing and blowing the flute and stealthily slinking along the walls. There is no doubt that such pictures possess more than merely narrative-historical value; in that remote era they were invested with a highly magical function. Ritual dances also took place before these paintings.

Art in this era thus stood in the direct service of medicine. But the other procedures which the medicine man used in the Stone Age, as well as those later used by almost all primitive races, bear a direct relationship to popular art. In the absence of any written accounts, we must continue to rely on such works of art in order to make deductions from them as to the prevailing medical practices. The most widespread methods of cure were, without doubt, those effected by fetishes, amulets, or talismans. The "fetish," a word originally derived from the Portuguese *feitiço* (the artificially manufactured), and ultimately from the Latin *facticius* (made by hand), was a powerful indigenous charm, existing most often in the shape of anthropomorphic or zoomorphic statuettes, whose effectiveness could, however, be controlled by the owner. As a perpetual reservoir of magical charms, the fetish could be used for imitative and contagious magic, i.e., through it the soul of the sickness-inducing demon was imitated or vicariously impregnated in the soul of a healthy person, to whom the respective illness was to be transferred. These were similar to the many African nail fetishes which were often accompanied by fragments of glass for warding off the evil eye and were supposed to be attached to the sensitive organ or body part so as to render the disease harmless. Hence such pins were never again allowed to be removed, and the fetishes themselves exhibited a great number of such needles.

Elsewhere fetishes exist which serve to venerate pathogenic spirits and are then mostly represented in animal shape. The physically unseizable demon is attainable through its idol by means of *participation mystique* and can then be pacified only by the medicine man.

Statuette of a king sitting on an animal symbolizing a throne.

This statuette depicting an ancestor was used for medical treatment. One orifice is specially included for the insertion of suppositories. Congo. Babembe.

Enema

Statuette of white wood. Cameroon, Douala. 19th century.

Representations of diseases or even of pregnancy, as pictured in statuettes from Oceania (sometimes quite realistically, with the placement of the fetus in the open abdominal wall of the mother), belong to the precursors of later figurines in this category. Some fetishes even have little openings similar to our little incense burners, in order to offer agreeable smoke to the demons.

In contrast to the fetish, the amulet (derived from the Latin *amoliri,* to push away) serves to ward off harm. It derives its power through a special incantation, a uniquely symbolic form, or else it is made of special material (precious jewels) or by special methods of production. Its usage spread far beyond the primitive races to the Islamic and Christian Middle Ages and has lasted to the present day.

The talisman is not actually a medical object but a general good-luck charm. Thus it is neither a therapeutic object nor a prophylactic, but rather a kind of mortgage, promising good luck on a trip as well as success in a business transaction. It corresponds in function to astrol-

ogy in the West and in the Orient. Often the medicine man also used an artistically fabricated mask. Ritual masks served most of all to frighten off demons, but also lent the magician a demonlike figure, enabling him to approach the demons unperceived. Occasionally they even indicated certain diseases, thereby pointing to the beginning of some degree of specialization.

Alongside the plastic arts, the medicine man also used music. The magical healing songs of the American Indians, for example, are addressed to the totem animal— the eagle who apparently can guard against sickness. Other rhythms are designed to exorcise departed souls from whom, according to many primitive races, a host of evil impulses can emanate. Still other melodies are meant to force the demon to give up his ill will and, through subsequent cathartic exercises, to dispel sicknesses caused by the violation of taboos. Finally the dance also serves to invoke good spirits who are to assist the medicine man in his battle against the sickness-causing demons. Today such healing dances as the "tarantella,"

Witchdoctor's mask
New Hebrides.

still used therapeutically in Apulia, Italy, as a cure against the allegedly dangerous tarantula bite, are quite familiar. The very name, "tarantella," derives from the nervous illness of *tarantism*.

A further practice, used by the primitive medicine man as well as in prehistoric times, was the mock operation. If one really believed that diseases resulted from the penetration of pathogenic substances into the organism, then their elimination had to be the main goal of therapy. If it was not possible to remove real objects such as arrowheads, etc., then the medicine man tried to extract an imaginary foreign body by means of draining, cauterizing, blood-letting, or an enema which he then "showed" to the patient in the real form of a small stone or wood particle. The legerdemain of these medicine men was considerable, but the credulity of their patients was also astonishing, although the current discussion of placebo therapy seems to express much sympathy for these practices. If a medicine man was not in the vicinity, then the tormented patient or his relatives had, of course, to rely on self-help. So it is no wonder that numerous prophylactic measures, from the house amulet all the way to preventive tattooing, found their way into popular medicine. Such a tattooed fetish, perched on a totem animal in the Congo with its odd headgear resembling a sun helmet, was ascribed by the natives as belonging to the Portuguese discoverers of the west coast of Africa, and must have been especially valuable.

A much more active therapy was widely practiced by laymen. Inducing enemas and vomiting belonged to the repertory of every household; and so we find many African representations—minute in their realism—showing people using enemas on themselves as well as on children, practices which have persisted into the twentieth century. Because of the absence of writing among the Central African peoples, popular art is an important indication of the medical practices which were in use there and which were personally observed in almost the same form by the explorers.

The various taboos are of course also to be viewed magically. (Taboo is derived from the Polynesian *tapu,* meaning "the marked, the unusual," and originally possessed a genuine protective function in regulating social and personal life.) Among cannibals the eating of fellow tribal members fell under a taboo. In almost all communities, as another proof of the elemental thought-process, menstruation was placed under a taboo. The realm of magical medicine also includes the strange custom of the "couvade," male childbirth, which doubtless serves to deflect the demons of puerperal fever. Among these people, during labor the married men lie down in special huts and wail and moan while the women giving birth produce

21

Fetish for amulet

When put into the abdominal cavity here, the amulet was supposed to cure belly-aches. Congo.

Symbolic depiction of the mother of a large family.

Kept in the home, this statuette was supposed to assure an abundance of offspring. Ivory Coast, area of Senoufo Tribe.

MAURICE RATTON
COLLECTION, PARIS

Baoulé Fetish

Woman administering an enema to her child by the old method of insufflation, which existed in most ancient cultures. Ivory Coast. Beginning of the 20th century.

their children in utter silence and unobserved. Then, while the men are carefully nursed in their "childbed," the women almost immediately get back to work. It is also true of course that recently the "couvade" has been interpreted sociologically as an attempt on the part of the male world to consolidate the patriarchy in these societies. The origin of circumcision as well as the infibulation of young girls may also be magical. These must originally have been viewed as the sacrifice of one part of the sexual organ to the demons, in order to prevent harm to the future offspring. On the other hand, they may also be seen as relics of human sacrifice, as they were still known in Greece and the Old Testament.

But with this we take leave of the medicine of prehistory and of the primitive races. With the rise of the ancient cultures of Asia Minor and the Mediterranean, animism and demonology give way to a new cultural development in medical science, theurgy. Now the dark and vaguely defined demons are replaced by divine figures with clearly defined rights and duties, and the medicine man of primitive provenance is transformed into the priest-doctor.

Cup of King Gudea, depicting a caduceus and a dedication to Ningiszida, the god of healing. Sumerian. 2200 B.C.

Sumerian and Babylonian Medicine

With the entry of mankind into historical times the first actual cultures began to develop. We have already pointed out that the primitive races of hunters and collectors differ from the civilized peoples through the absence of traditions, writing, and a sense of history. They use nature as a reservoir of life without trying to "master" it. By contrast we come now to the writing, understanding of traditions, and technology of the civilized peoples. This test applies equally well to the ancient Egyptians, the Sumerians, the Hittites, the Babylonians, and the Assyrians with whom we are now concerned. Actually the differences between primitive and civilized peoples are of a far more subtle nature. Theology, for instance, sees them in the transformation of animism into a codified belief in God; political economy believes them to be the passage from the momentary satisfaction of immediate needs to surplus productivity; sociology stresses the replacement of loose kinship or family ties by political institutions of the state; in medical history, finally, it is the passage from demonology and primitive magic to priesthood—medicine

or theurgy. But all these attempts at delineation have something in common: they assume the existence of certain guiding ideas over and above the mere struggle for existence.

In contrast to Egypt, the history of the "Land of the Two Rivers," which only in Grecian times received from the historian Polybius (second century B.C.) its present-day name of "Mesopotamia" (betwen two rivers), is extremely confused. Differing also from Egypt, which is surrounded and secured by sea and desert, is the geographical situation of that land, once also probably a desert, lying between the 2700-kilometer-long Euphrates, with its source in the Antitaurus, and the 1500-kilometer-long Tigris, with its source not far from there. First, an intricate canal system permitted the irrigation of the expanse, the most important cities of which lay much closer to the sea. Basra, the seaport; Ur, the birthplace of Abraham; and Babylon were all easily attainable from the coast. But open borders from the east, west, and south virtually invited foreign conquerors to take possession of the area.

Mother nursing her child

Hittite art, 2500-2000 B.C.

ARCHAEOLOGICAL MUSEUM, ANKARA

The first culture-carrying strata were probably the non-Semitic Sumerians, whose origins are still uncertain, and who assimilated the originally Semitic population. In their artistic representations they were already widely differentiated from the subsequent Babylonians through their brachycephalic skull shape accentuated by a typical aquiline nose. The curious, widely opened eyes, sometimes set with precious jewels, the overaccentuated brows, and the strangely placed bodies without any alternating construction of joints and muscles are quite typical. A strictly organized theocracy with a sharply defined temple service was the main foundation of the state. The real rulers of the people were the local divinities; and as the seat of the matriarchy, the mother goddess Innin held a special position. This is the era of the discovery of writing—first a picture writing similar to that in Egypt, which soon developed into a syllabic writing inscribed on a convex seal made of moist clay. Thus was laid the foundation for all European languages. From this period we derive the first doctors' "visiting cards" in the form of such seals. This Sumerian cuneiform, which was sometimes sent in "envelopes" (of clay) to the addressees, remained even after the subjugation of the Sumerians by other nations. Like the Greek language in antiquity and Latin in the Middle Ages, Sumerian continued to be the "high language" of religion and science. The famous library of the Assyrian king Ashurbanipal (669-627 B.C.) in Nineveh represented the most important collection of Babylonian-Assyrian writings, from which medical history also drew valuable evidence.

About 2350 B.C. a Semitic race, the Akkadians, subdued the Sumerians but took over the writing and culture of the vanquished, although the language now became Akkadian, which remained predominant in Asia Minor for hundreds of years. A king now reigned in an authoritarian manner: this was also manifested in the art of the period, with its stress on imperial dignity and power. Once more, in 2050 B.C., the Sumerians succeeded in taking over power and founded a new Sumerian kingdom. During this time the Viceroy Gudea of Lagash lived. A goblet was found in his possession, the outside of which shows two intertwined snakes, the first representation of the snake symbol in history. In all probability these emblematic animals were used as phylacteries to guard the drinker from harm, just as in Egypt the snake of the Pharaoh's crown was supposed to protect the bearer of supreme power.

About 1850 B.C. Babylon became the center of a great and powerful empire which reached its zenith under King Hammurabi (1728-1686 B.C.). Hammurabi was a remarkable reformer and lawgiver; his "Code of Hammurabi" even contains detailed medical paragraphs. His instructions regarding medical fees to be paid in the event of success and rigorous punishment to be meted out in case of failure are famous. We read for instance: "Given that a doctor has undertaken a heavy incision with a bronze knife and thereby has healed the person in question or has opened the stye with the bronze knife and thereby healed the eye, he may take ten bags of silver." This was actually a royal fee, as five bags of silver were sufficient to pay one year's rent on an entire house, and a worker under favorable circumstances could earn one-thirtieth of a sack of silver a day! But in line with the *lex talionis* (law of retaliation) there was another and extremely dangerous side to this regulation: "If, however, a doctor opens a heavy wound with a bronze knife and kills the patient or opens a tumor with the knife and thereby destroys the eye, he is to have both hands cut off." On a stele two meters high, Hammurabi had himself represented as praying to the God of Justice, Shamash. One is surely not wrong in seeing the origins of Old Testament justice in this era of Hammurabi's "merciless laws."

In the seventeenth century B.C. there was a new invasion by non-Semitic peoples from the east. First the Kassites, a mountain people from Iran, succeeded in invading Babylon. In the north the country was taken by the Churri-Mitanni originating in India. Both conquerors, however, quickly adopted the culture of the defeated and in this period was built the so-called "ladder to the stars," the Ziggurat, a giant temple observatory constructed for astrological purposes, and without doubt the model for the Biblical Tower of Babel.

Of greater independent significance was the Hittite empire expanding in Anatolia. Their capital, at present buried under the ruins of ancient Hattusa (in Turkish, Bogazköy), only recently has yielded magnificent works of art. One of them was, in its abstract beauty, almost too modern in style—a nursing mother from the second half of the second millenium B.C.

Shortly after the year 2000 B.C., the city state of Assur made itself independent of Babylon and developed alongside the Hittite and Egyptian empires into a great power in Mesopotamia. About 970 B.C. the conquest of the Aramaic states of Syria and Babylon began. These were occupied in 710 B.C. by the Assyrians, an especially cruel and warlike people—continuously portrayed in war char-

Code of Hammurabi

Hammurabi, 1728-1686 B.C., a famous reformer and legislator, whose code was carved on this stele containing highly detailed sections dealing with medicine. Hammurabi's decrees fixing the rates to be charged by physicians in case of success and ordering draconian punishments in case of failure, gained wide renown.

LOUVRE, PARIS

The seal of the male midwife Urlugaledinna
Sumerian, 2200 B.C.

iots in the art of the period. Equipped with sharp knives, they were greatly feared. The Babylonians, however, succeeded once again in regaining control for seventy more years. With the fall of Babylon to King Cyrus (d. 529 B.C.) in 539 B.C., the political and cultural history of this country between two rivers ended. But in contrast to the turbulent political situation, medical concepts changed very little. In all cultures the priest-doctors played an important part, especially in observing the stars and making prophecies from their observations. A strict mathematical mystique—our division of the week, which goes back to the Babylonians who consistently regarded the seventh day as bringing misfortune and so tried to pass it in utmost calm—led in medicine to a systematization and thereby to an exact observation of the conditions of disease. Astrology also led to the study of omens and signs, based mainly on the interpretation of dreams, the appearance of birth hindrances, birth deformities, or of so-called "water divination," in which a drop of oil was poured into a container of water and, depending on the behavior of the oil, a favorable or unfavorable prognosis was given. If the Sumerians had only four gods: Anu for the heavens, Enlil for the wind, Nintzi for the earth, and Enki for the water, they were all created from one original godhead, Eo. In the late Babylonian Empire the belief in demons again held sway. The spirits of the dead could become demons—e.g., those dead who had not succeeded in their earthly tasks, children who had died at birth,

those hit by lightning, those who had drowned, and those who had died by suicide were especially predestined for this fate. Higher spirits were those of the night, such as the masculine Lilu and the feminine Lilitu, as was pointed out by Isaiah (34.14) and by Johann Wolfgang von Goethe (1749-1832) in *Faust II*.

These spirits loved to appear in groups of three or seven, and they are still shown in this formation in the well-preserved amulet presently located in Paris. In the third row of this object an exorcism is being conducted in front of a reclining patient by two priests dressed as fish demons. Standing next to them are three differently disguised priests, two of them fencing in a mock duel, trying to trick the real demons; while in the row above the priests, again in the especially symbolic number of seven, the demons are doing a ghost dance. Above the demons, the most familiar of which were Ekimmu, the packer; Akhazu, the catcher; Rabasu, the lurker; Labartu, the oppressor; and Labasu, the conqueror, were different symbols of the gods. On the very bottom there was a reproduction of the Underworld. Individual demons, too, were often pictured, almost all capable of influencing disease or health. Thus for a migraine there was Tiu, for lung diseases Ashakki, for the liver Akhazu, and for female and children's illnesses Labartu. They were mostly pictured with an animal head together with ominous devils' horns and wings and there is little doubt that they constituted the model for the Fallen Angel, Satan, as he appears, as God's opponent, in the Book of Job. To protect against them, one attempted to banish them through amulets and magic incantations—a practice continued for thousands and thousands of years. Since they constantly populated the entire world, one had to be constantly on guard against them.

The comparison made by the outstanding medical historian Henry E. Sigerist (1891-1957) to the modern fear of germs is quite instructive. At that time no use was made of disinfectant lozenges or, as with the Chinese of our day, face masks for mouth protection; instead, there were prophylactic recitations such as the following: "A man may enter this house—but not you! A man may approach this house—not you! If someone enters—not you! You may not enter with the entering man! You should not enter with the departing man!" Finally, in Babylon special importance was attributed to study of the liver, a magical practice we subsequently find reappearing among other Mediterranean people, e.g., the Etruscans and the Romans. On the basis of a detailed study of the size and area of a sheep's liver, subtle diagnoses and forecasts were made; and the famous clay model of a sheep's liver used for purposes of divination and bearing appropriately inscribed cuneiform explanation, at present in the British Museum in London, doubtless served to instruct subsequent generations of priest-doctors. Actual lay doctors do not seem to have existed, otherwise statements made by Herodotus (490-ca. 420?)—cannot be understood. He expressed himself as follows concerning medical care in Babylon: "They bring their sick to the market, for they do not have physicians. Anyone can then approach the sick one and can give him advice concerning the disease, if he himself has had the sickness which is suffered by the patient or if he knows someone else suffering from a similar affliction. He then discusses the sickness with the patient and prescribes a remedy for him which had helped him or an acquaintance in a similar sickness. No one is allowed to pass by the sick man without asking him what illness plagues him."

Thus in Babylonian medical science we witness a curious paralleling of the first beginnings of scientific examination of disease. In the Babylonian Empire symptoms were defined for the first time and, for example, the jaundicing of the conjunctiva was traced back to a liver ailment. Side by side with the exorcism of numerous demons, there arose the equally justified systematization of medicine based on astronomy and astrology. But a genuine medical profession is still missing. We first encounter it in ancient Egypt.

*Thot was the god of magic
and medical secrets*

He supposedly performed an eye operation
on the god Horus. Ramessid period (New
Empire).

Art and Medicine in Ancient Egypt

About 2900 B.C. several city-states in Upper and Lower Egypt reaching back into prehistoric times were consolidated in the I dynasty: the so-called "Ancient Empire," which from then on united the whole desert vastness and the 850-kilometer-long fertile Nile Valley comprising Greater Egypt. The famous double crown of the Pharaohs became its symbol and Memphis its capital. In this era the famous pyramids of Cheops, Chephren, and Mycerinus were built; the cities of the dead of Gizeh and Medum arose. The Sphinx of Gizeh is the monumental expression in stone of the deified Pharaohs' might. Gradually there developed from the group of numerous city gods a hierarchy of gods more or less binding on the whole country—beginning with the god Isis, identified with the might of the rulers and the royal throne, her godly brother-husband Osiris, and their child Horus. The Pharaoh, till then venerated as a world god, eventually made room for the sun god Ra and the gods of the Underworld: Set, Prince of Evil and Osiris' murderer, and Thot, discoverer of the art of writing and the Guardian of Wisdom. They all played an important role thenceforth as did in the later times the god of medicine, Imhotep, depicted as a scribe. Utterly different from the lesser god of health and sickness Bes (who was sometimes pictured in the obscene posture of a dwarf figure, often with animal-like face and protruding eyes, emphasizing the navel and the penis, and who had risen from the ranks of archaic guardian demons to that of the venerated gods) was the position of Imhotep. Like Aesculapius in later Greek culture, he was venerated in the earliest times only as a particularly talented doctor and civil servant, who during the reign of the Pharaoh Zoser about 2600 B.C. may have been the builder of the step pyramid of Saqqara. His legendary descent from the creator of the world, the god Ptah who by "thought and utterance," i.e., through the power of "heart and tongue," set the universe in motion, gradually enabled Imhotep to occupy a place in the hierarchy of the gods. Imhotep, like his father Ptah, was never represented in zoomorphic form but in the anthropomorphic form originating at a higher cultural level. He was al-

Imhotep, the god of healing
Sixth dynasty.

ways shown with completely shaven head standing next to a learned scribe, hinting at the existence of a priesthood. The close connection between medicine and priesthood in the sense of theurgy was also clearly visible in this artistic rendition.

All statues of Imhotep, the god of health, show the finer hand of the artists of the New Empire, whereas the sculpture of the Old Kingdom is distinguished by a ponderous, throughly impressive, more elementary but also coarser artistic form. In addition to the myths preserved on papyri, art considerations alone would prove the relatively late theogony of this guardian of medicine reaching well down into the Ptolemaic era.

After an interregnum during which provincial princes continually fought one another, a second and so-called Middle Kingdom was resurrected around the year 2040 B.C. Now Thebes became the temporary royal residence. Sesostris I (1971-1927 B.C.) extended his influence as far as Nubia, while under Sesostris II (1897-1878 B.C.), Fayum was opened up. Sesostris III (1878-1840 B.C.) extended his might to Palestine. The art of reliefs and statuettes in the shape of the so-called "dice stools" was widespread. A second interim period, the so-called "Hyksos Kingdom," was succeeded in 1552 B.C. by the "New Empire," in which Egypt attained a position of world power under the rule of Amenophis I (1550-1528 B.C.). On the basis of elaborate concepts of the hereafter, subtle methods of mummification were developed. In the "Valley of the Kings" near Thebes, temples and cliff graves arose, guarded by oversized statues of kings. Under Thutmose III (1504-1436 B.C.), Egypt extended from the Euphrates to the Fourth Cataract of the Nile. The short intermission of the reign of Amenophis IV (1364-1347 B.C.), who called himself Akhenaton, introduced a monotheistic sun cult. This period has strongly impressed contemporary art with its turn toward sophisticated expressionism and its preference for asthenic bodies. The sculpted head of Nefertiti, wife of Akhenaton, marked the high point as well as the end of this era. With the death of Akhenaton, the old religion of Ammon took over once more under Ramses II (1290-1223 B.C.), a period of peaceful development and exceptional cultural flowering. Thereafter a decline gradually set in. In 664 B.C., Saïs became the capital; in 525 B.C., Egypt submitted to Persian rule, after many Greeks had already immigrated into the Nile country. In 332 B.C., Egypt fell to Alexander the Great, and after his death it succumbed to the Ptolemies, only to become a Roman province in 30 B.C.; then in 638 A.D., it was conquered by the Arabs.

Despite all developmental differences, the observer of Egyptian works of art must find this world inflexible and to some degree sinister in its ceremonial relations. The refined system of medicine, which throughout 3000 years

Mother and Child

This anthropomorphic piece of pottery was used in pharmacy. Its origin is unknown. New Empire, between 1500 and 1000 B.C.

LOUVRE, PARIS

Syrian Prince consulting an Egyptian doctor.

Polychrome painting, 1435 B.C., which decorated the tomb of Doctor Nebamon, was discovered in Drad'aboul Naga (Thebes).

of history hardly shows any development, was almost certainly equally rigid. It was quite different in the ancient Greek world, where the doctor of the Hippocratic era made thoroughly independent reflections on the causes of sickness and provided for extensive individual treatment. Such currents do not seem to have existed in Egyptian medical science. The approximately seven medical papyri extant, containing around 1200 different medical texts, give us a picture of a system of medicine partly religious and magical and partly empirical-rational. However, the rigid diagnoses and prescriptions lead to the conclusion that the Egyptian doctor had relatively little personal freedom of movement within his profession. Nevertheless in some areas the very specialized education in Egypt must have been outstanding. The *Odyssey*

praised the advanced standing of Egyptian medicine in the following words:

There the fruitful earth brings forth
A variety of Juices, of good and harmful mixture.
There everyone is a doctor, and surpasses in
  experience
All men.

Herodotus, who traveled to Egypt (in the fifth century B.C.), declared the Nile country to be a most healthy area, filled with doctors, "one of whom treats only the afflictions of the eye, another, those of the head, the tooth, the abdomen, or the internal organs."

Egyptian doctors were called everywhere. They were valued as much in Greece as at the court of the Persian

Healing statue in black basalt, covered with magic inscriptions. End of the native dynasties.

LOUVRE, PARIS

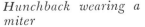

Hunchback wearing a miter

This statue was found in an intact "serdab" which contained eleven pieces of sculpture in all.
Beginning of the Fifth Dynasty.

EGYPTIAN MUSEUM OF CAIRO

kings. The relief—dating from the XVIII dynasty—of a Syrian prince undergoing treatment at the hands of an Egyptian doctor again proves their importance. To the left of the potentate, dressed in white and sitting on a chair, stands the doctor Nebamon, handing the Syrian prince a medical potion which he has just poured from a bottle held in his left hand. Behind the prince stands a helper, also dressed in white, who supports his upper arm. The prince is surrounded by several servants, who bring urns filled with provisions.

Indeed these frescoes have become more of a source of information for the medical history of Egypt than the papyri with their conservative dogmas. Here we find striking scenes of daily life. Thus a careful perusal of many thousands of grave paintings, which generally served to show the merits of the deceased in this world and to proclaim his entrance into the future world (and which were generally accompanied by legends in hieroglyphics), proves that those workers employed by the state to build the great temples, pyramids, and other monumental structures were by no means merely exploited as slaves, as might be assumed from accounts in the Old Testament. In connection with descriptions of such building projects made by highly placed personalities, we see repeated fresco scenes portraying the medical care of these workers. In a section of a mural done in 1439 B.C., an injured worker is being treated by the "work doctor." Imhotep's servant, who wears a loincloth, is rushing to examine the patient who has been undressed and lies on the ground with an expression of pain. In fact, social welfare for the state workers was quite extensive. We know from numerous documents that a kind of Sunday existed, a free day rotating at regular intervals. Before the worker was hired he was examined medically, and a kind of pension fund existed for those who became invalids while in service. This highly moralistic attitude toward the welfare of others was also apparent in the following command to the faithful:

> *Give to eat to him who is hungry.*
> *Give to drink to him who is thirsty.*
> *Clothe him who is naked.*
> *Let him ride across the Nile, who has no boat.*
> *Bury him who has no more son.*

Here one cannot avoid drawing parallels to certain Christian postulates, represented quite graphically in the weighing of souls, a practice that was pictured time and again during the middle Ages in many variations in churches and holy pictures, even though such a procedure is not to be found in the Last Judgment narrative in the Bible. This weighing of souls, which we can see in the famous *psychostasia* from the Book of the Dead of the royal scribe Hunefer, written on a papyrus now in

37

The Scales

Psychostasia (or weighing of the souls), from a mortuary register of the royal scribe Hunefer. Papyrus, thirteenth century B.C.

At the tribunal of the dead, Anubis leads the deceased before the balance which is adorned with the head of Maät, the goddess of truth and justice. On one scale we see the heart of the deceased, and on the other we see truth symbolized by a quill. Hunefer beseeches his heart: "Don't testify against me! Don't be my enemy at the tribunal!"

If the judgment goes against the deceased, the devourer of the dead (a being composed of elements of three animals) will consume his soul. But if he is judged to be good, Horus will lead him to his father Osiris, who in turn will admit him into his realm.

BRITISH MUSEUM, LONDON

38

the British Museum (thirteenth century B.C.), serves also to shed light on the psychophysical correlation in Egyptian thinking. For the Egyptian man, the heart was the center of life, not merely as the motor of the bodily functions but as the very center of spirit and soul. The heart, so to speak, took over the function of reason, intellect, and conscience. The Egyptian believed that canals flowed from the heart, and these canals contained the "breath of life," inhaled from the lungs. The heart was also the incorruptible witness of the moral behavior of its owner. After his death, it testified for or against him on the scales of death.

In the Judgment of the Dead, Anubis, dog-headed god of death, led the deceased before the scales. On one scale lay his heart; on the other, the symbol of truth, a feather. Anubis carried out the weighing of the soul under the supervision of the ibis-headed Thot, who is shown writing down the results. The transaction was worked out under the patronage of the goddess Maat, whose symbol of truth was also a feather, visible on the scales. If the beam of the balance pointed unfavorably for the deceased, he was devoured by a death animal nearby. If the beam pointed favorably, the falcon-headed god Horus guided the deceased before father Osiris, who finally admitted him into the Underworld. Osiris was endowed with the absolute power of the Pharaohs, complete with the dual crown, whip, and crozier, the last-named later used as a Christian bishop's symbol. Thus one single work of art can communicate more about the psychophysiological concepts of this people than numerous treatises, which particularly in the case of Egyptian literature fail to give a coherent picture of these problems.

Due to the special significance of the heart, it is no wonder that the latter was separated from the other internal organs during the process of mummification. The heart was placed in so-called Canopic jars containing, like the sarcophagus, the portrait of the deceased, to permit the Bird of Souls from time to time to visit the outer husk of its former owner, bearing the symbol of eternal life between its claws. Now too we understand various statements in wills that the heart must, in all circumstances, be buried in a different spot from the body. This was almost certainly done for fear that it might testify against its bearer at the judgment of the souls.

The example of the weighing of souls demonstrates that in order to understand everyday medicine in Ancient Egypt the discovery of abundant art treasures was as important as the papyri. Furthermore, the art of the Nile country is a valuable aid in clarifying the question of what diagnostic capabilities the Egyptian doctors possessed. It is especially interesting to note that surprisingly accurate representations of sickness which correlate with mummy finds are often found in the arts. Much evidence is found to support the assertion that the art of diagnosis

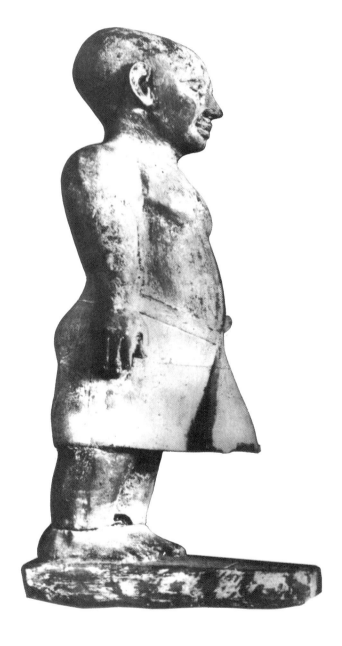

The dwarf Khnoumhotep. End of the Fifth Dynasty.
EGYPTIAN MUSEUM OF CAIRO

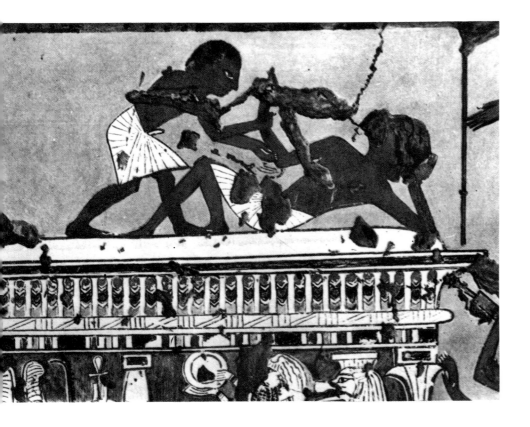

Injured worker being treated by a physician

The patient is stretched out on a large funeral chest, on which he was working.
Colored painting decorating the tomb of the sculptor Ipouy at Deir el-Medineh.

was extraordinarily well developed and that, above all, the different pathological manifestations were considered in their relationship to each other as symptoms. This was a development already hinted at in the Mesopotamian Empire but which was perfected in Egypt.

We are familiar, for example, with mummies which show clear signs of pronounced vertebral tuberculosis. In one case it is possible to see not only the vertebrae hardening with the consequent hunched back characteristic of Pott's disease but even to recognize a calcified, so-called "frozen" abscess in the loin as a typical result of spinal tubercular inflammation. A complement to this is the statuette reproduced here of a hunchback, caricaturized but showing the placement of the pointed hump in the upper portion of the vertebrate column which is pathognomonic. Orthopedic afflictions show similar parallels. A royal mummy exhibits a typical *pes equinovarus* or more accurately, a clubfoot; but on the basis of the autopsy results, it was not possible to make etiological comments. We are, however, in possession of the famous portrait of a priest in the Copenhagen Karlsberg Glyptothek Museum in which we can see that the *pes equinovarus* portrayed is apparently the result of the shortening of the right leg due to atrophy. We can hardly go amiss by assuming that the bearer of this deformity may have been the unfortunate victim of poliomyelitis. The medical papyri do not report on this type of case, and the existence of the memorial stone alone gives us an interesting indication of a particular case, of great importance in the history of infantile paralysis. Apparently of striking concern to the typical Egyptian artist was the portrayal of dwarfs. It seems that the Pharaohs, much like later princes of the West, had a predilection for such deformed creatures, and liked to bring them to their courts to keep them as jesters. This explains how statuettes of these disproportioned sculptured dwarfs rendered with typical facial and nose features are found relatively frequently in close proximity to the Pharaohs' palaces. These minor art pieces are familiar to us already from the Old Empire; the statue pictured here stems from the V dynasty (2470-2320 B.C.). Often it was by no means anonymous dwarfs who serverd as models for the artist, but celebrated personalities who sometimes were shown together with their wives and children on the stele and, judging from their appearance, seem to have been important people of the court. We also find portrayals of well-proportioned dwarfs, and various inscriptions tell us that the Pharaohs sent special expeditions to Central Africa to procure some from the Pygmy tribes. They were required by royal command to guard these dwarfs carefully, take good care of them, and bring them speedily back to Egypt.

We are also enlightened on the subject of excessive

obesity or leanness by the realistic art of sculpture. The representation of the queen of the mythical gold country of Punt, departing on a tribute-paying expedition to Egypt and pictured with overdimensional steatopygy and obesity of the lower limbs in a relief from the Temple of Deir-el-Bahari near Thebes, may be contrasted with the pronounced leanness of a peasant who can be seen on a cliff near Mer in Middle Egypt dating from the VI dynasty (2320-2160 B.C.).

That gynecology and obstetrics played an important role in Ancient Egypt is attested not only by numerous passages in the papyri, in which the most diverse medications from the suppository to the steambath are prescribed for gynecological ills but also through the now famous pregnancy diagnoses, lasting in the West well into the Middle Ages, by which a sack filled with wheat and spelt was watered with the urine of the woman to be tested. If the wheat grew more strongly, it was to be a boy; if the spelt germinated, a girl was expected—so it was stated in the Brugsch papyrus around 1250 B.C. However, we should not see in this, as is often maintained, a precursor of hormone diagnosis along the lines of the Aschheim-Zondeck tests, but rather a magical manipulation. Analogous birth deductions were derived solely according to the grammatical gender of the two terms for wheat and spelt.

If the written sources on the course of pregnancy are by themselves not too conclusive, we are compensated in the fine arts by the representations of parturition. According to these, diverse methods of birth seem to have been prevalent. In some illustrations we see the woman in labor sitting on a delivery chair in between two helping gods and evidently in pain, endeavoring to keep her upper thighs apart so as to free the way for the child. In other reliefs the situation is represented directly after birth. The woman, having given birth, is sitting in a crouched position on her heels, tended by midwives, one of whom has just taken the child and is handing it over to another attendant. The display in this ostensible delivery of the goddess Ritho is thus incomparably richer than on other bas-reliefs.

Circumcision, which was then taken over as ritual circumcision by the Jews returning from Egypt, is mentioned more often in the papyri, but it is the fine arts which give us a unique portrayal of the operation. A rather well-preserved relief from the Necropolis in Saqqara, dating from the VI dynasty, renders the most exact detail. We see here the surgeon crouching in front of the youth who is to be circumcised. The youth's hands are either held from behind by a medical aide or, so as not to disturb the surgeon, are placed on the latter's head by the aide. We may conclude that circumcision was undertaken as an initiation rite among the Egyptians as well as among many Semitic and African peoples. This was an important discovery in the sphere of intellectual history and ethnological relationships.

Ancient Egyptian art then, to a much greater degree than in the cultures considered thus far, is an irreplaceable and highly valuable aid in understanding medicine as well as the concepts of psychophysical anatomy and diseases in the land of the Nile. Despite a certain ceremonial stiffness, this art offers many indications of pathological symptoms and shows that artists, in addition to their predilection for the heroic and the grandiose, were also interested in the unusual and the comical. To the artists therapeutics was a highly regarded discipline.

Achilles bandaging Patroclos

A cup with red figures bearing the inscription of the
potter Sosias, originally from Vulci. Fifth century B.C.

42

Art and Medicine
in Ancient Greece and Rome

Whether we recognize it or not, we still derive intellectual sustenance from a cultural epoch commonly called "Classical Antiquity," which in a unique flowering embraced art as well as science. The artistic and medical concepts of the ancient civilizations of Asia Minor and Egypt discussed above had, oddly enough, little direct influence on the intellectual systems and artistic theories of the West. The Greek world and that of Hellenism have, however, to a disproportionate degree left their imprint upon Europe. They absorbed many Eastern influences and then disseminated them. It remains a peculiar phenomenon that a country geographically divided, consisting of hundreds of small islands and of the most diverse climate, traversed by mountain ranges and divided into many politically different city-states, where the power struggle of leading powers clashed—that such a country could produce such an exceptional flowering in art and science.

The people known as Greeks are those Indo-Aryan tribes who around 3000 B.C. immigrated from the Danube basin and the Balkans to the Peloponnesus or especially to the Greek islands and later from there to Asia Minor. They merged their language and intellectual concepts with those of the original inhabitants who lived there, the Pelasgians, and partly took over their customs. This original population had between 3000 and 2000 B.C. developed the so-called "Aegean culture," which can be divided into the Helladic-Mycenaean mainland civilization and the Cycladic-Minoan centered in Crete. The latter was mainly influenced by Egypt, even though most of the cultural and port cities were to be found on the northern coast of Crete facing Greece. About 1400 B.C. the early Greeks put an end to the Minoan culture in Crete. The legends of Theseus and Ariadne remind one of these archaic times. About 1200 B.C., the Dorians invaded Mycenae and founded Sparta. After the decline of the Hittite Empire in Asia Minor, the Aeolians settled in Thebes and the Ionians in Asia Minor. This may have precipitated the Trojan War. A kind of National consciousness developed from the eighth century on and

Ex-voto dedicated to Aesculapius
Bas-relief found in Thyrea, fourth century B.C.
NATIONAL MUSEUM OF ARCHAEOLOGY, ATHENS

the Greeks became Hellenes. The Homeric Epics, the Olympic Games, and the Delphic Oracle were proof and consequence of this new mental attitude, but the political consciousness of solidarity was insignificant. Greek patriotism hardly extended beyond the democratic *polis* (city-state), which was occasionally seized by a tyrant and which was in reality an aristocracy. The colonization of Sicily, Southern Italy, Africa, and Spain led to the expansion of the Greek intellectual heritage throughout the Mediterranean. The laws of Dracon and Solon in 624 and 594 B.C. introduced the so-called "classical era," during which the Persian Wars (ca. 480 B.C.) and the Peloponnesian War (431-404 B.C.) occurred. The period saw murderous massacres among Greek tribes as well as the most sublime creations in the fine arts. The last epoch of Greek high culture set in with the Corinthian Federation under the leadership of the Macedonian King Philip and his son Alexander the Great and lasted well into the time of the Roman Empire. To such a degree was this so that we hesitate to speak of an indigenous Roman art and even less of original Roman medicine. The basic Greek concepts of harmony and *kalokagathia,* of the four humors and healing power of nature, i.e., *physis,* also laid the basis for later Roman concepts; and Asclepius, Latinized to Aesculapius, was the god of health who influenced the Roman world.

The medical science of Crete was still completely magical, even though individual discoveries, especially as revealed in paintings and the other fine arts, indicate that an advanced body hygiene and admirable hygienic installations existed. Because Cretan linear writing is only now being deciphered, the artistic theories and comments of the Greeks are still the main source of our knowledge of ancient Cretan medicine. In Crete, the bull always crops up as the main cult animal and appears on many seals and coins in the renowned palace of Knossos. Apparently, great significance was ascribed to the mythical powers emanating from the bull.

If magical medicine still prevailed in Crete, we first encounter a more rationalistic concept of medical science in the Homeric epic. Yet magic is not totally banned in these epics, dating from 900 to 800 B.C. Thus Odysseus is wounded above the knee by a boar, and his hunting companions, the sons of Autolycus, bandaged the injury and cured the bleeding through an exorcism (as with the ancient Germans, whose so-called "Merseburger incantation" is preserved, or like the American Indians who used similar curative spells). In Homer, however, Aesculapius the father of the two legendary doctors Machaon and Podaleirios, is a prince of Thrace; the descriptions of the wounds of the Trojan and Greek heroes before the embattled Asian fortress are stark and very close to reality. The passages which describe the moment of death as a result of a mortal wound, and of the departure of the soul as the bearer of life, are told with exceptional drama. Thus the death of Alkathoos, felled by the sword of Idomeneus, is related as follows:

He fell with a crash, and the lance fixed in his heart,
That, still beating shook the butt-end of the spear.
Then at length mighty Ares spent its fury there.

(Iliad XIII)

44

Anatomical information was also used by the Homeric poet in his great epics. Not only did he know the seat of the urinary bladder but the breast region, with the life-supporting heart, particularly attracted him in his artistic portrayals. His subtle gift of observation is attested to by his description of the duel between Patroclos and Sarpedon, which cost the latter his life:

> *Now noble Patroclos swung his bronze,*
> *And his javelin flew not vainly from his hand,*
> *But struck Sarpedon even where the midriff clasps*
> *   the beating heart,*
> *And he fell as falls an oak, or a silver poplar,*
> *Or a stately pine-tree...*
> *Patroclos, setting foot on his breast,*
> *Drew the spear out of his flesh, and the midriff*
> *   followed with the spear,*
> *So that he drew forth, together, the spearpoint and*
> *   the soul of Sarpedon.*
>
> (*Iliad,* XVI)

It is to this day a matter of debate whether what was meant to be the seat of the soul was the "cover of the heart," the pericardium, or the midriff or diaphragm.

Less fatal injuries are repeatedly mentioned in the Homeric epics, proving that alongside the dramatization of the struggle for life and death there also existed a lively interest in medical questions which must have moved the poet. To be sure, self-help stood foremost, particularly since in the midst of battle no one could come immediately to the aid of the wounded. It was most important to remove the arrow or the spearhead, to stop the flow of blood with the aid of a tourniquet, and, in a given case, to apply a therapeutic salve. This third act, however, was actually left to those skilled in medicine. In this manner, Agenor helped himself when Menelaus' spear pierced his hand:

> *Menelaus of the loud war-cry smote the hand of*
> *   Agenor*
> *And into the bow, clean through the hand, was driven*
> *   the spear of bronze.*
> *Back he withdrew to the ranks of his comrades,*
> *   avoiding fate,*
> *With his hand hanging down at his side, for the*
> *   ashen spear dragged after him.*
> *And the great-hearted Agenor drew the spear from his*
> *   hand,*
> *And himself, bound up the hand with a band of*
> *   twisted sheep's-wool,*
> *A sling that a squire carried for him, the shepherd of*
> *   the host.*
>
> (*Iliad,* XIII)

The Peytel Aryballos

This perfume vase, 9 cm. high, is of exceptional interest because it goes back to the time of Hippocrates and reveals details of a medical consultation. We see a young physician making preparations to bind up the arm of a patient, after probably having bled him. The bronze basin near him contains the water and the sponges used for washing wounds. The stunted dwarf, a servant to the doctor, is carrying on his shoulder the hare his master has received as payment for a consultation.

Peytel is the name of the collector who donated this vase to the Louvre.

LOUVRE, PARIS

45

Only slightly less important was comradely help; here there are touching examples of friendship and willingness to help among the otherwise rather egotistical and pitiless Greeks who fought the Trojans. This subject occupies not only the Homeric poet but also the painters of vases in later times. But here too let the poet speak for himself. Eurypylus had in great pain dragged himself from the battle:

> *Badly wounded in the thigh with an arrow,*
> *Limping out of the battle, and sweat ran down*
> *Streaming from his head and shoulders, and from his*
> *   cruel wound*
> *The black blood was welling, but his mind was*
> *   unshaken.*

(Iliad, XI)

In the camp, he meets Patroclos, whom he beseechingly begs:

> *But me do thou succor and lead me to the black ship,*
> *And cut the arrow out of my thigh and with warm*
> *   water,*
> *Wash away the black blood from it and smear soft*
> *   healing drugs thereover,*
> *These good herbs whereof they say that thou hast*
> *   learned from Achilles.*

(Iliad, XI)

Patroclos is in fact the only one who can help at that moment because the two most famous Greek physicians are not available. One is still fighting in the battle, and the other lies wounded in the tent "himself in need of an experienced doctor." Achilles, who has received his pharmaceutical knowledge in the same manner as Asclepius, transmitted by the centaur Chiron, must also be found. Thus Patroclos begins to do the work for himself:

> *There he stretched him at length and cut with the*
> *   knife,*
> *The sharp arrow from his thigh and with warm water*
> *Washed from it the black blood. And thereon he*
> *   cast a bitter root,*
> *Rubbing it between his hands and ended all his*
> *   anguish,*
> *And the wound began to dry, and the blood ceased.*

(Iliad, XI)

Similar aid is lent by Achilles, who is skilled in medicine, to his friend Patroclos in the magnificent red-figured "bowl of Sosias" reproduced here. Patroclos knew from personal experience what considerable knowledge of therapeutics Achilles possessed, learned from his half-divine mentor. The picture, dating from the fifth century B.C., corresponds in every way to the spirit of the Homeric epic. The scene is rendered with objective realism. With admirable exactness Achilles is shown placing a bandage on the left arm of his friend, intent on his work, while Patroclus, his face turned aside and with painful expression, nevertheless helps with the thumb of his uninjured right hand in applying the classical bandage. Also from the *Iliad* and from other figured vases, similar scenes of comradely help are shown us. Thus Sthenelus removes an arrow from Diomedes' shoulder, and another vase shows him bandaging the right index finger of that same hero. Agenor bandages the hand of his friend Helenus and the doctor Machaon, wounded in the heat of battle, is aided by old Nestor.

Because of the numerous injuries, these few doctors were naturally highly regarded and much sought after. Their medical activity, however, still constituted an extra job since they also took part as combatants in the different battles. But the Homeric doctors differed from those in the cultures previously considered in that they were able to practice their duties in a completely secular manner, as human beings among human beings, without any priestly connection, just as Aesculapius was originally a prince with special medical knowledge who only was given godly attributes in the sixth century B.C. Greek doctors were highly esteemed from the beginning. This is made clear by the numerous representations of doctors in antiquity. In the *Iliad,* as we have seen, the special position of the warriors skilled in medicine was already emphasized. In the midst of a raging battle, after many a Greek hero has been wounded, the allied camp receives the communication that now Machaon the doctor has also been hit by an arrow. As a result Idomeneus asks the venerable Nestor himself to harness up the chariot in order to rescue that important man:

> *O Nestor... arise, get thee up into thy chariot, and*
> *   with thee let Machaon go,*
> *And swiftly drive to the ships the whole-hooved*
> *   horses!*

(Iliad, XI)

And now follow the classical words:

> *For a doctor is worth many other men,*
> *To cut out arrows and spread soothing medicaments.*

(Ibid., XI, 200)

From this time on, the medical calling possesses a strong tradition built on natural philosophy and Hippocratic medical science, from which, however, the cult of Aesculapius also stems. Interest in medical treatment is extremely intense among the Greeks, and numerous pictures on vases enable us to gain some insight into the medical practice of the pre-Hippocratic era, of which we here show a bloodletting and the "waiting room" of a doctor. The first scene shows a patient leaning on a crutch; he has

Philoctetes at Lemnos, bitten by
the serpent who guarded the altar
of the Nymph Chryseis.
Bowl from the end of the sixth
century B.C.

In all probability, an authentic bust of Hippocrates. Found in a necropolis of Isola Sacra, Ostia.

slung his tunic over his left shoulder so as to free his right arm, stretched out toward the doctor for bloodletting. An oversized vessel in the foreground is used for receiving the blood, as in later times the cupping basins of barbers, still used in Germany as signposts for hairdressers, the former barber-surgeons. With his left hand the doctor has himself located the vein in the elbow joint and is about to strike it with the sharp little scalpel, as was customary in the Middle Ages too.

In the second picture, beside two figures among the patients who attract attention (of whom one has had his leg amputated and is using a crutch) there is a little naked man who has certain characteristics of a Silenus—squat body, saddle nose, disproportion between rump and extremities—but who seems to lack the typical marks of the Centaur such as horse's ears, horse's tail, and horse's legs. Perhaps we are confronted with a dwarf or a chondrodystrophic. In any case these vases created in the fifth century B.C. show—alongside the more idealized portraits, which only later attained their highest flowering, especially in the sculpture of the harmonious and anthropomorphic figures of gods—throughly realistic traits, which have done much to enlighten us on the background of medical practice in Greece. There are bathing scenes, scenes of child rearing, massage, and the representation of exceptional psychic situations, in which we can, for example, see Charcot's famous *arc de cercle*, recognized by him as an especially impressive symptom of a major hysterical attack. All these were preferred subjects for miniature painting and relief sculpture.

After the sixth century B.C., a decisive turning point occurred in Greek culture. In the Homeric world the gods were already by no means the unrestricted lords of the world. They too, even if immortal, were also subordinate to inexorable fate. They were, so to speak, outsize humans, with all the human virtues and vices, and appeared as such in the magnificent statues which we as a rule associate with the concept of Greek art, whether it be the birth of Aphrodite from the sea, Apollo, Pallas Athene, the all-father Zeus himself, and lastly the numerous Aesculapius statues to which we shall return. Now Greek man began to reflect upon himself and, in a unique fashion, about the position of man in the cosmos; he began to reflect on the structure of the world in general. The age of natural philosophy began. The gods no longer stand over creation but alongside it, and all magic is widely denigrated so that everything is reduced to certain fundamental principles. The Greeks undertook the first attempt to objectivize the world.

The search for the prime substance was to be equally fruitful for medicine and art. For Thales of Miletus, one of the earliest natural philosophers of this more materialistic era, who lived ca. 640 B.C., the prime substance was

48

Torso of Aesculapius

Roman copy of Hellenistic original. Fourth century B.C.

Amphiaraos treating a patient
Fifth century B.C.

NATIONAL MUSEUM OF ARCHAEOLOGY, ATHENS

water. This substance was later translated by the Romans into *elementum,* and was the foundation for all vital functions, postulating a purely materialistic principle of the universe. Anaximander, living about 600 B.C., was less precise. He believed in a prime substance not tangible to the senses, which was simultaneously the idea of energy and form, from which emanated, as secondary qualities, water and cold. For Anaximenes, a disciple of Anaximander, air is the prime substance. All things stem, according to him, from condensation and evaporation. His teaching is the precursor of later pneumatic concepts, which saw in the *pneuma* the ether of life, the vitalizing principle; and sickness as being caused by the contraction or the dilation

of pneumatically filled pores in the human organism. Finally Pythagoras, in the words of the philosopher Stobaeus, "took numbers from the traders and made them the foundation of all thinking." Hereafter natural law is no longer considered mere accident, but as the principle which is inherent in numbers. Now it is held to be possible to measure all theories of life and to compare and to extract from individual objects, by the aid of number combinations, generally valid laws. The introduction of number as a theoretical concept further depended on the creation of the theory of contrast. One is originally not a number but a statement. 1:2, however, is the first antithesis. Tension arises from contrast, as was later expressed

50

Bacchic scene, the so-called
"Dying Bacchante"

In point of fact, a depiction of hysteria. At the far
right, a hysterical woman, her body bent in the shape
of an arc.

UFFIZI, FLORENCE

by Aristotle when he formulated the ten antitheses—for
example, straight-crooked, right-left, male-female, etc. Harmony then arises from the synthesis of opposites. Pythagoras called this harmony in the world "cosmos." Everything was subordinated to it, health as well as sickness, and
art as well. Health was thus no longer only bodily integrity,
but spiritual harmony and beauty as well. Conversely,
according to this doctrine, an ugly human being could be
neither completely healthy nor on a very high spiritual
level. Hence the ejection of deformed children, the contempt for cripples and ugly people. In art the primacy of
symmetry and the harmonious human being was the logical consequence of this philosophy. For this reason,

artistic representations of the pathological stigmata of
the sick, frequently seen in the art of the other ancient
cultures, now disappears. It reappears again only in later
Hellenistic times and most strongly in the period of the
Roman Empire when the naturalistic portrait crops up.
There are, however, some exceptions in classical art. The
anthropocentric natural philosophy, which was first of all
a cosmology in which man was only an imitation of the
cosmos, a microcosm within a macrocosm, reached its
apogee with Protagoras (ca. 460 B.C.), who saw man as
the measure of all things. But earlier Heraclitus had
claimed fire to be the prime substance and Leucippus and
Democritus had established the atomic theory. Whereas

51

Aesculapius and his daughter Hygeia

Aesculapius is preparing to save a patient sleeping on a small bed. Opposite him, friends or relatives of the patient are raising their right hands in a gesture of adjuration. These figures are depicted as somewhat smaller, which implies that they are insignificants compared with the illustrious physician.
Fourth century B.C.

Heraclitus recognized water and earth as basic substances besides the elixir of life, the atomists assumed that an infinite number of similar and indivisible particles perpetually move in an empty atmosphere and join to form new constellations, but fall apart again when these disintegrate. The manifold phenomena of the world, they held, were caused by different constellations consisting of like atoms. The harmony of the atoms as the basis for health also played a great role in Democritus' thinking. The contemporary of Pythagoras, Alcmaeon (ca. 500 B.C.), was prompted by this philosophy of harmony to see health as an equilibrium of forces. Sickness, on the contrary, was the dominance of a certain substance. He knew seven types of these: humid, dry, cold, warm, bitter, sour, and sweet. At about the same time, Empedocles (490-435 B.C.) taught that the rise and the disintegration of bodies resulted from the mixing and decomposing of the original particles, which he saw in the four elements of fire, water, earth, and air. Thus the theory of unity of the first natural philosophy developed into the theory of the four elements; it was finally introduced into medicine by the Hippocratics and codified by Galen (129-199 A.D.), becoming a leading medical system, still held valid in the Middle Ages and in modern times as humoral pathology.

In considering these principles of natural philosophy, we see that in a different form the same concepts were also binding for theoretical medicine. These were theories stemming from the philosophy of harmony, yet on the

other hand they were dynamic and vital and resulted in the later pneuma concepts. It is interesting to note that the same principles were at work in art. The theory of harmony, of *kalokagathia,* was closely connected with a definitely dynamic artistic power of expression, as seen in the medical reliefs, especially the gravestones of famous doctors. The oldest and most famous, the statue of the Greek doctor Somrotidas of Megara Hybla in Sicily dating from the sixth century B.C., still shows the remains of a nude and youthful body, the head and right arm regrettably not preserved, reminding us of Egyptian sculpture in its rigidity. If this statue can only be identified by the inscription as that of a physician, the picture of the doctor in later Greek art changes considerably. A typical example is the gravestone of the Athenian doctor Jason dating from the second century B.C. We see pictured here a representation of a distinguished man in his prime, dressed in a chiton, sitting on a cushioned stool and undertaking a typically dynamic action—a palpatory examination of the epigastrium. His profession is not only proven by the inscription on the stone, but by a "visiting card," an overdimensional cupping glass in the right lower edge. It is also interesting to note that the patient being examined is portrayed considerably smaller than the seated doctor; thereby the social distinction between the two is made visible. This was a practice current in other old civilizations and was still used to illustrate differing positions in the Middle Ages. Other reliefs always show the doctor in some activity, either as a scholar reading, corresponding to the late Hellenistic theory earlier ascribed to Hippocrates: "The doctor who is a friend of knowledge resembles the gods"—or he is undertaking an operation, emphasizing the other side of the practice of medicine, the wandering doctor. These paintings or reliefs almost always show the attributes of medicine, such as surgical instruments and especially the cupping glass, as can be seen on the previously discussed vase painting of a bloodletting, where it appears between doctor and patient, and also several times on the upper left corner.

This artistic emphasis on the doctor as a scholar is not new in antiquity—it also existed in Egypt—but the position of the doctor who could now work, free of the restrictive ties of religion, was immensely higher. This had an effect on the activity of several medical schools, the most familiar of which were located in Knidos and Kos. Hippocrates (460-375 B.C.) was born in Kos, and to this day his name is associated with a main trend in medicine. Plato already considered him one of the most important

doctors; his fame has reached down through the centuries, sometimes overshadowed by the second most famous doctor of antiquity, Galen. It is still a matter of debate among philologists and medical historians what part of the *Corpus Hippocraticum* is really Hippocrates' work or whether it dates to earlier or later times. Yet a certain intellectual tone permeating the whole corpus permits us to speak of the medicine of the Hippocratics. Completely reliable observations of the course of a sickness and all its symptoms, the consideration of all personal and environmental factors (for example, climate), support of the *physis* of the patient and his natural healing powers attest that the doctor could stand as a common ally by the patient's side in the struggle against disease. This method also allows for freely acknowledged confessions of failure; and to learn from failure is one of the most important factors. Thus we find a highly ethical view of the dignity of the medical profession culminating in the "Hippocratic Oath." It is regrettable that portraits of Hippocrates, hitherto asserted to be authentic, are mere objects of fan-

Sthenelos bandaging Diomedes' index finger

Sixth century B.C.

NATIONAL MUSEUM OF
ARCHAEOLOGY, ATHENS

tasy, as is also the case with pictures of Galen. (Medieval portraits of other personalities are also seldom original. Often existing woodcuts were slightly altered in order to picture quite different people.) The fact that the artists were not interested in an individual expression but in a principle is quite impressively illustrated by a fresco from the twelfth century A.D. in the cathedral of Anagni in Northern Italy, where both pagan *principes medicorum*, the ancient Hippocrates and Galen (in actual fact separated by five hundred years) are peacefully sitting together at two lecterns like those used by the medieval monks and holding a conversation.

Most supposedly late Hellenistic statues of Hippocrates seem to be statues of Aesculapius or of Apollo. This is true of a bust, today preserved in the museum of Kos, found in 1929 in the Odeon of the island, bearing a poetic inscription which seems to describe a relatively young Aesculapius. In the third century B.C. there was a cult of the healing-god on Kos. The experts assume that a bust discovered in 1947 in the necropolis of the Isola Sacra near Ostia bears the name of Hippocrates. In contrast to the idealistic portraits of Aesculapius, it shows a face of maturity, bearing certain traces of resignation and fatigue—traits that often occur in doctors at the end of their careers when they have seen too much misery and death and have lived through too many disappointments. This intellectual head in no way corresponds to the principles of the youth-obsessed *kalokagathia*, nor is it accidental that it resembles the bust of Socrates. We must not forget that this statue also, which might closely correspond to the actual appearance of the great man from Kos, only dates from the Hellenistic era and thus cannot lay claim to authenticity. The personality of the important physician thus remains in the dark, even though a host of legends have been woven about him and his work. The best known is his examination of Democritus, accused of mental illness by his fellow citizens of Abdera. Hippocrates tells the Abderites that he has found Democritus to be the only normal being in the infamous city.

The later influence of Hippocrates and of the works ascribed to him may be illustrated by four further examples which touch on the two areas of medicine and art. We possess a wonderful miniature, dating from the fourteenth century, in a Parisian manuscript, showing Hippocrates in the Byzantine manner, sitting on a foot stool, over which a crown floats. He has placed his chiton on his head as a kind of nimbus, so that a certain resemblance to representations of Christ by artists of that period cannot be denied. Above him floats a blue, expensively decorated canopy. In his left hand he holds an open book with the original Greek text of the famous aphorism:

Life is short, art is long, the moment fleeting.

This warning, as appropriate today as it was 2500 years ago, should be inscribed in the notebook of every medical student.

A statue in the minster of Constance has a quite different effect on us. In the chapel of the Holy Grave, we find among the deceased the grave of an "ointment salesman" marked, however, by two peculiarities—one that he bears the name of "Ypocras," the other that he wears an unusual habit for a simple salesman, a mortarboard and a gown reminding one somewhat of the scholars of the period. In his hand he holds a magnifying glass, certainly not an instrument for an ointment salesman. It is now thought that the misspelled name "Ypocras" is reminiscent of the great Hippocrates and that the gown denotes a pharmacist, especially since in medieval pharmacies medications received the name "Ypocras."

Another later representation of Hippocrates gives the supposed Greek doctor not only the robe of the period but a typical pair of riveted glasses held in his hand to stress all the more clearly his status as a scholar. This too was of course a historical anachronism.

Finally we should mention the artistically appealing illustrations in individual portions of the *Corpus Hippocraticum*. These were added to the books of the *Corpus* or, as in this case, to the commentaries, this one by Apollonius of Kitium (ca. 60 B.C.), primarily for didactic purposes and not for gratuitous artistic reasons. They offer, however, despite the almost theatrical triumphal arch with its open curtains (behind which the actual medical procedure of a maxillary setting—as still practiced today—is taking place according to the Hippocratic writing *On the Joints*), a good idea of the importance of the Hippocratic writings three hundred years after his death. These diagrams and the illustrated teachings of bandaging by Soranus (98-138 A.D.) are typical products of so-called Byzantine medicine, which may be viewed as the inheritor and preserver of the medical science of antiquity; they stand at the beginning of a long line of such didactic illustrations which later embellished the scientific manuscripts of the Middle Ages as miniatures and initials. This genre lasted until the introduction of the woodcut and printed books, when a new kind of illustration found its way into literature. Better than the dull and distorted texts of the Middle Ages corrupted as a result of countless recopyings, the illustrations here give us an insight into the medical life of the times—the surgical processes, methods of observations, therapeutic measures, and anatomical as well as physiological concepts. In contrast to our own strictly scientific illustrations, in earlier times it was customary to embellish such themes, either with the aid of valuable scenery, as in our picture, or with vignettes or cartouches.

We have already mentioned that during Hippocrates' time several medical schools existed. These not only served to elucidate methods but also represented a different conception of medicine as a science. These medical theories were fed from different sources. In one case, the influence of the great idealist philosopher Plato is unmistakable. If at the beginning of Greek philosophy there prevailed a very materialistic world view, the Eleatic philosopher Parmenides at the beginning of the fifth century B.C. represented more idealistic concepts in his didactic poem *On Nature*. He was the adherent of a strictly monistic theory, according to which there was only one true being. Thought and existence were identical and being was indivisible, immovable as in a perfectly rounded sphere. The opinions of those who claimed the existence of antithetical principles, or Heraclitus' theory that "everything is in flux," were, according to Parmenides, illusionary truths that stood in contrast to real existence. Parmenides thereby became a forerunner of the Platonic theory of ideas, and perhaps influenced Democritus, who was the first to differentiate the perception of external phenomena by the senses from genuine cognition. The discrepancy between perception and thought is henceforth also important in medicine, where practice and theory flowing from these two modes of perception now distinguish the "philosopher-physician." Aristotle even maintained that only the doctor who was also familiar with philosophic problems could claim to be scientific. His magnificent system of nature as a deductive method, the derivation of general laws from empirically gathered individual facts, was for many centuries the standard for the entire system of knowledge and medicine; it was not completely replaced by the inductive, experimental method until the beginning of the modern period.

The stronger regard for theoretical concepts led moreover to new medical directions. If the Hippocratics particularly emphasized the artistic elements of medical science and treated them in an individualistic manner, emphasizing ethical judgment by the individual, the Khidian school, on a peninsula of Asia Minor across from the Island of Kos, attempted to lay greater stress on generally valid scientific viewpoints. As a precondition, they believed in the regularity of the healthy normal body and in closer scrutiny of its functions. In this respect they based themselves on the theory of the pneuma. This school was first called the dogmatic, then later became the pneumatic school. Its main adherent was Diocles of Carystus in the first half of the fourth century B.C. Galen may also be said to belong in a certain measure to this school.

In the third century B.C. another school arose in Alexandria, connected with the names of Herophilus and Erasistratus. They made anatomical studies the basis of their theory, without neglecting physiology, which was

Jason, a physician, examining a patient's liver

We notice a giant cupping-glass next to the patient. Second century B.C.

BRITISH MUSEUM, LONDON

Hippocrates

Roman statue of the Hellenistic period. Fourth century B.C.

so important to the Greek physician. Here too we see the decided tendency to place the dynamic before the static— *Dynamis* before *Hyle*—as clearly demonstrated in all Greek works of art.

In Roman times, additional schools grew up to compete with one another. The Methodicalists under the spiritual guidance of Themison of Laodicea (end of the first century B.C.) and the teacher Asclepiades of Bithynia (died 30 B.C.) believed they had a simple method of considerably simplifying the treatment of patients. Starting out from two extreme conditions, the *status laxus* and *strictus,* it was necessary, according to this method, to achieve through appropriate therapeutic measures of relaxation and tension a return to normal.

The eclectics had finally grown tired of the bickering of the different schools and attempted by critical examination of all existing observations and theories to create a diagnostic, therapeutic, and theoretical system best corresponding to the actual conditions. To this school belong several outstanding descriptions of certain clinical cases of disease, such as epilepsy, migraine, and asthma, by Aretaeus and perhaps even Galen. It was Galen himself who finally succeeded in collecting and ordering the entire body of knowledge of the physicians of antiquity beginning with Hippocrates (a 20-volume Greek-Latin edition by Kühn), and on the basis of numerous self-observations and experiments wrote a commentary on the *Corpus.* In collecting the knowledge of antiquity first place belongs to Galen and not to the *Corpus Hippocraticum.* If Hippocrates was, so to speak, the symbol of medicine, Galen may be viewed as his scientific disseminator. If Hippocrates is "the father of medical science," Galen was for the Roman, Byzantine, and medieval doctors of the West—as well as of the East—the true *princeps medicorum* (foremost of doctors).

Up to this point we have followed the development of medicine in antiquity to a science based on philosophy. On the basis of the representations of doctors we have been able to gain an impression of the high regard in which the best representatives of this profession were held in Greece. But it should be remembered that, next to it, a kind of religious medicine, theurgy, was practiced in Greece, spread from there throughout the entire Mediterranean area, and later held sway in the Roman Empire. This system was closely connected with the name of Aesculapius. Even more abundant than the portrayal of doctors are the statues of the healing god, whose attribute was a caduceus, retained to this day as the symbol of medicine in all countries of the world. Wherever wandering physicians could not be found; for all those who could not afford the required fee (because there were no social provisions for the treatment of the poor); and for those who suffered from chronic diseases or were consid-

Adonis wounded, assisted by Venus and being bandaged
by cupids. Pompeian painting.

ered incurable and were forbidden for this reason to be treated by a physician—for all these the only solution was to turn to Aesculapius and his priests for help.

We have mentioned above that Aesculapius was originally, as stated in the *Iliad,* a prince of Thrace and was regarded as an important physician who was first added to the Olympians in the sixth century B.C. The oldest god of healing encountered in the Homeric epic is Paeon, the "doctor of the gods." Almost all gods were designated as Paeonii, when they were engaged in acts of healing, so that the father god himself was sometimes called "Zeus Paean" or "Zeus Soter." Actually the god of healing and protector of medical science, but also the sender of pernicious diseases, was subsequently Apollo, the god of light, who is the first to be invoked in the Hippocratic Oath. In Homer he is still shooting down disease-laden arrows to avenge himself against the humans.

Hesiodus first reported the wonderful birth of Aesculapius in the seventh century B.C., as the son of Apollo and the mortal Coronis, whom the latter had seduced. As Coronis was to be married by another, she was murdered by Apollo's sister Artemis; but the god let the innocent child live in the pregnant body of the mother and cut it while still living from the body. Aesculapius was then entrusted to the centaur Chiron, who initiated him in the secrets of medical science. Pindar also repeated this legend with slight changes in the fifth century B.C. He portrays Aesculapius as a mortal, but as son of a god. In later accounts his birth is seen as a divine miracle and it is surely no coincidence that the legend of his descent from a godly father, Apollo, and his birth from a virgin mother, Coronis, later greatly added to his being the sole Greek god to offer real competition to Christ, the Saviour. Thus his cult was especially singled out for battle by the rising Christians; whereas they usually recognized heathen authorities in medicine such as Hippocrates and Galen, as their representation in a Christian church proves.

Aesculapius' oldest cult establishment is to be found in Thricca in Thrace, the same locale which yields the earliest accounts of the mortal physician. From there his worship seems to have spread rapidly. Certain cult centers were established in Epidaurus at the end of the sixth century, 420 B.C. in Athens, 408 B.C. in the port of Piraeus, and on the Island of Kos in the middle of the fourth century B.C. About this time, the cult also reached Pergamum in Asia Minor and finally, in 291 during an epidemic in Rome, spread very rapidly through the whole Roman Empire, in the provinces as well as the city itself. In all these cities so-called Aesculapius statues were erected. These were places of pilgrimage, toward which the sick and suffering wandered, in order to be cured by the god in a temple sleeping ceremony. In the midst of a holy grove, in which neither a child could be born nor a human being

Aesculapius and his daughter Hygeia

"Don't forget we owe Aesculapius a cock," said Socrates before drinking the hemlock.

VATICAN MUSEUM, ROME

Japyx and Aeneas

With the aid of an instrument, Japyx, a doctor, removes an arrow from the thigh of Aeneas, the hero of Troy. Pompeian painting.

NATIONAL ARCHAEOLOGICAL MUSEUM, NAPLES

Bone-setting of jaw

This miniature is the ninth-century A.D. copy of an illustration in Kition's "The Commentary of Apollonius," composed around the year 60 B.C. The patient, suffering from a dislocation of the lower jaws, is sitting on a stool. The doctor seizes the dislocated jaw between his fingers and puts it back into place while an assistant holds the patient's head.

BIBLIOTECA MEDICEA LAURENZIANA, FLORENCE

die, the holiest of temples was to be found, always with a statue of Aesculapius, a holy spring, and a round construction, the Tholos (to this day unexplained), in which perhaps the harmless ritual snakes were kept by the priests. It further consisted of the Abaton, the incubation hall, which as a pergola-shaped portico often surrounded the smaller area. These temples resembled theaters, for the pilgrims had prepared themselves for the coming great event, the temple sleep of a physical and psychic catharsis, with the aid of water from the spring and fitting theatrical presentations. These preparations were supposed to result in a kind of expectant tension. The pilgrims also had to make sacrifices to the godheads and the priests, either before or after the procedure, mainly consisting of figurines which still give us a good picture of the sicknesses treated by Aesculapius and the details of the therapeutic process. Powerful suggestions by the priests raised the receptivity of the patient for the expected visit of the god during incubation. Serpents, his symbol, and disguised priests who helped carry out healing measures gave the semiconscious patients the impression that the god had personally taken over their case. And there seems to be no doubt that the dreams and daydreams of these neuropathic or hysterical patients could certainly have led to the cure of their functional afflictions. Actually, most of the sick belonged to this category. This wonder-working intervention on the part of Aesculapius is repeatedly represented in votive tablets. Here the moment is portrayed on a relief of the fifth-fourth century B.C., which today is in the Piraeus museum: Aesculapius with the help of his daughter, Hygeia, is about to aid the patient lying in a therapeutic sleep on a stretcher, the slumber bed. Across from him, three observers are standing, perhaps friends or relatives of the patient, who together with the even smaller-sized slaves (portrayed according to social rank) have raised their right hand in an incantation and are awaiting the outcome of the miracle cure.

The votive picture renders rather well the patient's conviction that in the dream he is actually seeing Aesculapius—here not only as *deus ex machina* but also as the actively examining and treating divine physician. The description is quite different from that of Christ's miracle cures in the New Testament which are, as a rule, cures by the power of word and faith. The memory of Homer's "incomparable physician" still seems to be alive in this Aesculapius. Similarly active, but still much livelier in an almost mannerist fashion, Aesculapius is pictured with Hygeia at the sickbed in another Greek sculpture from Tanagra. This one, however, has to be pictured in color in order to realize the full impact of its aliveness. Here too the patient is resting, half reclining on the stretcher. Hygeia has however graduated from the role of passive companion to that of an active helper. In fact, later stat-

Aesculapius with poppies

In the Iliad, Asclepios was only a prince. The Romans deified him under the name of Aesculapius. Here, he is leaning on the staff that eventually became the physician's symbol.

VATICAN MUSEUM, ROME

61

ues show her always holding a medical basin or feeding the snake, so that eventually she becomes the protective patron of pharmaceutics. On this sculpture the hypnotic effect, expected by Aesculapius' patients, has worked especially well. The authority of the divine doctor, the force that can make things grow, is clearly visible and contrasts with the marked lethargy of the exhausted and emaciated patient.

Aesculapius is very often portrayed not only with his favorite daughter Hygeia, who sometimes appears as his wife, but also with his whole family, as on the relief before us. Here again, in double lifesize, worshipers bring sacrificial offerings while two slaves are standing across from Aesculapius and his numerous relatives, equally pictured as godheads. The god of cure can be recognized by his (Aesculapian) caduceus, on which his right shoulder leans. Behind him, hardly to be recognized, is Hygeia, wearing a veil. Following her are the familiar sons, Machaon the surgeon and Podalirius, from the *Iliad*, who are usually invoked for diseases of the internal organs or mental illnesses.

The poet Arctinus has expressed this differentiation in his poem "The Plundering of Troy" in the following way:

To the one, he (their father) gave more dexterous hands, to pull arrows from the flesh, and to heal all wounds; to the other, he gave the power to see in his heart all invisible things and to heal the incurable. He was the first to understand the strangely gleaming eyes and to point out the depression of the mad Ajax.

There follow on the relief the three other daughters, whose names are directly related to medical science— Akeso (in Greek, "cure"), Jaso (in Greek, "to cure"), and Panakeia (in Greek, "all-healing") from which our term "panacea" originates.

On this relief, Aesculapius appears in classical form—a well-built, bearded man with benevolent, mild, spiritualized traits and of mature years, in order to lend him the attributes of the wise. He was often represented as a youth as well. This may be traced back to the Apollo statues, which showed the bringer of light as a glowing youth. Aesculapius was in the area of medicine his legitimate successor, a fact which influenced the early Christian portrayals of Christ, where the Lord also appeared as a victorious youth and rarely as a man of pain. Both Aesculapius and Christ, as we already know, were accorded the name *Soter* or saviour!

In this way, too, he almost always appears with his daughter Hygeia in Roman representations, sometimes standing or leaning on his caduceus, sometimes sitting on the throne, as in the temple of Epidaurus. But there are older chthonian (earth-dwelling) symbols of the snake, which appears as a phylactery as early as 2000 B.C. on the

famous vase of King Gudea of Lagash, in the Old Testament as an animal of seduction, and also in the story of the brazen serpents of Moses as well as in Egyptian and Cretan lore. The staff, which is next to him, is assumed to symbolize the branch of a pine tree from the holy grove.

Other, less familiar symbols were ascribed to Aesculapius, as shown on the pedestal of an Aesculapius statue, where worshipers or the children of Aesculapius bring a sacrificial cock to the god. So Plato has his teacher Socrates say with his last words: "I owe a cock to Aesculapius," because the god of healing was also the lord of euthanasia, the gentle sliding into the other world, the Empire of the Dead; it was he who controlled the harmonious crossing over the river Acheron.

Aesculapius was not the only one who aided sick persons who could not expect help from the doctors. Among the other gods or heroes of healing the figure of Amphiaraus stands out. His ancestor, the seer Melampus, had accomplished miracle cures among the raving mad. Amphiaraus seems also to have been a chthonian earth-god. The legend relates that pursued by enemies, he was hidden by Zeus in a chasm and was thus made immortal. His most important cult sites were found in Thebes, Oropus in the Attic peninsula, and Athens. Pilgrims who journeyed to his holy abode had to refrain from eating for three days and from drinking for one day; then they had to sacrifice a ram and lie down on its skin for the healing sleep. Some time ago, a votive relief of someone named Archinus to Amphiaraus was found in Oropus, originating in 380-370 B.C., and affording an interesting insight into the extensive secularization of the Greeks' world of gods, which also found its parallel in art under the influence of natural philosophy. The one who commissioned the work of art was perhaps still completely convinced of his cure by the divine helper. Not the artist, however, who in the foreground represented the patient's dream and in the background, i.e. synoptically, pictured the healing process as he imagined it. In this specific respect, this relief is a unique artistic and historical document. Whereas to the left a bearded god of healing, portrayed in a likeness to Aesculapius supporting himself on a staff, is tending the shoulder affliction of the standing patient—in this way, Archinus imagined the healing process—the artist shows the patient in the background lying on the stretcher, his shoulder being licked by a temple snake, while a priest is reciting the fitting verbal incantation. In this representation, we see the transformation in thinking which

*Roman soldiers
treating their wounded comrades*
Fragment of the Trajan column, 113 A.D.

ROME

62

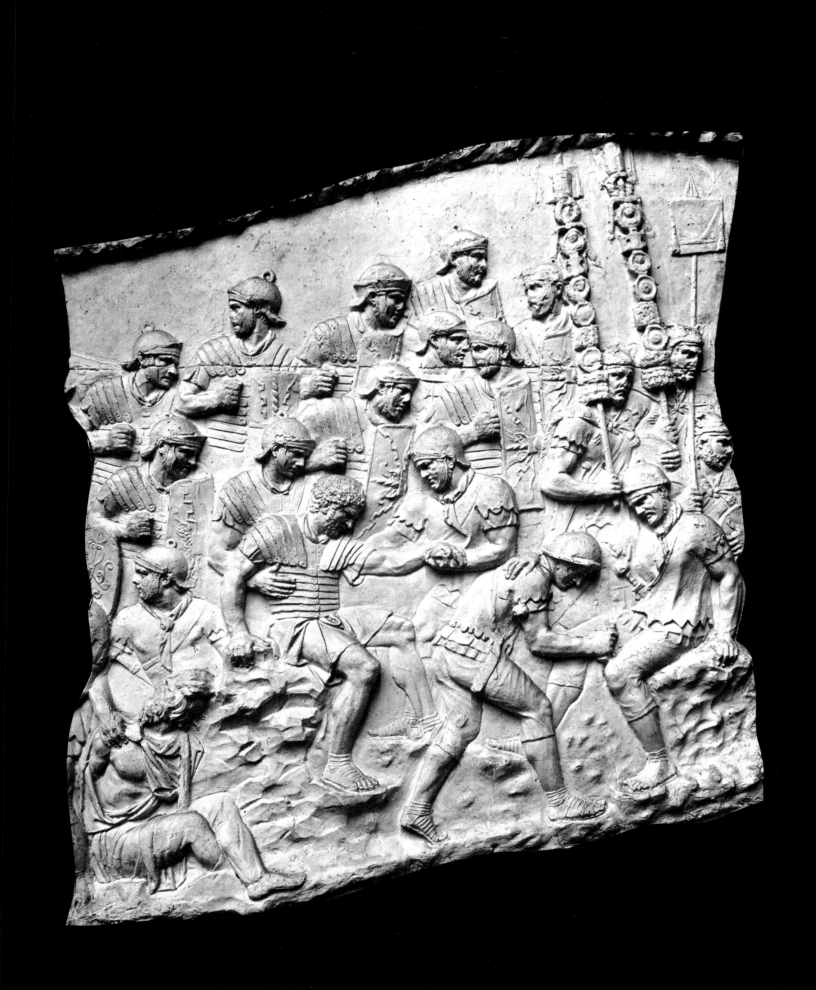

marks the beginning of the dethroning of the old gods. We are reminded in this respect of the statement in the *Corpus Hippocraticum,* that epilepsy was not, as previously held, a special malady, a holy disease, but that its origin could be explained in the same way as all other disease.

The doctor in Rome played a comparatively modest role in contrast to his greatly respected position in Greece. Down to the time of Julius Caesar (100-44 B.C.) only slaves and Greek doctors who were freed men practiced medicine. Any respectable Roman citizen would have been outraged if he had been required to earn his living as a doctor. Cato's invectives (234-149 B.C.) clearly reveal the image of the Greek physician, but they also disclose that, despite all contempt for medical achievement, there existed great interest in medical problems. Caesar finally bestowed Roman citizenship on all who practiced medicine and the Emperor Augustus (63 B.C. - 14 A.D.) freed all doctors from taxation as a result of a successful cure by his personal physician Antonius Musa.

Roman girl with arm-injury.

The representation of a Roman military dressing station on Trajan's column, the remains of various invalids, a kind of army hospital, and many discoveries of instruments show that military medicine was given high standing. However, the only classical Roman author who edited a fundamental work on medicine was Aulus Cornelius Celsus (25 B.C.-50 A.D.), himself not a doctor but a landed proprietor, who in a kind of encyclopedia also discussed medical science. In fact, only this section of his work has survived. It was only in the Christian era, with its completely different attitude toward the physician as a servant and subject of Christ, and the consequent high esteem for medical science, that there emerged some important late Roman doctors such as Cassius Felix, Vindician, and Caelius Aurelianus.

The fine arts and painting as well as poetry often liked to use medical motifs. As the cult of Aesculapius also spread rapidly in Rome, it comes as no surprise that numerous Roman statues of Aesculapius were produced, in part copies of Greek originals and in part original creations by Roman artists. Without exception they all retained the previously mentioned attributes of the divine doctor, often showing his daughter and companion Hygeia and sometimes the little hooded Telesphorus, the god "who brings to an end," i.e., the happy end of a sickness, recuperation. Increasing interest in naturalistic portraits was shown by Roman art. Not only were emperors portrayed with stark realism but also sickness itself. The sick human being was revealed for the first time with his special physiognomy. An art arises which attempts to redraw the face of the sick person as if the artist no longer (a sign of the disintegration of classicism and *kalokagathia*) feels bound to the laws of harmony. Thus contradictory statues appear, such as the portrait of a sick old woman and on the other side the statue of a young and very lovely Roman girl with an arm injury. One piece of art seems to show the resignation of old age, the other budding hope for early recovery. Both statues, however, are equally far removed from the strict harmony of Greek antiquity; both are, so to speak, snapshots, whereas Greek sculpture consistently attempted to throw light on the essence of things.

Once again a special development occurred in Roman art: in the mosaic and the fresco. We possess in some Pompeian frescoes representations with very interesting medical themes. Subjects from antiquity were chosen by preference. Virgil's *Aeneid* brought the Trojan War back into popular appeal, and it is not surprising that among the Pompeian paintings there is also a scene representing the doctor Japyx removing an arrow from Aeneas, the founder of Rome, with a pair of tongs. This was a wound received at Troy; Venus appears in the background, with a jar of ointment containing soothing bal-

Sick woman
Roman bronze discovered at Vichy, France.

LOUVRE, PARIS

sam. Here the old theme of medical help is again treated in a realistic manner, as was the case of the Greek vase painter, Sosias.

We encounter this motif, the healing of injuries, in another fresco at Pompei, in which Cupids are bandaging the wounded Adonis. Such scenes seem to have been very familiar to the martial Romans, but one should not forget that statues of doctors and representations of ointment sellers were well known in Rome; and, as in Greece, the Romans liked to add the attributes of their profession, surgical instruments as well as ointment jars, or even an Aesculapius staff which, in the case of Augustus' personal physician Musa, identified him as outstanding.

A new movement began, Christianity, which cast its shadow over late antiquity. Not only did it exercise important influence on medical ethics, though in other respects it took over the scientific structure of medicine in the ancient world; but it also followed new paths in the arts, whose relation to medicine we shall trace below.

65

Tlazolteotl

She was the goddess of childbirth as well as of fertility and of corn.

Here, she is depicted giving birth. Of all the positions used for childbirth among primitive peoples, this one seems particularly unfortunate. Goddess though she may be, Tlazolteotl's face is distorted by a grimace of pain, while the delivery itself is not very felicitous for the baby, who normally would strike the ground.

Mexico, Aztec period.

The Medicine
of the Aztecs, Mayas, and Incas

It is a curious phenomenon, explainable only in terms of the European-centered viewpoint of Western medical history, that the medical science of the ancient American civilizations has until recently awakened very little interest. This despite the fact that after the discovery of the new continent, in addition to the reports of the conquistadores and missionaries, numerous proofs of medical skill became known to the Old World, in the form of splendidly illuminated pictorial codices, through information imparted by Spanish doctors sent to the young colonies, and through the introduction into Europe of many new and effective drugs.

Only in the last few decades have archaeologists, art historians, religious philosophers, and medical historians concerned themselves with these largely forgotten civilizations; now one discovery follows another.

Because of the lack of any real historical understanding of the original inhabitants of Central and South America, it was the custom up to the twentieth century to speak only of pre- and post-Columbian culture. It has now become necessary to broaden and complete this too primitive scheme of things. For we have discovered that in all of America there existed two high cultures, geographically divided by the Isthmus of Panama and the Andes. These cultures, like high mountain peaks, towered over a mass of otherwise primitive accumulators and hunters who comprised nomadic Indian tribes. These two cultures are now labeled "Mesoamerican" (i.e., Middle American) and the "Andean culture." The so-called " Mesoamerican cultural area" includes Mexico and parts of Guatemala and Honduras. Here at the time of the conquest of Mexico (1519-1521) by Hernan Cortes, of Guatemala (1524) by Pedro de Alvarado, and of Yucatan (1527-1546), were found the empires of the Aztecs and the Mayas. These two cultures show a close relationship without merging into each other. Both erected their state structures on the ruins of much older, archaic high cultures, mostly named after their place of discovery. One such older culture may be that of Tlatilco, on the plateau of Mexico, which according to archaeological evidence and modern radiocarbon methods can be dated at around 1500 B.C. About 600 B.C., a special cultural development began in the zone of the Gulf of Mexico, around the place of discovery, La Venta: it was that of the tribe of the Olmecs. At approximately the same time as the birth of Christ, we can place the ceramic cultures on the west coast of Colima, Nayarit, and Jalisco as well as near Mexico City—the Teotihuacan culture, carried on by the forerunners of the Aztecs, the Toltecs.

For the history of the Mayan cultures we can reach back to the magnificent Mayan calendar—the calendar hieroglyphs are the only ones that have been deciphered up to now—and to various monuments, not quite in the distinct style of the Mayas, found in the Gulf zone, at the scientifically verified date of 21 B.C. By contrast the first typical Maya-dated monument, a plaquette in Leyden, can be placed in the year 317 A.D. It can thus be maintained that the historical development of the Mesoamerican cultures spanned a much longer period of time, about 2000-3500 years, than was heretofore thought.

In South America those Indians living in the western Andes, in the mountain valleys and plains of the border region, were culture bearers. We differentiate here in the area of modern Peru between the Inca empire, which in the twelfth-thirteenth centuries A.D. first consolidated itself and subsequently extended far beyond present-day Chile, and a developed splinter culture, the so-called " Chimu Empire," developing about 400-1400 A.D. in the region of the present-day Peruvian coastal strip and later forced to pay tribute to the Incas. Both cultures were wiped out with inhuman cruelty by Pizarro in 1532.

Knowledge of their fine arts is also of some importance for medicine, since neither the Aztecs nor the Incas possessed any actual written records: the Quipu writing of the Incas served solely for registration and tax collection, and the hieroglyphs of the Mayas, except for the numbers, have to this day not been deciphered. There are only the wonderfully illuminated picture codices, almost all produced at the incentive of discerning Spanish monks shortly after the Conquest. These were often translated into Spanish and bore commentaries on the events pictured, thus permitting a closer insight into a world completely foreign to Europeans. The contemporary Spanish reports also give interesting details, which are naturally subjectively colored; yet despite revulsion at the Aztec practice of human sacrifice, they confess repeated admiration for the magnificent architectural and artistic creations of the Mesoamerican peoples. There is, for instance, the description of the old residence of Tenochtitlán (Mexico City),

Maternal idol

Pregnant woman.
Valley of Mexico, tenth century.

LE CORNEUR ROUDILLON COLLECTION, PARIS

68

which was originally situated in the midst of a salt lake and served as a defensive barrier. At the time of the Conquest, it contained 300,000 inhabitants and was highly regarded by Cortés' co-warriors as the "Venice of America" because of its many canals and garden installations. The still preserved step pyramids, on the platform of which temples were erected in honor of the sun god, and which witnessed untold human offerings were, in contrast to those in Egypt, very rarely used as burial places. Even the harsh Spanish conquerors admired them. Today still we continue to discover pyramids in the domain of the Mayas in the Yucatán jungle—evidence of cultures long since disappeared.

The foundation and guiding principle of these Mesoamerican cultures was their pronounced polytheism. The Aztecs, for instance, worshiped a large number of gods enjoying equal rights who, they believed, also influenced health and sickness. To each god certain attributes were ascribed. The famous white god of the winds and peace, Quetzalcoatl, who according to Aztec belief was to reappear from the East after a period of collapse (a belief that greatly facilitated Cortés' conquest), was represented with a pointed hat and, completely unexpectedly, a goatee. A legendary early king of the Toltecs, he is supposed to have disappeared to the East in 987 A.D. His return, like that of Jesus Christ in the imagination of the first Christians, was expected at a definite time. Whereas the Christian religion then left the reappearance of Christ to the unexaminable decision of God alone, the Aztecs believed they could predict the return of their god on the basis of calendar calculations. They had just predicted his return for the year 1519, the so-called "Cane-year 1" when Cortes landed on Central American territory with his private army.

Known as the god of war and fighting, Hitzlilopochtli, may be considered his opponent. To honor him, thousands of unfortunate prisoners were slaughtered, because the Aztecs believed that he had to be nourished by human blood; in the event of lack of this divine food, the sun would remain in the underwold and would not rise again. In the light of this concept, we may get some understanding of the sacrificial orgies of the Aztecs, who murdered their prisoners not in pure sadism but in a state of panic over an impending world catastrophe. This elemental sacrificial act was repeatedly illustrated in the picture codices. The process is particularly impressive in one picture, painted in blatant colors. We see the pyramid temple and the enthroned god of the underworld Micttlantecuhtli, who is usually symbolized by a skull and skeleton limbs and with a black banner of mourning. On the steps of the temple a human sacrifice has just been

Man showing an injury in his right leg
Western Mexico, Nayarit culture, Eighth century.
LE CORNEUR ROUDILLON COLLECTION, PARIS

Head sculpture

A tumor in the lower left eyelid, another in the earlobe.
Gulf of Mexico, Vera Cruz culture. Sixth century.

LE CORNEUR ROUDILLON COLLECTION,
PARIS

made. The high priest has just ripped out the heart of a prisoner lying on the sacrificial altar, making a quick incision with the obsidian knife from underneath the ribwall through the diaphragm. The incident had to occur with lightning speed, for the god was only interested in the blood and the emanation of the still-beating heart; and these two are just rising heavenward in the shape of torchlike offerings. The dead person was then rolled down the steps of the temple where the corpse was immediately seized upon by a large, silently waiting crowd, so that they could also participate in the superhuman emanation. Everyone tried to retrieve a part of the body so as to devour it in a sacred rite of cannibalism at home among the family circle. The victims themselves were not supposed to utter a sound during the ceremony and, if possible, were supposed to climb up the narrow, steep steps to the place of sacrifice under their own power. This was undoubtedly possible only because they had been prepared through medications and drugs, so that they entered a kind of trancelike state. Curious idols, designated as *Caras Sonrientes* (Smiling Faces), dressed for the sacrificial scenes in the typical minimal dress—loincloth and necklace—and were seized with peculiar convulsions, throwing their arms and head upwards. According to many scholars, these were supposed to be the specially prepared prisoners. As a matter of fact, in recent years drugs that strongly affect the psyche have been discovered and extracted from two old Aztec plants, Teonanacatl and Ololiuqui. One of the alkaloids belongs, according to researches of Cerletti and Hoffmann at the Sandoz laboratories, to the group of lysergic acid derivatives; the other one was made available for research as psilocybin. Earlier, mescaline, possessing similar effects, had been extracted from the peyote cactus. Actually the use of such substances does induce in the person in question a state of indifference toward his environment. Through hallucinations the immediate environment is no longer recognized. The taking of these drugs can lead (as shown by the personal experiences of explorers and through various scientific experiments) to a kind of serenity. This it is that explains the individual's stoic acceptance of his inevitable end. Moreover, the belief persisted among the Aztecs and the many peoples oppressed by them that those who died on the sacrificial altar would go to the highest of the three otherworldly empires. This conviction too eased the "passage."

The distinctive otherworldly concepts of the Aztecs are closely linked to medical problems. Into the lowest sphere, the Shadow Empire ruled by Mictlantecuhtli, all those voyaged who had died from disease and old age. For those who died suddenly through natural phenomena such as lightning or drowning, but also for those who lost their lives through contagious disease, a higher domain was foreseen—a kind of earthly paradise, located above the clouds and under the rule of the rain god Tlaloc. A far higher place in the hereafter was destined for those who had fallen in battle, for warriors butchered on the sacrificial altars, and, surprisingly enough, for women who died

Hunchback with tattooed face
Western Mexico. Jalisco culture. Sixth-seventh century.
NATIONAL ARCHAEOLOGICAL MUSEUM, MEXICO CITY

in childbirth. They ascended to the heavenly paradise and, while the warriors accompanied the sun every day from its rising to its zenith, the women who died in childbirth then took over the task, until the setting of the sun.

If not enough prisoners were available for the sacrificial scenes, special wars were fought by the Aztecs to obtain the required number for sacrifice. Then too the Aztec nobles had to offer their own blood through blood-letting with an obsidian knife, wounding feet, ears, nose, or, in the most extreme case, by gouging out an eye. Here too the picture codices present appropriate examples. Similar concepts existed among the considerably less bloodthirsty Mayas. Relief sculptures show the self-castigation of priests who pull a thick rope through a hole in their tongue.

The special female patron of medicine among the Aztecs was Tlazoeteotl, the earth goddess and protector of the main article of food, corn. She was often pictured wearing the skin of a sacrificial victim, but in most cases during the act of birth of the real corn goddess. This sculpture, interesting for art as well as for medical history, permits us to draw some conclusions about the process of birth in the Central American civilizations. The goddess is bending in a typical crouching position, whereas the newborn baby is presented most often from the position of the forehead. However, the two upper extremities as proffered are only to be understood ritually. The suffering facial expression, almost distorted into a grimace, shows the painfulness of the delivery.

A special god, the god of spring, known as Xipe Totec, "Our Lord of the Oppressed," existed for certain very prevalent skin diseases of Central America. He was especially associated with the skin of sacrificial victims, with which he appears clothed on the numerous reliefs preserved. The flayed skin was a symbol of nature's renewal; at the same time a kind of generating power to cure skin diseases was ascribed to it. This human fleece was always represented in a realistic manner on the statues. The eye and mouth areas were carefully cut out of the scalp and this skin was then knotted together in the back of the head. The upper and lower part of the body was completely covered by this skin, which was also tied together in the back. The flayed skin of the hands and feet hung loosely from the extremities, and the modern observer can often see the fatal sacrificial wound in the breast region, through which the priest reached to tear the living heart from the dying victim's body. On the god's days of worship, the "day of human flagellation," orgiastic sacrificial celebrations took place. The priests of Xipe Totec wrapped themselves in the still-steaming human skins and ran for days dressed in this fashion through the streets,

touching every person afflicted with a skin disease so as to cure them, until the ever increasing odor of decay of the disintegrating organic material forced them to take off the terrible garment.

Numerous other gods coexisted, each one for a specific area of disease. The abovementioned rain god Tlaloc was held responsible for rheumatism and colds. One of the five female demons, Giuteotl, was held to be the originator of epilepsy and hemorrhages and was therefore mostly pictured with convulsed limbs, ulcers, and in the *status vomiendi*. A special god, Xolotl-Nanahuatzin, was considered capable of spreading the abscess diseases we now associate with syphilis or frambesia, because he was described with "rubberlike boils" and "flowerlike growths." Such symptoms may, of course, also be leishmaniosis or other tropical diseases. Often the god with pronounced *gummata* or bubonic boils was pictured as cleansing himself by burning himself in a pot, only to reappear later in a cured form. There also exist artistically impressive face masks attributed to him—examples of artistic mosaic work set with jade, obsidian, and other jewels, and possessing ceremonial attributes. Syphilis apparently was not recognized as a sexual disease, since we know that special gods existed for the diseases of the sexual organs, the god of music and dance Xochipilli, and the goddess of love, Xochiquetzal. The magician god Tezcatlipoca was always represented with the underarm bone (the radius) of a woman who had died in childbirth, which he is supposed to have stolen and with which he hypnotized his victims—a forerunner of the magic wand in our fairy tales. The magician god spread dropsy and leprosy, with its early and so typical symptom, the falling out of the eyebrows. Amimitl and Atlana were held responsible for diarrhoea; Xolotl for miscarriages and the equally feared birth of twins, which in many early cultures was viewed as an omen fraught with danger.

The mask of Xoloto-Nanahuatzin

This mask is considered one of the finest works of art in pre-Columbian Mexico. It is covered with tiny turquoises representing Nanahuatzin's syphilis. He was one of the gods who foregathered at Teotihuacán to create the sun. He was the only one willing to fling himself into a brazier, and his heart flew towards the sky and became Tonatiuh, the sun.
Aztec civilization.

BRITISH MUSEUM, LONDON

Human sacrifice

A priest has just torn out the heart of a prisoner and is presenting it to the gods. At the foot of the temple stairs, another captive is lying, with his chest slashed open.
Codex Magliabecchiani. Sixteenth century.

Similar gods reigned over health and illnesses among the peoples belonging to the Mayan civilization. The god Zamna had the same function generally speaking as Tlazolteotl: protector of medical science. He was, like Aesculapius and Christ, viewed as both god and human and was considered a "saviour" and the founder of medical science. Two other gods, Ixchel and Cibolontun, were looked upon as the discoverers of numerous healing drugs.

Artistic representations from this cultural area still teach us today through many sculpturally rendered diseases. The little piece of sculpture shown here, from the eighth century A.D. in the vicinity of Teotihuacán, again has birth as its motif. It may have been used as an incense burner. It shows a wide vaginal opening together with an amorphous dummy of a child. In contrast to the much more realistic portrayal of the earth goddess, everything is rendered abstractly here, with the exception of a phantom's rich and magnificent headgear. On the other hand, the sculpting of the head with a large tumor in the left ear region is, without doubt, very realistic, and here the "blear-eye" is again the most marked symbol of disease. Odd little sculptures in crouching positions show scar marks on the upper arms, which could have stemmed

either from an injury or from a past sickness, for instance, the *lues*. Only one diagnosis that might come to mind can be excluded with certainty: the pox. It is a known fact that smallpox was first brought into the West Indies after the Spanish conquest in 1517 and led to the annihilation of many Indian tribes. These epidemics also were used by the Aztec artists; however, not until Spanish rule, in the much-loved and typical calendar representations. The Aztecs and the Mayas were familiar with two differing but subtly interwoven calendar systems: the sun calendar with eight twenty-day-long months to which were added five rest days, so that in fact 365 days were obtained; and the augurian calendar which was exceedingly important for medical prognoses and consisted of twenty thirteen-day-periods, designated in the calendar books as the so-called Tonalamaxtl, from a combination of thirteen point-shaped day symbols and twenty symbolic animal-and-plant pictures. Altogether this calendar numbered 260 days. Certain combinations of days were thought to be lucky; others as bringing bad luck. Especially feared were the last five days of the sun calendar, the Nemontemi, on which no work was done. During this time no doctor could be persuaded to bring help; it would have been useless anyway. Calendar soothsayers, as well as corn-kernel throwers and water-seers, as pictured in the codices, were, next to the quite highly esteemed doctors and midwives, much sought-after quacks. Interest in medicine and in sick persons was apparently very great. In Mexico and Peru a large number of statuettes and earthen pots was found, representing pathologically deformed human beings or parts of the body. Particular attention was paid to hunchbacks. Repeatedly, we see humps, resulting either from atrophy, so that we assume tuberculosis, or without atrophy, heads with pronounced marks of disease, with hairlips, and cleft palates as well and typical chondrodystrophy with the familiar disproportion between hands and limbs and extremities.

Mesoamerican pathogenetic concepts are undoubtedly based on thoroughly rational maxims, especially in regard to external afflictions; but they also embody the world-wide notion of "sickness as a result of sin." Excesses of various kinds, especially sexual, overindulgence by the young and healthy in intoxicating drinks which could only be prescribed by doctors and priests to the sick and men over sixty, and other violations could make those involved vulnerable to the harmful influences of the different gods. Consequently, therapy consisted in a kind of confession and absolution, exercises which were occasionally represented pictorially and in which the sinner, the Tlaelquani, was forced to eat the excrement streaming from his anus. If the violation on the part of the sick person had been unconscious, intoxicating and hallucinatory drinks served to transport the patient into a kind of trancelike state, making it possible to discover which sin lay behind the sickness. The doctor was thus both confessor and healer.

The Incas also had similar pathogenic concepts, despite their otherwise extensive cultural differences from the cultures of the Mesoamerican area; these, however, had much more far-reaching consequences. Their religious concepts were altogether different. Basically, a kind of sun cult was embraced in which the godhead was personified by the Inca Great King, whose prosperity and well-being were intimately connected with that of the whole population. The higher the rank of the personality who became sick, the greater his sin appeared to be, and therefore it was almost a catastrophe if the God King himself fell sick. The entire population then had to make heavy penance. Hundreds stormed to the river edges to make private confessions, thereby wanting to help absolve the sick king. Here too human sacrifices similar to those of the Aztecs, though not practiced to the same degree, were prevalent. Numerous drugs and such surgical measures

Ciuateotl, a goddess or female demon, the dispenser of epilepsy and ulcers, holding the signs of these illnesses. Codex Vaticanus. Sixteenth century.

Indian eating psychotropic or hallucinatory mushrooms. before the god Mictlantecuhtli. Codex Magliabecchiani. Sixteenth century.

Birth

Divinity with the plumed headpiece that supposedly enabled sterile women to become fertile. In the lower opening, a symbolic depiction of the child was placed.
Mexico, San Juan Teotihuacán.
Eighth century.

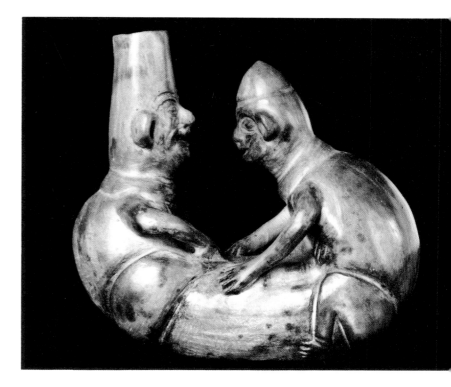

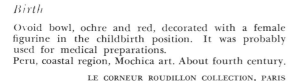

Birth

Ovoid bowl, ochre and red, decorated with a female figurine in the childbirth position. It was probably used for medical preparations.
Peru, coastal region, Mochica art. About fourth century.

Doctor treating a patient
Peru, Mochica ceramic. About fourth century.

as trepanation, which seems to have been used fairly often, were available to the Incas. The same predilection as among the Aztecs and their forerunners is to be found among the Incas in a larger number of impressive, artistic, and often quite appealing, representations of diseases. The latter, in view of the distinct lack of pre-Columbian written remains, give us some insight into the medical situation. The medical consultation—with the almost classical animated discussion between the dignified listening doctor and the vehemently complaining patient—is this illustration from the Mochica culture of the fourth century, which gives a direct impression of the patient-doctor relationship. It stands at the beginning of a tradition which was carried on by the great Western painters, in particular the Dutch, after Greek sculpture had already treated this valuable theme.

Especially famous are the earthen pitchers and vases from the North Peruvian Mochica culture and their very numerous representations of disease. The pitchers probably developed from the custom of using the skulls of slain enemies in the form of drinking cups—the purpose being to imbibe the strength and power of the slaughtered enemy. Later an entire new genre of art developed from this usage. One often finds representations of oddly mutilated upper lips and noses, which look as if they were amputated with a knife: we must regard them in part as caused by sacred and punitive incisions, but they are also remnants of past abscess diseases such as *lues* and *leishmaniosis*. The touching mother-and-child portrayal shows the typical flat nose indicative of syphilis, which is also visible on the child, so that discerning researchers see a *Lues connata* here. The process of childbirth is also rendered on these vases. Of great value to medical history was the birth scene portrayed on a handle from the Mochica culture of the fourth century A.D. We see here a woman in labor in a seated position with a greatly arched body, before whom a midwife busies herself with the progress of the child's head. A helper is sitting behind the pregnant woman and holding firmly the body of the mother-to-be. But this representation of a birth from the

77

Hunchback

Peru, Chicama valley. Sixth-tenth century.

MUSÉE DE L'HOMME, PARIS

Woman giving birth

Peru, Mochica art. About fourth century.

MUSEUM FÜR VÖLKERKUNDE, BERLIN

Mochica culture of the fourth century may be set against another one in which the woman giving birth is seen in the same crouching position, as with the Aztec goddess, Tlazolteotl.

Trepanation played an important role in South America as contrasted with Central America, where it was practically unknown. Many skull finds demonstrate that, if the trepanation hole has completely healed or if it shows a hardened callus formation or if several trepanation holes are found at the top of the skull, the patient survived this heroic operation. Whether these operations were for cult purposes or for therapy of the mentally ill cannot be

Doctor and a sick child

Peru, Mochica art. Sixth-tenth century.

Blind man

Peru, Mochica art. Fourth century.

Syphilitic woman with her child

Peru, north coast, Mochica art. Fourth century.

definitely ascertained; the idea was that through the hole induced in the highest place on the human body a harmful pneuma or personal demon could be expelled. We must also mention that sculpture concerned itself with surgical instruments as well; and we know of a little sculpture of a T-shaped knife, which can be identified as an instrument for a trepanation. We can see on it the proceedings of an operation. Again three persons are visible: a patient, a doctor who is just about to begin the operation with the above-mentioned knife, and a helper who is supporting a patient who has probably been previously treated with drugs.

It is still unclear as to what led the Mochica Indians to form pictures of the sick and crippled on many of their utensils whereas, by contrast, their skull pitchers bore almost classical portrait sculptures that now, in the symmetry of their racial features, inspire the admiration of all who see them. Since we always come across skeletons among these works of art, we may perhaps conclude that we are here faced with a *memento mori et aegrotandi* which the Indians sought always to recall when using such vessels. But in this as in so many other aspects of the ancient American cultures, many questions still remain unsolved and need clarification.

The Good Samaritan

Emperor Otto III's Gospel book. End of the tenth century. Note the means of conveyance: the injured man, riding on a horse, is supported by two splints (bottom register).

Art and Medicine
in the Middle Ages in the West

Just as for the ancient physician a concern with philosophical questions was the basis for the practice of his profession, so the new era—which began with the recognition of Christianity in Europe and Asia Minor, in the Western as well as the Eastern Roman Empire—the Christian religion became the basis for medical practice. The invasion of Germanic tribes in the age of the great migrations which then set in did of course uproot the old order; but in no way did it destroy the cultural and intellectual accomplishments of the ancient world. An extensive adaptation of the old cultural heritage by the new conquerors occurred. As a result we see two currents in medicine. Whereas scientific medicine held fast to the foundations worked out in antiquity which, as we have seen, were organized by Galen into a convincing system of humoral pathology, with its theory of the four Humors, the practice of the medical art and the medical ethos was now shaped by the Christian attitude. This is particularly true of the relationship to the sick person (in antiquity generally considered an inferior individual), which

changes fundamentally. From now on, even the most miserable human being had a right to pity and aid—*misericordia* and *caritas* as the *Imago Dei* (Image of God) and as the "neighbor" in the sense of the New Testament. Christ himself appeared in the Gospels in numerous passages as the Saviour and legitimately took over the functions of the old *soter* or saviour, Aesculapius. Jesus was looked upon not only as the doctor of souls; he was also the saviour in bodily afflictions. Numerous miraculous cures were described by medieval men with great joy in both word and picture and were handed down in countless legends of the saints.

It is no surprise that in the fresco paintings and book illustrations, in miniatures and illuminated initials, and especially in the ivory carvings of artistic book bindings, the theme of "Christ and the sick" constantly recurred as a kind of pictorial Bible of the miraculous cures of the Lord. The healing of the blind-born was frequently the theme as was the expulsion of impure spirits, all treated with reference to the holy image. This carving.

Funeral stele of a woman doctor, found in Metz. This is the only known Gallic portrayal of a lady physician.

for instance, also shows the swine into which, according to the legend, the "exorcised" spirits were supposed to have entered. Other motifs were the curing of the cripple whose faith permitted him "to take up his bed and walk," a scene which could hardly be pictured more dramatically than on these ivory carvings where usually the first act of the miracle, the confrontation between the sick person tied to his bed and Jesus, is rendered. The healing of the leper afforded the medieval artist particular freedom in the portrayal of the pathological signs of leprosy. In such pictures we encounter for the first time the attributes of the lepers, who were excluded by the emerging medieval society in the West as well as the East, so that they could be known from afar as "outcasts": the leper's rattle and costume with bells still survive in perverted form in the carnival costumes in many regions of Germany, although the bearers today seldom realize the tragedy that was earlier connected with such dress.

The story of the hemorrhaging woman must have been especially disturbing to contemporaries, showing as it did the hopelessness of a woman given up by the physicians, to whom apparently only the heavenly doctor could give superhuman help. Mark relates this in 5.25-29 of his Gospel: "And there was a woman, who had had a hemorrhage for twelve years and had suffered much from the doctors and had spent all her fortune thereon and all this helped her nought; rather she became worse. As she had heard about Jesus, she came from the people, from behind and touched his gown, and said: 'If only I could touch his robe, I would become well.' And thereupon the source of her blood dried up and she felt in her body that she was healed from her plight."

In art too a new development resulted. From then on the harmonious, glowing, healthy, and godlike human being no longer stood in the center, though the first early Byzantine representations of Christ still show this ideal. Now rather the downtrodden, sick, and martyred figure became central, a figure often modeled on Job. Faithful to Christ's answer to the question of the Pharisees as to whether a person born blind had himself sinned or his parents had sinned, were the words: "Neither he nor his parents have sinned, but God's deeds are manifest upon him," proving God's almighty power and Christian mercy. Here we see one of the sources of the increasing interest in the sick person as a *testimonium Dei* (God's witness) in the now-frequent portrayals of sick people, cripples, paralytics, and the deformed.

Christ as doctor—in later times quite often pictured as the divine apothecary preparing in a contemporary apothecary shop beneficent medicines on the scales of justice, consisting of the ingredients of tolerance, compassion, moderation, etc.—was soon followed by the martyrs and the saints. Some of the latter were promoted in the popular mind to patron saints of specific diseases, because they had themselves suffered from these sicknesses and had been cured in miraculous fashion. Thus Saint Roch was patron of the plague. Others became patrons because they had suffered their martyrdom in a particular organ of the body. This happened to Saint Apollonia, all of whose teeth had been ripped out and who has since then been revered all over Europe as the patron saint of dentistry. In antiquity a similar process had occurred. Zeus himself, especially in the form of "Zeus Meilichios," was regarded

Wonder-healings

Three ivory plaques, depicting (from bottom to top) the healing of the possessed, the paralytic, and the woman "ill from a loss of blood." Italy, end of the fifth century.

LOUVRE, PARIS

as lord-protector of medical science; later Apollo and finally Aesculapius were given this post, and individual members of his family took over clearly delineated special tasks: including Hygeia, Panakeia, Machaon, Podalirius, and Telesphorus. Jesus too was replaced as direct patron of medical science by other personalities. Luke the Evangelist had been a doctor, and his symbol, the flying bull, adorns many a medical faculty seal. Thus the fourteen emergency helpers stepped into the place of Jesus. In particular the two brothers, Cosmas and Damian, became the patron-protectors of medical science, especially in the late medieval period with its dual development of medicine and pharmacy. The flowering period of the artistic representation of these martyrs, who probably date from the time of Emperor Diocletian in the third century A.D., came in the fourteenth, fifteenth, sixteenth, and even the seventeenth centuries. These examples in art will be discussed in a different place, but we may already point out here that the many representations of Cosmas and Damian offer interesting insights into the medical concepts of the laymen of that period. The saints were depicted either as undertaking one of their miraculous cures, the amputation of an abscessed leg and its replacement by the leg of a Moor, or with the then typical attributes of medicine and pharmacy, the urine glass or the book and ointment jar with spatula, or an apothecary jar. The attributes of doctors and pharmacists are taken from reality, as we can easily ascertain by comparing the pictures with preserved specimens; but the pictures of operations have purely symbolic value. They permit of no conclusions concerning prevailing operating methods, and thus interest medical history only in terms of theme and not of detail.

Quite different is the case presented of the numerous miniatures that offer such abundant evidence for our theme in the Latin manuscripts of both early and late Middle Ages. These codices were first of all meant for the educated monks, who appeared as the first and sometimes the only vehicles of culture. In this capacity they also became the protectors of medical tradition, and in numerous schools—to mention only a few: Chartres, Toledo, Monte Cassino, later Salerno, and Montpellier—they copied and disseminated throughout the West the ancient works of Greek doctors, mostly from Syrian-Arabic translations, and the Latin books of late Roman medicine. Nor was popular medical science neglected; in this work of enlightenment Saint Hildegard of Bingen (1098-1179) was especially active. Contrary to the still widespread opinion that the Middle Ages were concerned only with the saving of souls and that medicine was then in a period of retrogression, we must emphasize that this period took a lively interest in medical science, and in things of the body in general. The Church Fathers' concept of the body

as *vox animi*, as "garment or voice of the soul," and the dogma of the resurrection of the flesh were both mighty forces making for concern about the body. Of course, spiritual salvation consistently took precedence over physical salvation, and that was why confession and communion by the priest stood above medical therapy.

In this connection, there were frequent portrayals of the Good Samaritan, which occupied artists until Rembrandt and even down to our own time. In countless representations, the various stages in the divine narrative were laid before the eyes of the beholder, demonstrating the hard-heartedness of the Levites and the Pharisees and the mercifulness of the Samaritans whom the others held in contempt. Christ's teaching then became a part of the famous Benedictine rule of 529 A.D. in which it is stated: *"Infirmorum cura ante omnium et supra omnia adhibendum decet,"* "Care for the sick goes before everything and over everything"; and further, "One should serve them as did Christ, whom one is really serving in them, for He says: I was sick and you visited Me and what you have done to the lowliest, you have done to Me."

The idea of a hospital for the care of the wretched and weak in the Samaritan sense was taken up in Byzantium as early as 350 A.D. The Church Father Basil (330-379) founded a home near Caesarea, called a Xenodochion or Gerokodochion. This soon developed into a larger nursing compound, the Basileion. However, here the care of patients and the taking in of wearied pilgrims played a far greater role than actual treatment of the sick. It was the Islamic world that first developed the genuine concept of the hospital. From then on, nursing of the sick, whether in one's own home or in homes of the wealthy landowners in a *nosocomium* or a hospital, became a favorite motif for the artists, who thus sought by their example to praise these good works. At first more emphasis was placed on general things, as is shown in the miniature of the treatment of a sick person from a French manuscript of the thirteenth century. We see numerous people of both worldly and clerical rank standing in almost theatrical postures around a patient who is lying naked in his bed, according to the custom of the times, while another patient is having a fainting spell. The representations in the fourteenth and fifteenth centuries become more and more realistic, as the artist's interest in the details of the event becomes greater and greater. It seems as if even in this art, the turning away from abstract scholasticism to a newer, more individualistic philosophy of life has become noticeable.

But we must not make it appear as if there had been no interest in the rendering of detail in the Middle Ages. There can be no doubt about this. For example, the bizarrely shaped gargoyles on the Gothic cathedrals testify to the subtle gift of observation of the stonemasons who

Saint Cosmas

Saint Cosmas and his case of medical instruments, on the famous mosaic of the apse of the church of Cosmas and Damian in Rome. It dates from the time of Pope Felix IV (526-530). At the right side of the mosaic, Saint Peter, his hand on Cosmas' shoulder, is pointing at Jesus, sitting in the center. In his hands, hidden by his toga, Cosmas is carrying the crown of martyrdom. His instrument case, red and marked with a white cross, is attached to his belt.

worked on them. Notice this figure captured in the very act of vomiting who is shown after having taken an emetic—which next to blood-letting and purging was the most important method of therapeutic evacuation, and was supposed to bring about eucrasia—well-being—by normalizing and harmonizing the four Humors. The gargoyle is portrayed holding his breast with the left hand and reaching with the right hand for his head, so as to assist in the painful vomiting procedure. The decidedly expressionistic sculpture of the Cathedral of Strasbourg, although a hundred years older than the gargoyle mentioned above and dating from the high Gothic period, also demonstrates the artist's excellent gift for observation; it leaves no doubt as to the diagnosis of facial paresis—the ptosis of the left eyelid is portrayed in realistic fashion as is the downward-drooping corner of the mouth.

This realism is also clearly visible in the miniatures of a surgical manuscript of the school of Salerno from the eleventh century. Gradually the medical profession had passed from the monks to the lay doctors and had simultaneously undergone a separation of internal medicine and surgery, which was brought about by the Church's concept of *Ecclesia abhorret a sanguine*. According to canon law a priest lost his religious authority if he committed an

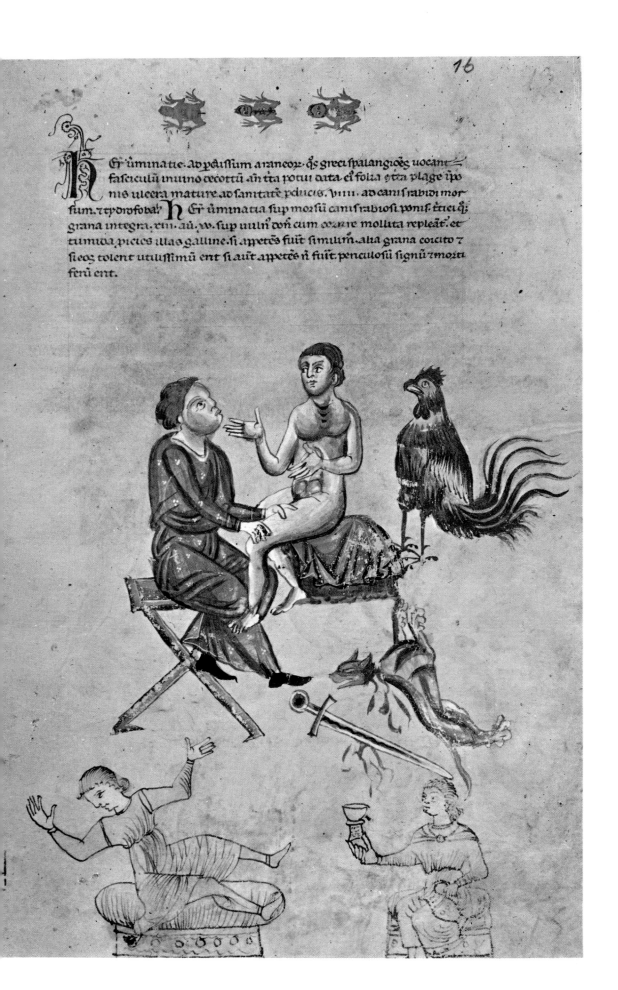

Er uminatie ad pdistium araneor. qs greci spalangices uocant fasciculu muino cecottu an tra potui data ei folia eta plage ipo nis ulcera mature ad sanitate pducis. vm. ad cam srabidi mor sum. rhydrofoba? h Er uminatia sup morsu cam srabiosi ponis. trie q grana integra. xm. au. xv. sup unln don cum cozine mollita repleat. et tumida picies illas galline. si appetes fuit simlim. alia grana coleito r si eos tolent utilissimu ent si aut appetes n fuit. periculosu signu rmorti feru ent.

The Verbena

Illumination, Italy, thirteenth century, after a lost manuscript dating from the fourth century.

1. Infused into wine or mixed with honey, and then applied to a wound, verbena soothes tarantula bites (but the drawing at the top shows frogs, an error probably to a confusion between "ranae" and "aranae.")

2. When used for bites by mad dogs, verbena is applied to the injury, from which the humor is running. Then the seeds are to be thrown to a cock. If he eats them, there is a chance of a cure; if he refuses them, this constitutes a sure sign of death (middle illustration).

3. Remedy for jaundice (bottom drawing).

Childbirth

Illumination, thirteenth century, copied from a lost manuscript of the fourth century.
The most original pages of this medical compilation uniting several treatises are nearly all taken from the work of Lucius Apuleius, called Barbarus, an Italian naturalist.

irregularity, i.e., if he became coresponsible for the death of a patient, as in the case of an unsuccessful operation. Consequently, first surgery, then general medical science divorced itself from monastic medicine. The secular *physicus* can be traced back as far as the tenth century along with the less trained and less reputable *chirurgicus*. In Salerno, Italy, there arose in 900 A.D. a completely secularized school of medicine, the forerunner of later medical faculties, the oldest of which was probably Montpellier, first mentioned in 1180. One monk, however, though a lay brother, had considerable influence on the school of Salerno: Constantine of Africa, who came to Salerno in 1060 and died in Monte Cassino in 1087. Numer-

ous medical writings based on Greco-Roman-Arabic sources but also giving hygienic advice based on actual experience developed here: e.g., the *Circa instans,* a collection of prescriptions "for emergency use," as the title states. Another one was the famous, subsequently enlarged *Regimen sanitatis,* which was still printed in countless editions in the age of the printing press and whose advice has remained popular in folk medicine to this day. One of these verses was of this regimen, *"Post coenam stabis aut mille passus meabis"* ("After eating one should rest or walk a thousand steps"). Miniatures were created to accompany these works, which were not so much indigenous works of art—but in the Middle Ages, were not all artistic

Aesculapius discovers the betony plant. Miniature of the treatise *Herba Vettonica*, falsely attributed to Antonius Musa, the celebrated physician to Augustus. The manuscript from which this painting is taken dates from the eighth century.

BIBLIOTHÈQUE NATIONALE, PARIS

endeavors subordinate to definite pragmatic goals?—as they were meant to be technical illustrative material. For this reason they particularly fascinate medical historians, although the art historian can also claim interest in them. The miniature before us vividly shows three surgical operations, apparently conducted by secular physicians, whereas the illustrations to the *Anathomia* by Guido of Vigevano, dated 1345, still shows some illustrations of monastic clerical doctors. The removal of hemorrhoids, an operation for nasal polyps, and a cataract removal are cleary rendered by this picture, and certain reminiscences of Byzantine painting are unmistakable. The examination of the epigastrium of a sick knight in standing position and the depiction of the pulse diagnosis with one hand pointing to the arteria radialis and the other to the arteria brachialis from the textbook by Guido of Vigevano reveal a completely different style. The treatment is considerably more lively; doctor and patient, whether standing or sitting, are not wooden and uninvolved with each other as in the codex from the eleventh century. In short, the doctor-patient relationship is essentially stronger. Here too we see the radical change in the spirit of the times, which is hinted at long before the advent of the official Renaissance. As a further example, we can point to the sleeping Daniel, in an illustrated commentary to the Book of Daniel. This illustration, also dating from the eleventh century, is similar to the surgical pictures. The Old Testament seer is portrayed as lying isolated, resting on a couch, whereas in the upper part of the picture is a kind of vision, as is related in the Book of Daniel, 8.16:

> *And I heard, from the middle of the Ulai, a human voice call and speak: Gabriel, show your face so that he may understand it. And he came close to me. I, however, was startled, as he came and suddenly appeared before my sight. But he spoke to me: Pay attention, you, mortal child! for this face is approaching its end. And as he was speaking to me, I fainted with my face upon the earth.*

But let us return to the hospital compound, which apparently evoked lively interest among the artists in the late Middle Ages. It is easy to understand why the hospitals, especially those founded by the Crusaders because of their intense concern for their sick and wounded companions in the Holy Land, had already become familiar as such to the outside world. Naturally, the House of God with its tower was always the central point of the entire complex, as the visitor can still see today in Beaune—and as was the case with similar installations in the Arabic world, e.g., the Muristan in Cairo. But the portals and capitals often indicate the denomination of such institutions, as can be seen from our picture. This relieflike representation from the twelfth century is scarcely differentiated in style from the one in the surgical manuscript. Whether the person hiding in the background is a physician, we cannot distinguish. We must again stress that until the modern era hospital care by monks and sisters of the various orders always had priority over treatment by doctors. The doctor was mainly called upon at his home. It was often sufficient to send him a urine specimen, since in the meantime, from the thirteenth century on, the urine test or uroscopy, already current in antiquity, had now become the most important procedure.

Here the fateful penchant of the Middle Ages for mystical speculations showed up particularly. As a filter of the four cardinal humors, color and substance were supposed to determine the so-called primary qualities in the organism (cold, warmth, humidity, and dryness). Locating the individual's disease was assumed to be possible by means of the urine analysis, because as an extension of the old magic belief in analogy and the ancient micro-macrocosmic notions, transformations were ascribed to definite urinary layers of individual regions of the body. It was believed for a fact that by such subtle urine diagnosis one could

Hippocrates and Galen

Twelfth-century fresco in the cathedral of Anagni, Italy.

89

get from the different urine qualities not only exact diagnoses but also prognostic deductions. The urine glass thus became the stand-by of the physician, just as today the stethoscope or the otoscope. From the thirteenth century on, the doctor examining urine became an oft-depicted theme down to the Dutch Little Masters. It was anatomical research that finally put an end to uroscopy, although the knowledge of the diagnostic value of urine never was lost. Thomas Willis (1621-1675) discovered the honeylike taste of the diabetic's urine. Thus this relief, designated quite simply as "the medication fabricator," really offers us the portrait of a doctor who is just lifting a urine glass for testing, while in front of him two maids are standing with the then typical urinary containers made of woven straw, meant to keep the urine glasses from breaking during transportation. These maids are obviously supposed to bring the results of the medical examination to their sick master, at the same time bringing the effective remedies. These medications can be found in the containers on both shelves. This whole scene is part of a representation of human skill in art on the Campanile of the Duomo in Florence which was inspired by Giotto (1266-1337) and fashioned by Andrea Pisano (1295-1349?). The spirit of a new era is already visible here, specifically in the lively and individualistic artistic style despite the thoroughly medieval subject.

The founding of the universities also had considerable influence on medieval intellectual life. A school for higher learning was founded in Bologna in 1119, in 1275 in Paris, in 1222 in Padua, in 1224 in Naples, in part as successor to the already mentioned school of Salerno. In the twelfth century Oxford was founded and in the German-speaking area Prague in 1348, Vienna in 1365, and Heidelberg in 1386. As early as 1140 the Norman king Roger II of Sicily (1095-1154) enacted a decree stating that only tested and approved doctors were allowed to practice in his realm. The school of Salerno awarded the title of Magister, and the Emperor Frederick II (1194-1250) issued detailed decrees in 1231-1234, separating once and for all the doctor's profession from that of the pharmacist. In the thirteenth century the highly esteemed title of doctor was created: the bearer of this title was given a rank equivalent to that of the lowest nobility and was recognized all over Europe. The "doctor" also had the right to give lectures at the university. A special gown, doctor's hat, and ring also distinguished him outwardly. We see this academic costume in the miniature of the great French doctor Guy de Chauliac (1298-1369), who here is respectfully approached by three sick people showing their infirmities. De Chauliac, editor of one of the most famous surgical textbooks of the time, apparently has turned away from his reading desk, an additional symbol of erudition, and is paying attention to the patients seeking advice. All this is enacted

The Vision of Daniel

In the "Commentaries on the Apocalypse," written and illustrated by the Abbot Gregory Muntaner at the monastery of Saint-Sever.

BIBLIOTHÈQUE NATIONALE, PARIS

Three surgical operations

Ophthalmology, oto-rhino-laryngology, and proctology
as conceived of and practiced in the eleventh century.
Miniature illustrating a surgical manuscript of the
School of Salerno.

BRITISH MUSEUM, LONDON

91

Care given to the sick

A twelfth-century capital, found in the city hall of Puy. It seems to come from the front gate of the Church of Saint-Esprit, which was torn down in 1716.

according to medieval art concepts. There is no perspective either of the people or of the checkered floor. De Chauliac is sitting on a canopied " study chair," a regular " cathedra." He is receiving the patients in his study, which in the university also served for lectures and conferences with small groups of listeners.

Just as the contemporary illustrations enable us to obtain insights into the daily lives of the doctors and professors of that time that are not to be obtained from the manuscript sources, so the portrayals of hospital interiors or of private sick rooms give us a clear concept of the nursing of that time. The Cosmas and Damian illustrations of the fourteenth and fifteenth centuries almost always are set at the bedside of a patient suffering

from a serious leg injury. Only later do the double statues and portaits of the two patrons of medical science appear. But the doctor's visit to the sickbed was readily used as a motif. The doctor can always be recognized by his special dress. His dignified appearance and his chief occupation as seen by the layman—feeling the pulse and uroscopy—were particularly stressed.

In the hospitals, on the other hand, nursing scenes were emphasized. A French woodcut of the fifteenth century is especially typical. Here, moreover, in contrast to the above-mentioned scene with the French doctor Guy de Chauliac, the technique of perspective has found its way into art. This woodcut shows that the hospital building was related to church architecture and that large rooms for the

sick were preferred in which the beds were always turned to an altar. Actually this arrangement, with the crucifix as focal point, formed an important component of the medieval hospital, here too emphasizing the primacy of the clergy in caring for the sick. The patient was supposed always to have Christ's salvation before his eyes, a theory expressed by Ambrose (340-397): "We have everything within Christ. If you want to heal a wound, He is physician. Do you have fever, He is a fountain! If you are oppressed by evil, He is justice. Do you need help? He is the power. Are you in fear of death? He is life..."

The sick in these hospitals had mostly to fear death, and once the doctor had to lay down his instruments, only the consolation and succor of the church could accompany them on their last earthly journey. Our artist here has graphically expressed the perpetual threat to the hospital inmates by his portrayal of nuns in the foreground busy sewing up the corpses, which in reality occurred in another room. The juxtaposition of the offering of spiritual and worldly nourishment, in the right and left half of the woodcut, is pregnant with symbolism. While on the one side a priest is giving Holy Communion, the nuns on the other side are handing out earthly food. Another interesting detail in this picture is that often one bed had to

Vomiting man
Thirteenth-century gargoyle, Saint-Urbain de Troyes.

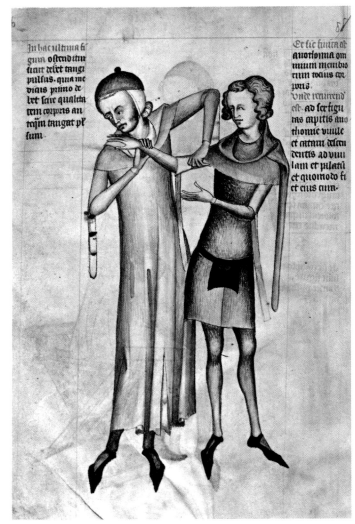

Physician examining a patient

These two miniatures are from a book by Guido de Vigevano, produced in 1345.

serve for two or even more patients at the same time. Numerous other illustrations show that this case was not unique, as in this example from the Hôtel-Dieu in Paris, one of the most famous hospitals of the era. Here we see clearly the cramped space and crowding of sickbeds— despite the architecturally flexible design of the nave, which offered ample space for air and ventilation, and often provided for almost modern sanitary installation (in the Frankish hospitals, for instance, sewage and garbage were directly drained outside the city walls). The hospitals often had their own little door in the city walls to receive contagious patients, so as not to have to transport them through the city gates. Such patients however often produced catastrophic cases of hospital gangrene and other contagious sicknesses which, when they occurred in a hospital, were considered tantamount to a death sentence.

Epidemics in general left their powerful mark on the medieval world view. The theory of contagion in epidemic diseases is an achievement of this period. In the literature of antiquity there is occasional talk of infectious disease (we need only recall the so-called plague in Thucydides, or allusions to the spread of the plague in Galen, who during an epidemic in Rome in 166 A.D.

fled from the capital, or leprosy in Aretaeus). But in general, atmospheric factors were held responsible for the outbreak of an epidemic. With the rise of the medieval city and its crowded space within the limits of the city walls, there was an increase in infectious diseases. Now for the first time in medical history these were clearly recognized as being contagious. First of all, in the case of leprosy, isolation measures were carried out. All suspects had to undergo a leprosy examination by the city doctor and other officials in public life; and they were unconditionally banned from the city if they were declared lepers. They had to live out their lives in special leper houses far from the gates of the city. In Germany these were euphemistically called "good-people-houses." They

could only enter the city at certain high holidays, recognizable from afar by their leper rattles and colored garments furnished with bells. Then they could listen to mass, go to Confession, and occasionally also beg. Such a scene has been portrayed by a Nuremberg artist in 1493. The approaching march of the stricken, the sermon, Confession, and Communion as well as the concluding festive meal are rendered here. The viewer should pay particular attention to the central Confession scene. There the person hearing Confession is carefully holding in front of his nose and mouth a cloth saturated with some disinfectant, such as juniper. The leper who is kneeling at quite some distance is recognizable as such by his rattle. Naturally artists have also frequently given us pictures of the disease itself. Often

Josaphat as a child, meeting a leper and an old cripple at the gates of Jerusalem.

Miniature taken from the "Miroir Historial" of Vincent de Beauvais. Middle of the fourteenth century.

BIBLIOTHÈQUE DE L'ARSENAL, PARIS

The Plague in Tournai, 1349
MUSÉE DE L'ART ANCIEN, BRUSSELS

the sick person is only marked by ulcerous sores; but the countless representations of all kinds of cripples, including not only the casualties of the many wars or the victims of accidents, remind one, especially when the infirm limbs are shown in bizarre positions, of the neuritic form of leprosy, in which such paralytic contractions are actually known. The painter of fantastic realism, Hieronymus Bosch (1450?-1516) had a special preference for these unfortunate pariahs and has drawn and painted them in many versions. Here again the medical historian can study the most diverse models of crutches and of prostheses used by these unfortunates.

Much more destructive for medieval man than leprosy was the epidemic of the plague, which came from the East in the fourteenth century and reduced all Europe to fear and horror. There was absolutely no doubt about the contagiousness of this epidemic, and isolation measures were put into effect. Thus there were soon quarantines in the port cities where ships suspected of carrying the plague were held in a special place of anchorage. They were detained in Ragusa in 1337 for one month, then in 1383 in Marseilles and in 1403 in Venice for forty days (*quadraginta dies*), before they were able to land and discharge their cargo. These were the most important countermeasures to the plague.

In hundreds of plague tracts and regulations the most important preventive measures for the public and the doctors were discussed—measures which could be taken before the outbreak of a plague and the therapeutic possibilities as well as personal and general treatment that might be used after the onset of the dreadful epidemic. The picture by Gentile Bellini (1429-1507) is a graphic rendition of a doctor's visit to a patient sick with the plague. The doctor very carefully approaches the patient, who lies on a platform. In order to feel his pulse, the doctor holds a sponge soaked with a disinfectant in front of his nose and mouth. Two servants are carrying flaming torches and one of them is holding a vessel hard to distinguish—either a urine glass or an incense burner. In the background, relatives are carrying a bowl which probably contained disinfectant vinegar.

These measures remained for the most part without success. That is probably why time and again in the art of the period we see illustrations of the dance of death or *ars*

Hippocrates
Byzantine miniature of the fourteenth century.
BIBLIOTHÈQUE NATIONALE, PARIS

ὉΙΠΠΚΡΑΤ῾ ΚΩΟΣ

ΟΒΙΟΣ ΟΛΕ
ΒΡΑΧ ΚΑΙΡϹ
ΥΣ ΗΔ ΟΞΥϹ
ϹΤΕΧ
ΜΑΚΡΗ

Two miniatures from the book "Grande chirurgie" by Guy de Chauliac, four-teenth century.

moriendi, as for example in this woodcut. Here the overturned table indicates the hopelessness of all earthly endeavors; the woodcut places in the forefront preparations for eternal life through meditation and repentance. Now the very old *media vita in morte sumus* by Notker Balbulus (ca. 840-912) again became a topic of unprecedented importance. On the other hand, signs of a new era, which we have already repeatedly encountered, are evident in the representations of man's revolt against his fate, as portrayed by Andrea di Cione, called Orcagna (d. 1368) in his fresco, the "Triumph of Death," for the Camposanto in Pisa. It represents the revolt of the sick and stricken against death, a deeply moving document of human defiance and a symbol of a new anthropocentric self-understanding, foreshadowing the more humanistic Renaissance period.

98

From the Middle Ages
to the Renaissance and Humanism

The concept of a new epoch of cultural history replacing the Middle Ages and beginning with the fall of Constantinople in 1453 goes back to Pierre Bayle (1647-1706) and the young Voltaire (1694-1778), the first historians of the Renaissance, who trace it to the migration of numerous Greek scholars and the hitherto unknown documents they brought with them to the West, first of all to Italy. This viewpoint is rarely maintained today. It was already refuted by the statement made by Giorgio Vasari (1511-1574). It was he who first used the term *rinascita* solely for the fine arts and traced its beginnings to Giotto and his teacher Cimabue (1240-1301). If Jules Michelet (1798-1874) specifically saw in man's quickening consciousness with respect to himself and the world the decisive factor

ANONYMOUS ARTIST
Visiting the sick.

CHURCH OF SAN MARTINO, FLORENCE

100

The anatomy lesson
Wood Engraving. Fourteenth century.

of the Renaissance, Jacob Burckhardt (1818-1897) developed the notion: discovery of the world (i.e., of this world) and of man, and was really the first to give this cultural movement its now undisputed validity. In it too the genuine intellectual-scientific movement of humanism found its origins. Nor did humanism begin with the expulsion of the scholars from Byzantium, but with the argument against scholasticism; hence with the so-called "universality controversy." In early and late scholasticism it was held that the general concepts of being stemmed from the differing metaphysical-objective reality of individual things. In short, the theory of *universalia ante rem* prevailed. At the same time it was linked to the old philosophical theory of ideas. It required a more deductive world view, with the particular derived from the general. In opposition to this concept stood nominalism, especially as represented by Duns Scotus (ca. 1270-1308) and William of Ockham (1285-1349), and which stated that *universal* only consisted in names, *nomina,* and that reality consisted only in individual objects, *universalia post rem.* According to this philosophy, only the individual possessed true objectivity. This led to an inductive world view, which was later disseminated especially by Francis Bacon (1561-1626) with his demand for *observatio et experimentum,* observation and scientific testing.

So in the philosophical as well as the artistic life, the individual, the return to the human being, man's self-reliance, played a decisive role. Individual observation became the basis of philosophy and the natural sciences—and so it was in medicine as well. In science there began the preoccupation with specific self-enclosed problems, with introspection, self-observation, and *autopsia* (seeing with one's own eyes); problems were no longer solved with the aid of scholastic or traditional devices. Since no prior *universalium* was recognized, there was renewed emphasis in science on the mass, which had been so important in antiquity. Now, according to Nicholas of Cusa (1401-1464), the individually perceptible could be compared to other realities. The principles of modern scientific methods of work—measuring, weighing, comparing—were thereby acknowledged, as was the role of the individual.

In summary we may say that all the features of the later Renaissance and of humanism were prepared in the twelfth century and became apparent in the thirteenth. By the fourteenth and fifteenth centuries, they finally became the dominant ideas of their time. Among these were the following: the rise of individualism, the awakening of the urge to beauty, the triumph of mundane pleasures and happiness, the conquest of earthly reality, and, above all, the consciousness of the human personality in its natural relationship to the world.

Forerunners of individualism were Dante (1265-1321) and Petrarch (1304-1374). The latter's invectives against medicine contain little that is flattering. Yet he clearly recognized the weaknesses of the scholastic intellectual position, as he called out to the doctors: "How often have I said: Doctor, treat! Rhetoric is your enemy! If you want to be poets and rhetoricians, then stop being doctors."

Both poets first attempted to awaken moods by the description of landscape. Hand in hand with this goes the discovery of nature and distances as well as the third dimension, through perspective, on the part of the artist, who now also made the individual portrait the focus of his art. At the same time biography received renewed literary recognition, and now, with a backward glance at antiquity, historical thinking set in once more. In the middle of the fifteenth century the first Western presentation of the history of medicine, *De medicina et medicis,* by Giovanni Tortelli (d. 1466), was written.

If the first portraits of the Middle Ages were, so to speak, interchangeable, because more attention was paid to the general appearance of royalty, of physicians, or judges, they were looked on as the symbol of a higher idea. But from the thirteenth century on, we encounter ever increasingly individual portraits, which also enable the medical historian to make some discoveries. The canon Van der Paele in the famous painting by Jan van Eyck (ca. 1390-1441), for instance, is depicted not only with the characteristic traits of an old man (just look at his arteria temporalis) but is also portrayed with a pair of eyeglasses. We know today that the first pair of glasses were created in Italy around 1300. Around 1270 the first convex eyeglasses were said to have been ground in the little island of Murano near Venice, famous for its glass blowers. Such glasses were surrounded by a thick ring of iron, wood, or

Capital of Aesculapius

A physician receiving a patient in his alchemist's laboratory. A peasant is bringing him an offering. Beginning of the fifteenth century.

RECTORS' PALACE, DUBROVNIK

102

The impatience of the sick man

The demon of fever (or sickness) was not neglected by the medieval artist. He is contrasted with the angelic patience of the nun in the foreground.
Wood engraving of the fifteenth century.

horn and equipped with handles, the whole soldered together. These "riveted glasses" had to be held with the hand at the desired distance, as is shown in the familiar picture of the so-called "Wildunger Altar" by Konrad von Soest from the year 1404. Thereafter glasses became a rather significant factor in the cultural development of the West, permitting far-sighted scholars to continue their work, from which they had hitherto been excluded once vision had failed them. Indeed, glasses became an attribute of the scholarly man. The above portrait should be considered in that light, especially since the half-opened book furnishes additional evidence. Even more interesting for the medical historian is the second portrait exhibited here: that of an old man and his nephew by Ghirlandaio (1449-1494), in which the pathologically transformed nose of the grandfather immediately confirms the diagnosis of rosacea, which can be traced back to alcoholic excesses and here had already assumed the shape of rhinophyma. Such a characteristic picture of a sickness can hardly be a mere symbol of a disease, as was the case with the medieval artist in his rendering of leprosy. For this portrait a patient, if not a model, had to sit. Here the new artistic perception is clearly present and at work.

In still another example we can clearly illustrate the process of individualization in the Renaissance in the fifteenth century. In the years 1440-43, the important Italian painter Domenico di Bartolo (ca. 1400-1447) had made frescoes for a hospital still preserved as such in the Ospedale della Scala in Siena. We have already encountered representations of hospitals in the early and late

103

ANDREA PISANO (1270-1349?) traditionally after
a design by GIOTTO

*The medicine maker. In reality, a uroscopy by
a physician.*

CAMPANILE, FLORENCE

DOMENICO DI BARTOLO (1400?-1447)

Treatment of the sick.
Fresco in the Hospital of Santa Maria della Scala,
Siena.

105

These four wood cuts are from the incunabulum "Hortus Sanitatis" by Joannes de Cuba, printed in Mainz in 1491. The first picture shows a man resorting to the tears of a deer (a remedy whose utility has long since been forgotten). They were thought of as an aphrodisiac.

The second picture shows a beauty treatment with crushed toads. The third picture shows a physician who has just removed a bladder stone from the patient. Finally, in the last picture, the "large belly" is a symptom of ascites.

Woodcut from the "Hortus Sanitatis."

Two physicians are surrounded by their usual patients: a woman in bed, a cripple with a stunted leg, a child, and a man with a swollen, ulcerated leg (probably a varicose ulcer).

Middle Ages. But there is surprising movement in the fresco by Domenico di Bartolo. While in the foreground we can see a kind of policlinic, in the middle of which a man wounded in battle is being washed by the hospital monks before being bandaged, to the left another friar is nursing a very sick man who has just been brought in on a stretcher. Clerics and doctors complete the scene. In the rear of the picture is the hospital itself. Here too the altar is the focal point of the room which has been divided into little cells—an example of which we can still see in Germany in the St. Ann Hospital in Lübeck. The artist must have had quite a unique and lively picture before his eyes when he created this series of frescoes. In contrast to the older representations of hospitals, the marked difference in the new art is noticeable also in the dynamics of the action, sharply contrasting with the static nature of the medieval illustrations.

This advance from static to dynamic also appears in a special kind of medical picture, the anatomy scene, which also captured the interest of great artists. These scenes appear more and more as miniatures, adorning the written codices; and after the invention of printing ca. 1440 (the significance of which for medical history we cannot go into here), they were added to the textbooks and encyclopedias of medical science in the form of woodcuts.

We know that at the time of the Ptolemies in Alexandria dissections were made and that Erasistratus (310-250 B.C.) and Herophilus (335-280 B.C.) owed their anatomical knowledge to autopsies; but mummification in Egypt was carried out by the socially inferior and by persons completely indifferent to science, so that even from the point of view of technique they transmitted no knowledge of the inner construction of the human body. The aversion to corpses and the belief in the resurrection of the flesh were probably the main reasons that hindered dissection in the early Middle Ages. The doctors preferred to follow Galen's anatomy which, as was later recognized, was primarily derived from animal anatomy. The first dissections were not meant for scientific purposes but arose from more practical needs. In 1286 the corpse of a person who had died during an epidemic in Cremona was opened up, in order to discover the possible cause of the mass deaths. In 1303 the first forensic medical dissection occurred in Bologna because of a suspicion of poisoning. In 1316 the first "textbook" on anatomy appeared, the *Anathomia* by Mondino de' Luzzi (d. 1326), a work which even after the introduction of book printing went through numerous editions and was often embellished with illustrations of dissections. These, like our woodcut, render a good impression of the *Lectiones anatomicae* of that time. However Galen's work held sway: the professor still did not conceive of descending from his lectern to convince himself through his own observations, through

FRA ANGELICO (1387-1455)
Saint Palladius being treated by Saints Cosmas and
Damian.

JAN VAN EYCK (1385?-1441)

Detail from *The Madonna of Canon van der Paele*.
The wart on the canon's ear, visible in this reproduction, has become quite controversial, since it disappeared during the restoration of the painting in 1934.

MUSÉE COMMUNAL DES BEAUX-ARTS, BRUGES

autopsia, of the position and the relations of the organs in the human body. It was enough for him to read from one of Galen's tracts or from the *Corpus Hippocratum* or, if he was unusually modern, from the Latin translations of the great Islamic doctors, in particular Avicenna (980-1037). It was the duty of a demonstrator to point out, from a corpse laid out on a simple wooden table, those places on the body treated in the text, or to show the respective organs to the interested students, university graduates, or doctors. He was given an additional demonstrator, who did the actual work of cutting open and preparing, while the other demonstrator used a pointer. In all this the anatomical dissection was simply a confirmation of Galen's teachings. If deviations from the text of *Principes medicorum* occurred, it was assumed that the corpse had undergone a pathological transformation, rather than that the great Galen had made a mistake.

Forensic medicine thus shaped the beginning of modern anatomy and only gradually did dissection occur for its own sake. Dissection, after serving simply as visual background for the "lectures," first gained greater importance with the introduction of the new ideas of the Renaissance. Now attention was also paid to the *singularia* of the human body, and curiosity about man also extended to his anatomical construction. The professor was now actively brought into the dissection process. He himself was now eager to penetrate into the mysteries of the human body, even prior to Andreas Vesalius (1514-1564). And we see him in this miniature from a work by Bartholomaeus Angelicus (ca. 1225)—the writing, however seems to stem from the fifteenth century!—standing in the midst of his listeners who have now also become onlookers, carrying out the dissection himself, while the scholar standing to the right is closely studying an organ. Indeed, under the influence of the static thinking of the Middle Ages, the subtle description of individual organs or organ systems and illustrations of them had become the main endeavor of early anatomists. But in some cases pathological observations challenged the medical casuistry that had long prevailed, as in the work of Antonio Benevieni (d. 1502) or Alessandro Benedetti (d. 1525). The dynamic thinking of the Renaissance led to a change in attitude in the field of anatomy as well. All of a sudden the so-called *situs* was "discovered." The interconnection of muscles, bones, and organs, the functional unity of a joint, for example, now interested doctors and artists. It was an age in which Leon Battista Alberti (d. 1472) first demanded exact anatomical knowledge for the artist and attention to bodily forms in the work of art. But medicine required the delicate and incorruptible powers of observation of a Vesalius, really to effect the great breakthrough to a new anatomy. He was ably seconded by Jan Stephan van

MASTER OF FRANKFURT (b. around 1460)
Saint Roch

Saint Roch eternally shows his pestiferous bubo, traditionally in the middle of his thigh.

WALLRAF-RICHARTZ MUSEUM, COLOGNE

111

DOMENICO CURRADO called GHIRLANDAIO
(1449-1494)

Presumably a portrait of Count Sassetti and his grandson

The realism of the period makes for a faithful and exact reproduction of the Count's "rhinophyma," a kind of nasal acne, which provoked the unpleasant pimples on the nose.

LOUVRE, PARIS

Head of a man with facial paralysis
Pink sandstone. Second half of the fifteenth century.
MUSÉE DE L'OEUVRE NOTRE-DAME, STRASSBURG

Calcar (ca. 1499-1545), an artist uncommonly gifted in draftsmanship.

The printing press opened up unimagined possibilities for the artistic representation of scientific problems. Soon not a single important work appeared without the addition of more or less successful woodcuts. Some printers employed the same process-blocks for works that differed in content and were often completely unrelated; hence the illustration often had only a very loose connection with the text. In contrast to the works of art of the fourteenth

and fifteenth centuries, the woodcuts of this genre often bore the stamp of medieval art. Standing on the borderline of the two eras are, for example, the illustrations in the famous *Hortus sanitatis*, which was published in Mainz in 1491 as an incunabulum, a highly valued botanical-pharmaceutical book of reference of the period containing pictures of magical and obsolete medicines. It enjoyed several editions in the German language as the "handbook of health." Here too the doctor is represented symbolically between the two poles of his activity:

113

Reception of patients in the Hôtel-Dieu

Miniature illustrating the "Book of the very active life of the nuns of the Hôtel-Dieu of Paris." Fifteenth century.

Sick ward at the Hôtel-Dieu

Miniature illustrating the "Book of the very active life of the nuns of the Hôtel-Dieu of Paris." Fifteenth century.

GIOVANNI DELLA ROBBIA (1469-1529)
Examination of the sick

The physician is very serious about taking the patient's pulse.

OSPEDALE DEL CEPPO, PISTOIA, ITALY

115

scientific research on the human organism with the help of anatomy, and practical medical activity, denoted by the giving out a pill-shaped medication. The prescription for the preparation of theriac, a panacea highly esteemed until modern times and used especially as an antidote, has been portrayed in another picture, which shows the doctor or pharmacist surrounded with the most important ingre-

dients: snake fragments, jewels or bezoar stones (calcified concretions from the stomach of a north Persian bezoar goat), and a deer as the source of the *cornu cervi*.

The artist of the fifteenth century also liked to depict scenes of operations, in which he presented rather realistically observed settings of fractures. These could be seen in contrast to imaginative illustrations such as one showing

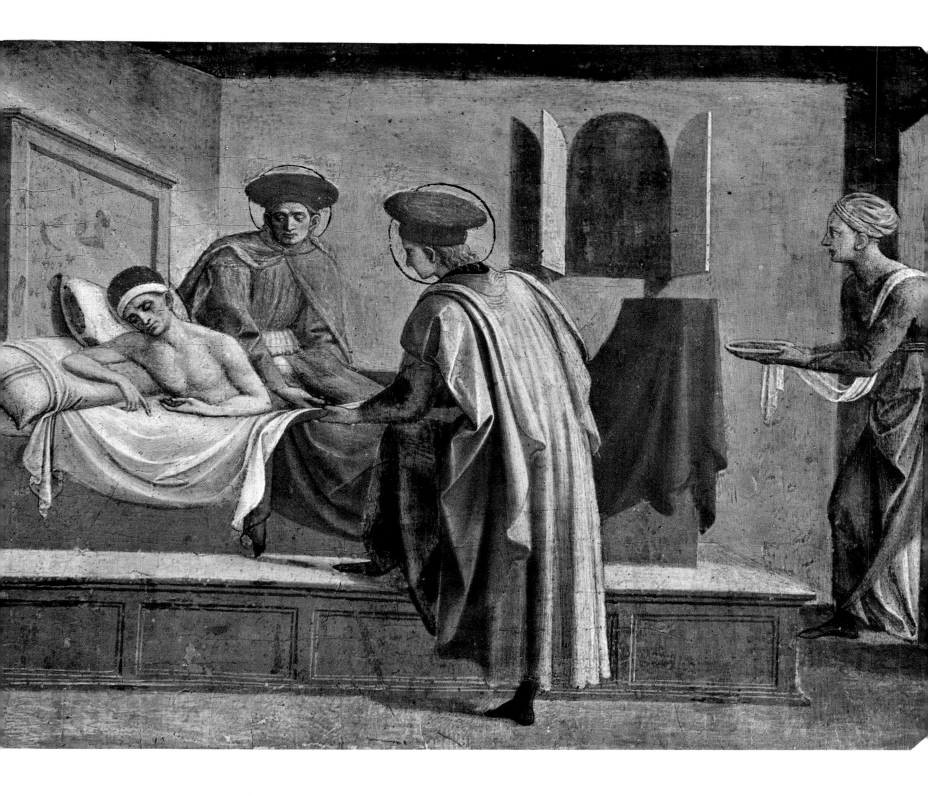

FRANCESCO PESELLINO (1422-1457)

Saints Cosmas and Damian

Fragment of the predella of a painting illustrating episodes in the "Golden Legend" by Jacobus de Vora-
gine. The two patron saints of medicine acquired
their reputation by transplating the leg of a Negro to
the body of a white man.

LOUVRE, PARÍS

117

Treatment of a fracture

Wood engraving from Hieronymus Brunschwig's "Dis ist das Buch der chirurgia," published in Strassburg in 1497.

Intestinal suture

Wood engraving from Hieronymus Brunschwig's "Dis ist das Buch der chirurgia," published in Strassburg in 1497.

Depiction of treatment for injuries due to dangerous animals: mad dogs, scorpions, snakes.
Wood engraving from Hieronymus Brunschwig's "Dis ist das Buch der chirurgia," published in Strassburg in 1497.

GENTILE BELLINI (1429-1507)
Examination of the patient
Engraving.

animal excrement being used to heal wounds. In any event, we must admire here the sense of movement in the consultation or operation, another indication of the now pervasive dynamism. Even the *Buch der Chirurgia*, written by Hieronymus Brunschwig (1450-1533) and published in 1497, which contains the first specifically medical woodcut illustrations, and is further noteworthy in that for the first time it discusses in detail the treatment of gunshot wounds, offers rich illustrative material for this final transitional phase from the Middle Ages to the Renaissance. Thus we find besides the surgical illustrations one of the interior of an apothecary shop—in which the meaning of the crestlike inscriptions on the orderly arranged apothecary jars standing on the shelves is still a matter of debate—and in which an expensively dressed doctor or pharmacist (his exact status is also unclear) is using a pointing cane, while another figure seems to be gathering information from a volume lying on a heavy table.

The charming picture from a French manuscript of the fifteenth century of ladies in pastel dresses picking sage,

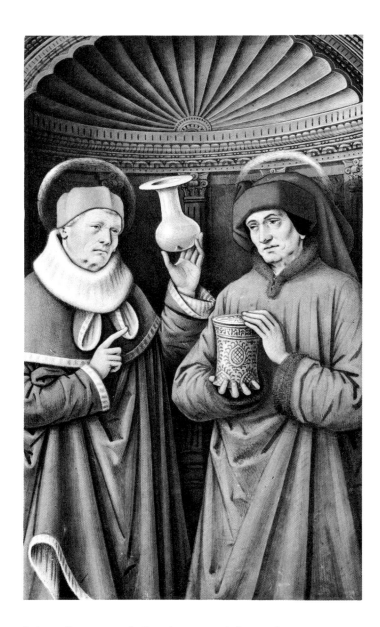

Saints Cosmas and Damian examining urine
Miniature illustrating the "Hours of Anne of Brittany."
BIBLIOTHÈQUE NATIONALE, PARIS

will be a fitting conclusion to this brief analysis. The new mood of the times, the urge for beauty and the joy of life, the individuality of man as focal point of the universe, and not least the renewed interest in antiquity are tellingly expressed. The picture demonstrates the same optimism as that which filled the *poeta laureatus*, the knightly poet Ulrich von Hutten (1488-1523), himself destined to become the victim of a new epidemic brought from the New World at the end of the fifteenth century, syphilis, and who enthusiastically wrote to his friend Willibald Pirkheimer (1470-1530):

Vigent studia! Florent ingenia!
O saeculum, o literae!
Juvat vivere.
Heus Tu, accipe laqueum,
Barbaries, exilium prospice!

Long live studies!
May the spirits flourish!
Oh century, oh knowledge!
There is a lust to live!
But You, Barbarity, hang yourself,
And await exile!

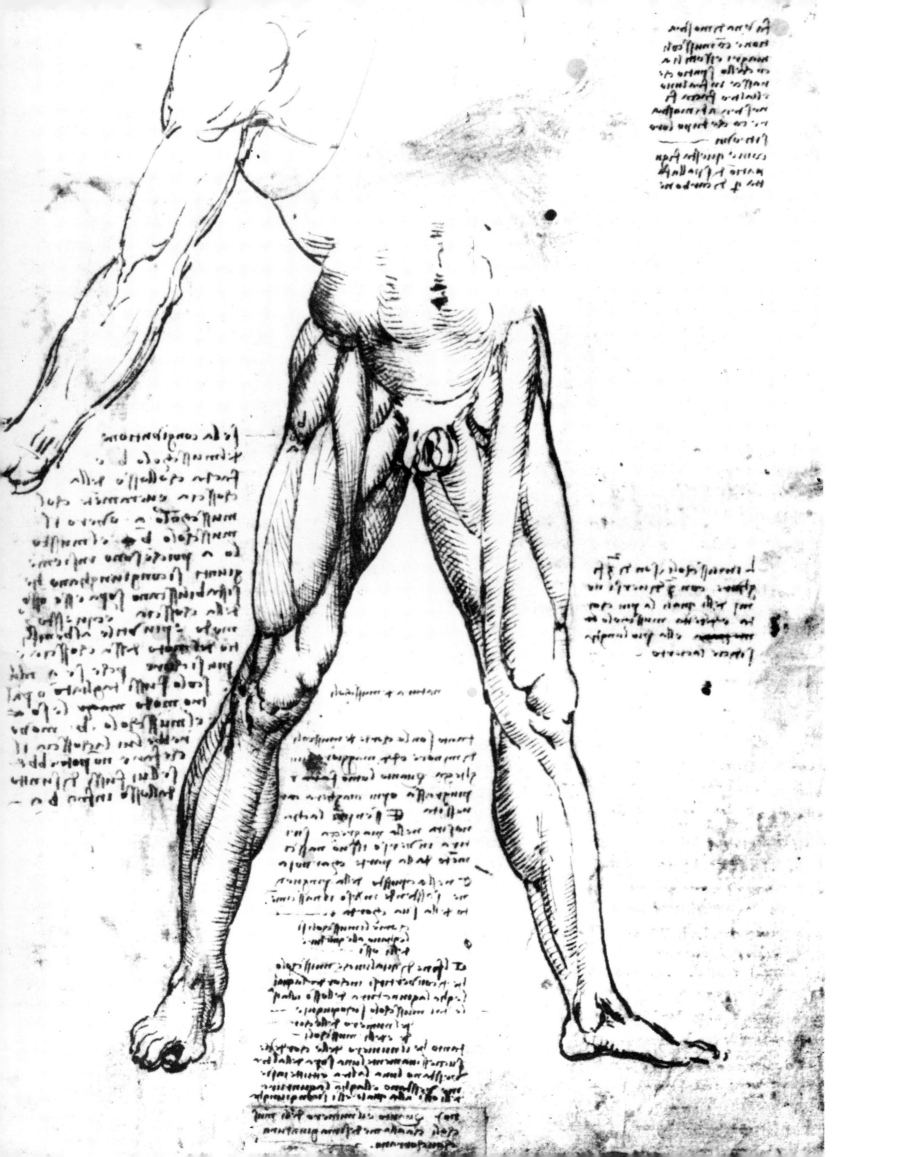

LÉON BINET   CHARLES MAILLANT

THE SIXTEENTH CENTURY

The Heritage
of the Middle Ages

Élie Faure: "The Renaissance is the affirmation of a new ideal that demanded the perilous conquests of intuition and faith be submitted to the double control of experience and reason."

It would be difficult to find a better symbol for the sixteenth century, and at the same time it would be hard to find a more appropriate frontispiece for this chapter than Hans Holbein's (1497-1583) splendid *Allegory of the Medical Arts*. Why is this? Because here Practice and Theory are seated upon their chariot, drawn by wild beasts and led by Melissa, Mentha, and Artemisia, and

LEONARDO DA VINCI (1452-1519)
Depiction of the legs
(This drawing was probably a study for the *Battle of Anghiari*).
A deeper knowledge of the human body is one of the essentials in the work of Leonardo da Vinci, who dissected some thirty corpses and very nearly discovered the circulation of the blood.

ROYAL LIBRARY, WINDSOR CASTLE

plowing up all human miseries; fevers, dropsy, and the plague. Although one is not surprised to see a skeleton with its hands crossed seated in the coachman's place, illnesses and epidemics are wiped out by this rational and intelligent trio. But things are not really quite as simple as the painter makes them out to be. The same can be said for medicine during this period.

Although the "century by century" format of a history like this one may appear to be the most practical, it must nevertheless be highly and even fatally arbitrary. In whatever field under discussion, history is a continuation of events, joined together in some sort of chronological order. It is only natural that each century should have a particular meaning for us and give rise to some particular emotion. But although every painting impresses us in a particular way, containing as it does a local color of its very own, there is no real cleavage between one epoch and another.

This is especially true in the case of the change from the Middle Ages to the Renaissance. One must, therefore,

123

Hans Holbein (1497-1543)

Allegory of the Medical Arts

On her chariot, drawn by savage beasts under the guidance of Melissa, Mentha, and Arthemisia, Medicine is enthroned in glory between Practice and Theory.

BIBLIOTHÈQUE NATIONALE, PARIS

attempt to determine the origins and phases of an evolution that was in fact a revolution, and outline some of the main events that took place and should be remembered.

Toward the end of the fifteenth century, the momentary conquest of the kingdom of Naples (1495-1498) brought about an increase in cultural and artistic exchanges between France and Italy. In that period too the discovery of America and the invention of the printing press changed the image that Europe had of the geographical and intellectual world, thus affecting radically the psyche of Western man. Finally, men of considerable stature were to influence the birth of a new spirit that in its turn was slowly to change the rapport between art and religion, between scientific and human activities, and, in particular, to bring about a change in medicine. The future Pope Julius II was born in 1442; Leonardo da Vinci in 1452; Erasmus in 1465; Copernicus in 1473; Michelangelo in 1475; Martin Luther in 1483; Ignatius Loyola in 1491; Paracelsus in

1493; Rabelais in 1494; Calvin in 1509; Vesalius in 1514, and lastly Ambrose Paré in 1517.

In this so-called "Age of Discovery" man's horizons were broadened in many ways. To Renaissance man the New World represented not only the beginnings of a reaching out to far places but also the beginning of a real awareness of the world in which he lived. While in the Early Renaissance of the fifteenth century, people's eyes had been opened to the wonders of nature in a relatively external fashion—which was mirrored in the arts by the discovery and development of perspective, the flora and fauna of nature, and most particularly by the awareness of the human body—the sixteenth century (the century of the High Renaissance, the Reformation and the Counter Reformation) became more internal in its viewing of nature. In the plastic arts this is represented by the fifteenth-century sculptors and painters looking at anatomy more carefully, estimating its bulk, weighing its mass,

124

ALBRECHT DÜRER (1471-1528)

Self-portrait drawing meant for the doctor, the artist
asking for a long-distance consultation. The text reads:
"there, on the yellow spot, where my finger is pointing,
is where my pain is."
If it is hard for us to figure out—with this single bit
of information—Dürer's malady, how much more per-
plexing was the diagnosis at the time!

KUNSTHALLE, BREMEN, GERMANY

and developing devices to convey this data in visual form.

The early sixteenth century saw the actual practice of
dissection by artists such as Michelangelo and Leonardo
in aid of their art. But, although we can certainly relate
these sketches to the development of scientific anatomy
in the strictest sense, the sketches themselves do not
represent any effect on the history of medicine as such.
The fabulous drawings of Leonardo, centuries ahead of
their time in accuracy of anatomical detail as well as
physical beauty, remained unknown, i.e., unpublished,
until the late nineteenth century. Yet with the development of the printing press it became possible during the
generation following Leonardo for Vesalius' great work
on anatomy to published as the first real "text" on
anatomy in modern times.

In the same way as it was possible for anatomical ideas
to be disseminated through illustrated books, it was also
possible for other ideas to be diffused throughout various

parts of the world. It is a period during which we become
aware of the medical man as such, of people like Paracelsus and Paré and even Dr. Rabelais. Yet we are still
far from the true age of science, and the medical knowledge of this period appears in brief flashes out of a still
murky background.

The Middle Ages, "massive and delicate," as Verlaine
called them, were the age of Faith, with the Church as the
real government. It was a government that exercised its
rights in every activity and in all the disciplines. Doctors
were under the control of the Church; nearly all of them
were members of some religious order, and the few laymen
permitted to practice the art of Hippocrates were not
exempt from certain religious obligations. It was by order
of the Church, therefore, that doctors were celibate, until
1462, at which point Cardinal d'Estouteville in France
permitted them to marry. As for surgeons, they were
looked upon as mere subsidiary medical aides, with some-

125

126

what the same status as that of barbers; and indeed they practiced barbering on the side.

If the painters of this period were interested in medicine, it was not out of a deisre to depict the subject matter realistically. Rather, since they were illustrating the lives of saints, they perforce had to depict activities that would liken them to healers, or to inspired surgeons. An example would be Saints Cosmas and Damian, martyred together under Emperor Diocletian in Cilicia in 303. It was these two men who performed the first human graft by giving a white man the leg of a Negro. This miracle, which made them the patron saints of surgeons, was to inspire, from the fifteenth century onward, a large number of works of art.

One of the most famous of these is the large reredos in the church of Santa Maria in Tarassa (Spain), attributed to Jaume Huguet (active 1448-1487), depicting several episodes in the lives of SS. Cosmas and Damian. The extraordinary grafting operation is shown in one of the panels. The superb predella by Giuliano Giuochi (called Pesellino, 1367-1446) hanging in the Louvre, depicts the same miracle of surgery and faith. Divine intervention has just taken place and the two saints contemplate the result of their surgical work.

During the sixteenth century, Fernando del Rincon (active 1510) in a lively canvas (Prado, Madrid) takes up the same theme, changing it sufficiently to cause the viewer great uneasiness. The saints, not content with the grafting of the Negro's leg onto the white man (the latter is lying on the floor, presumably already on the way to recovery!), are in the process of grafting the white man's ulcerous leg onto the Negro.

At about the same time an Italian, Giovanni Battista Tinti (active 1590) also painted the two saints, though in this picture one is not quite sure that they are performing a grafting operation. One can be sure, however, that in an anonymous bas-relief at Valladolid they are performing the same activity. In this picture, the Negro with the amputated leg seems to be managing perfectly well without it, and there is no question of inflicting a pernicious graft.

In certain books of hours, in particular the *Book concerning the active Lives of the Nuns of the Hôtel Dieu* (Musée de l'Assistance Publique, Paris), we can see minia-

tures which give us an insight into the atmosphere of a hospital during the Middle Ages. However, these illustrations, presumably intended to reproduce a lifelike example of the hospital environment, are primarily religious and edifying. If there is realism, it is accessory, not doctrinal. The artist's aim is to glorify the holy women who, in the name of faith, looked after the sick. They are watched over by four large figures dressed in black representing the cardinal virtues of Prudence, Temperance, Strength of Soul, and Justice.

Even if these miniatures cannot be considered scientific documents, they do in fact show us autopsies, anatomy lessons, the dressing of broken limbs, etc. This iconography, which was to become more popular during the sixteenth century, changed radically in style, as did the subject matter and spirit in which they were executed. One might say that as far as concepts and techniques were concerned, art, medicine, and surgery were to evolve along parallel lines.

The Early Renaissance

The sixteenth century marked the height of the Renaissance in Italy as well as in the rest of Europe, particularly in France where it became a *French Renaissance* due to the assimilation of such artists as Francesco Primaticcio (1504-1570) and Giovanni Battista Rosso (1495-1540). But, it would be impossible to ignore the fact that this "High Renaissance" was the direct result of the flowering of an earlier Renaissance that began well before 1500, and did not leave the Italian peninsula.

For centuries the profound influence of Byzantium on the art and thought of Italy had been so pronounced that the Italians hardly noticed the monuments and antiquities from which their art had sprung. They raided the countryside without much care; builders took material from ruins, as in Palermo, where the dismantled old buildings were often used as foundations for new ones.

The first Italian artist to come under the influence of antique culture was undoubtedly Nicola Pisano (1206-1280). The art of ancient Rome was the inspiration for his sculptured panels of the baptismal font at Pisa. Soon poets and humanists were to draw practically everything from antiquity; and indeed, so strong was this influence that it is to them that we owe the continuity between the two worlds, the antique and the Christian. Dante, whose master was Virgil; Petrarch, inspired by Cicero and Ceneca; and finally Boccaccio, for whom the ancient world was the "mirror of nature," are the most glorious artisans of the Renaissance and of this synthesis.

The relationship between art and anatomy is a crucial one in the early Renaissance of the fifteenth century. The

127

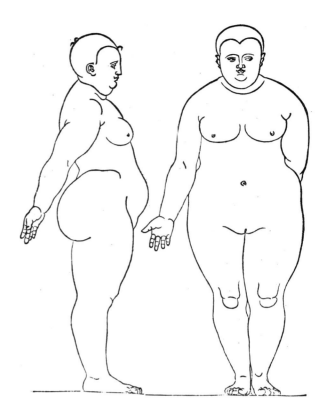

ALBRECHT DÜRER (1471-1528)
Thinness and Obesity

BIBLIOTHÈQUE NATIONALE, PARIS

need for greater and more exact knowledge of the human body by sculptors and painters in an age increasingly concerned with the world rather than the spirit eventually led to closer observation—at first externally, then internally—of the human body. Even before the fifteenth century, in the time of Giotto (ca. 1266-1337), we are impressed by the painters's mastery of mass and weight, by his arranging the folds of drapery so that they hint at the solid form beneath. By the early fifteenth century, in the time of the sculptor Donatello and the painter Masaccio, the nude as such becomes an increasingly frequent element in art and is observed in movement and at rest. In Donatello's sculpture the skin of the human body is tightened and loosened alternately to suggest the mass of a face or shoulder. Thus, the fifteenth-century artists became the first genuine students of anatomy, and were thoroughly aware of the skeletal framework of the human body. In an age when anatomy was still not being taught in any systematic fashion, the study of art supplied this impetus.

At the same time, we can see that the evolution of medical art did not fail to leave its mark on painting, and in a general way on the other plastic arts. Mindful of Galen's instruction, doctors seriously set about to study anatomy. This serious approach to a relatively new subject did not manifest itself without certain excesses. Experiments were made not only on bodies that were lifted from cemeteries late at night, but also on bodies that were still warm! In the early sixteenth century Cosimo de' Medici, Grand Duke of Tuscany, delivered two men condemned to death to Fallopius, the Pisan anatomist, saying: "Kill them in whatever manner you wish and dissect them."

Of course, medicine was still empirical, concerned at the same time with divine intervention, magic, and alchemy, and attributing ills that befell the human body to the occult. But medicine also began to take an increasing interest in the structure of the human body. In fact so much so that by the year 1500, one might well say that the combination of the new science of anatomy and an art form that returned to antiquity for its inspiration brought into being, as Baudelaire said, "...an era of nudity, in which Phoebus amused himself gilding statues." It was an historical meeting point that was of benefit to the

128

NICOLAS MANUEL DEUTSCH
(1484?-1531?)

Detail of an ex-voto (tempera on canvas): Saint Anne between Saint James the Greater and Saint Roch

In this ex-voto, the artist has shown the different contagious diseases that afflict humanity. The detail we have reproduced shows a leper in the center. His hands, reduced to stumps, are supported by a linen sling wound about his neck; his legs are dreadfully deformed.

KUNSTMUSEUM, BASEL

129

LEONARDO DA VINCI (1452-1519)

Mona Lisa (study)

Does this study reveal the reason for the mysterious smile of the Mona Lisa?
This preparatory drawing for the painting has the merit of realism. What do we see?
One eye was darker than the other, and the lady squinted. When she learned or saw that the artist had made this minor failing vanish, a failing which—in modern parlance—must have given her a complex or two, is it at all astonishing that she assumed that enigmatic yet satisfied expression, which has given rise to so much speculation?

MUSÉE CONDE, CHANTILLY

artist. From this point onward, the artist tended to depict not only religious subjects but also profane ones. We shall witness the detail they were to lavish on the drawing of a man, a woman, or a child. Children, formerly depicted as a smaller version of an adult, are more properly proportioned; indeed, the children carved by Andrea della Robbia, for example, are as accurately drawn as those of Dürer or Gerard David.

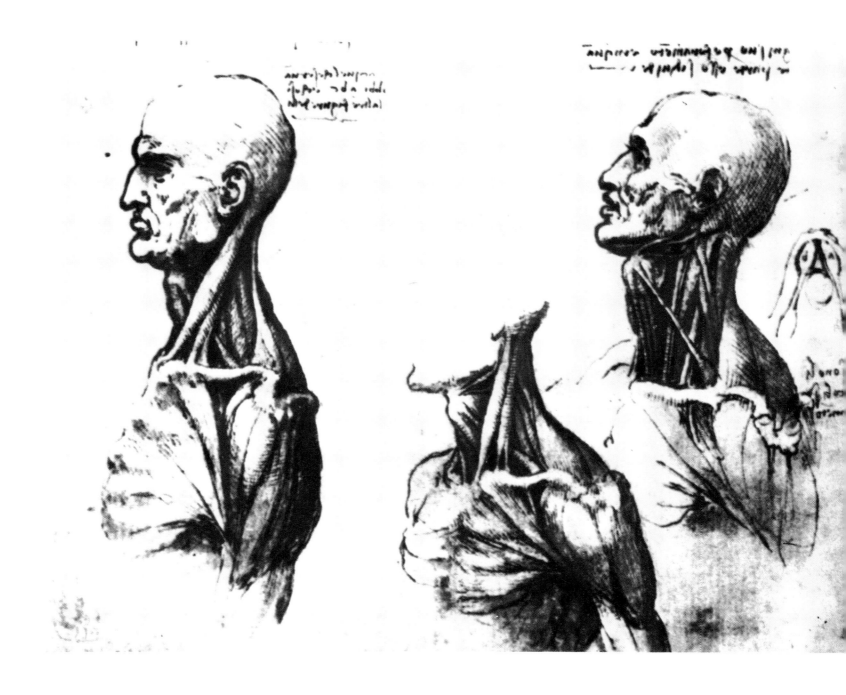

The Renaissance: Anatomy

Not so many centuries ago it was considered a sacrilege to apply a scalpel to a dead body (was not man, even when dead, created in the image of God?) and the punishment for doing so was severe; rather a curious paradox in an era when war, pillage, tournaments, murder in the name of family honor, and summary executions were daily occurrences.

Thus, for many years, the study of anatomy had to be pursued clandestinely. Finally, the authorities in certain states, beginning with Italy, came to understand the use of this new discipline. It was only to placate increasing

LEONARDO DA VINCI (1452-1519)
Outer and inner muscles of the neck

ROYAL LIBRARY, WINDSOR CASTLE

public fury over the violation of tombs that they permitted corpses, usually those of prisoners, to be cut up for the greater good of science.

The gradual linking of medicine with art that started with the official sanction of the study of anatomy, became

131

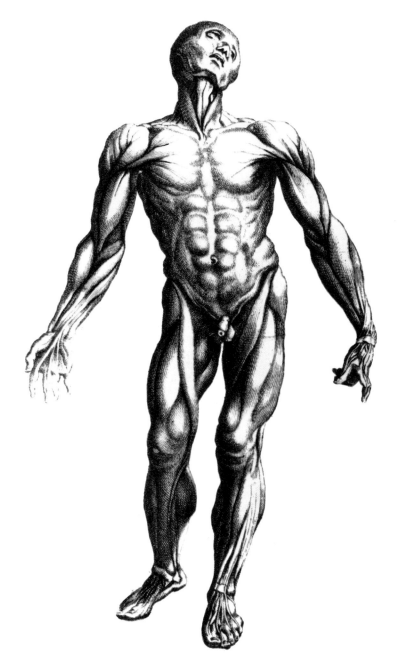

more evident when artists of the stature of Leonardo da Vinci, Albrecht Dürer, Michelangelo and Raphael devoted themselves to scientific studies of the human body.

One of the most fascinating examples of this interest is seen in the amazing artistic career of Leonardo (1452-1519). Leonardo's deep and profound knowledge of the human body is one of the essential foundations of his work. This man of genius would rise late at night in order to examine the plants in his garden by candlelight in the hope that he might be witness to some of the transformations in plant life, and then he would examine the entrails of a corpse with the same enthusiasm. Leonardo was a scientific explorer and practitioner, as much as an artist and a philosopher. His aim was to discover the most secret of mechanisms in man and to show them to the world. The determination with which he set about his researches, the audacity of his inquiries, and the richness of his discoveries make him one of the most important precursors of modern anatomy. He himself dissected over thirty bodies, both male and female, and of various ages; furthermore, it was he who had the idea of making cross sections of the organs of the body and of using injections into vessels and internal organs in order to study them better. We have him to thank for studies of the brain ventricles, of the genital area and the fetal envelope, and for his detailed study of the heart and blood vessels; indeed he was just a step away from discovering the circulation of the blood. Unfortunately Leonardo did not publish his findings, so they remained virtually unknown among his contemporaries. The manuscripts are in the Royal Library at Windsor Castle and some were published in Paris (1898), others in Turin (1901), and the remainder by the University of Oslo.

Leonardo's interest in medicine was not confined to anatomy. Optics and optometry interested him just as much. There is that strange drawing in the Musée Condé at Chantilly, in which the celebrated Mona Lisa is depicted with her right eye dark and her left eye light, and a squint that must have caused her some embarrassment. Indeed, Leonardo performed an imaginary operation on Mona Lisa in depicting her in his famous portrait with the deformity corrected.

Although Albrecht Dürer (1471-1528) and Leonardo da Vinci were contemporaries, they were as diverse in their work as much as in their anatomical studies. Dürer, content with artistic anatomy, plunged more deeply into the Middle Ages, whereas Leonardo, conducting scientific dissections, was the embodiment of the Renaissance.

In *The Four Books* Albrecht Dürer (Vier Bucher von Menschlicher Proportion, Nuremberg, 1534, Latin ed.), reveals his inclination toward the artistic rather than the scientific. The male and female bodies are well proportioned and carefully inserted into squares. There are also

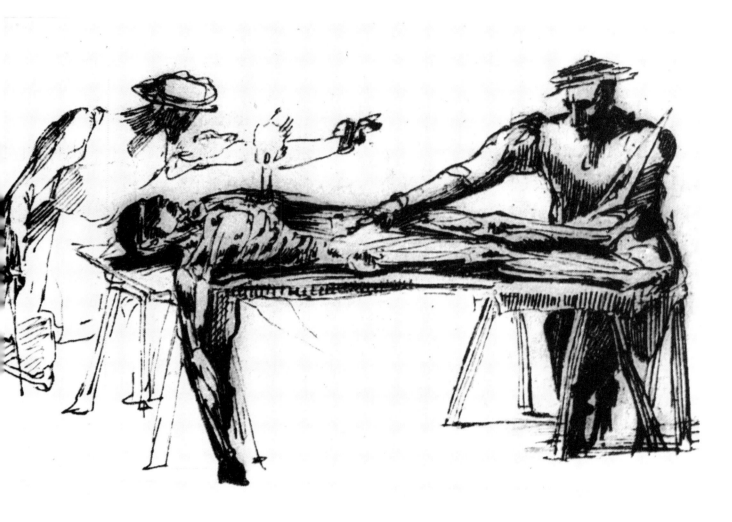

MICHELANGELO BUONARROTI (1475-1564)

Dissection of a corpse

Like Leonardo Da Vinci, Michelangelo was as adept
with a scalpel as with a paintbrush.

OXFORD UNIVERSITY

included drawings of physical anomalies, either of extreme
slimness or of obesity. In his famous *Melancolia* engraving, one can see the detailed drawing of a state of depression. The model is also a prototype of one of those
powerful women that abound in German legends. Or
again, we have the anomalous head of the child (Louvre,
Paris) with side whiskers and an enormous beard.

How about Raphael and Michelangelo? A pen drawing
in the British Museum proves that the former was interested, like Dürer, in external anatomy. On the other hand,
Michelangelo wielded the scalpel like Leonardo. The
anatomical plates that the latter composed are precise in
detail and distinguished in drawing.

Among the anatomists proper, Johannes Günther of
Andernach, their precursor, a universal man—belletrist,
philosopher, and physicist—taught Greek at Louvain
University and pursued his medical studies in Paris. We

are indebted to him for a study of muscles especially of the
hand, and above all for having developed a pupil of
genius, Vesalius, the real father of modern anatomy.

Vesalius was born in Brussels in 1514. Completely
dedicated to his researches he fought against all obstacles,
and ran the risk of being branded a heretic or a sorcerer.
He was reputed to have been seen in Paris fighting the
crows for the remains of criminals beheaded at Mont-
faucon. While teaching anatomy in the Italian universities—he was only thirty-six at the time—he was hounded
by the Church. Then in Madrid, while in the service of
Philip II, he heard himself condemned to death by the
Inquisition for allegedly having performed an autopsy on
a gentleman who was still breathing. He was only saved,
in extremis, by the intervention of the king and as penance
was forced to make a pilgrimage to the Holy Land. The
trip proved fatal; on the return journey he was ship-

133

PRIMA MVSCV-
LORVM TABVLA

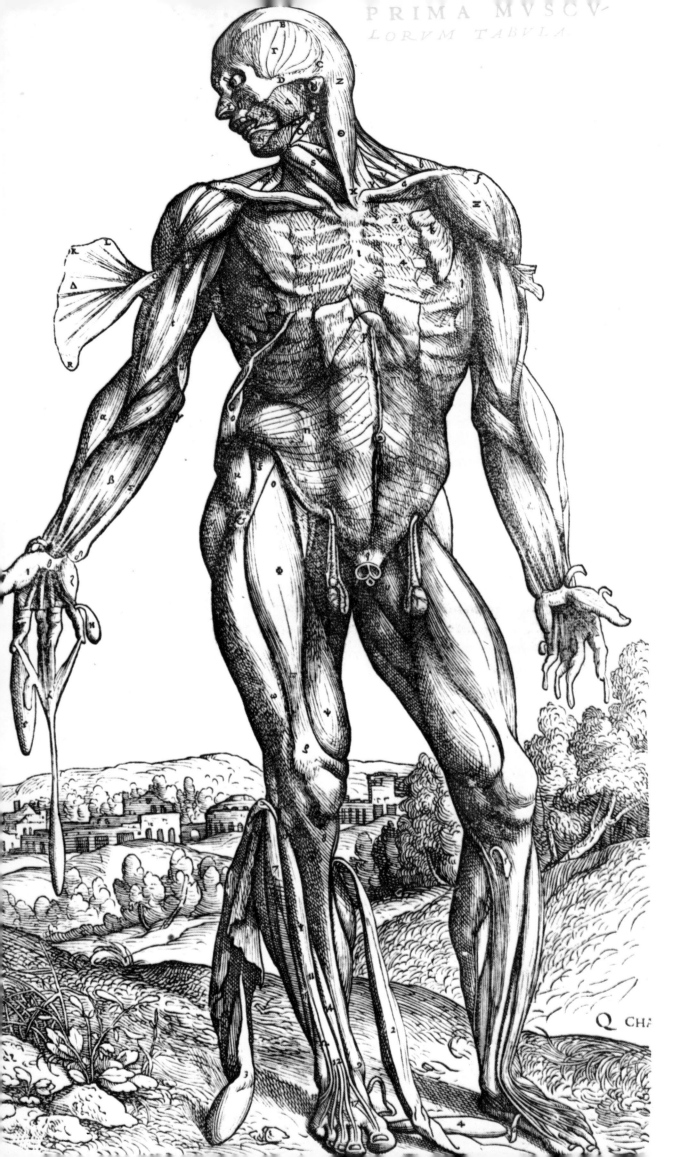

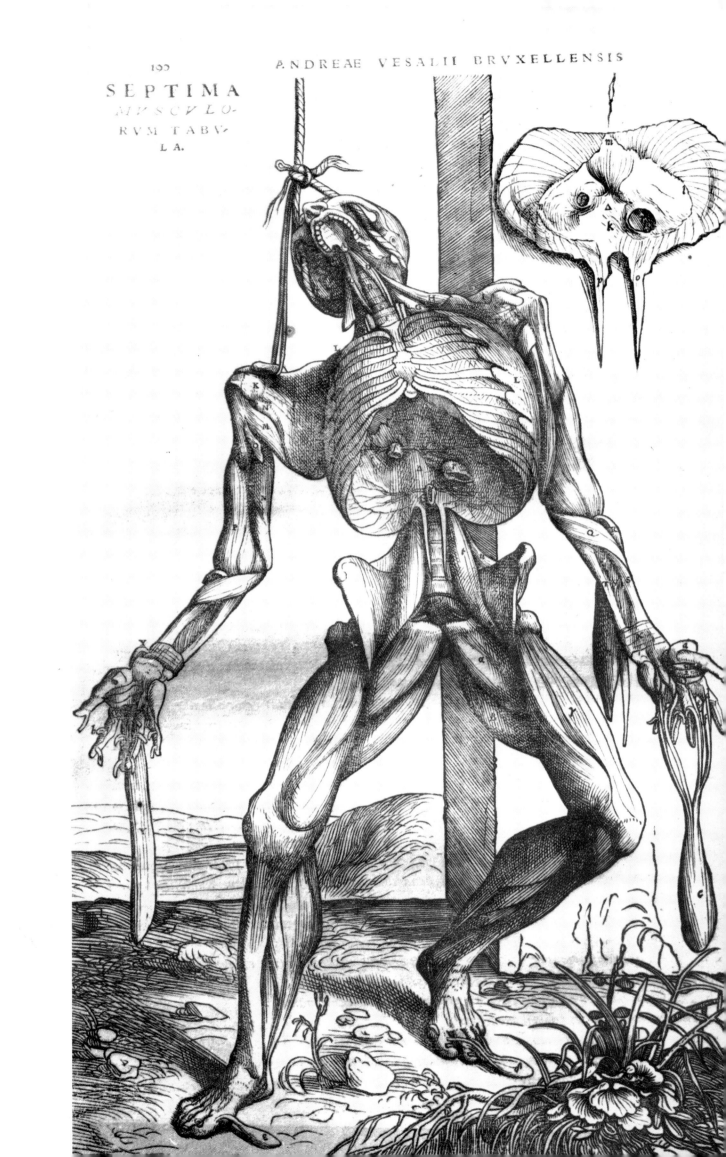

FAMOSO · DOCTOR   PARESELSVS

wrecked on the coast of Zante, where he apparently died a short time later of typhus.

A victim of envy, superstition, and stupidity, Vesalius was nevertheless able to produce a work of major importance, namely his *De Humani Corporis Fabrica,* published in Basel in 1543, and illustrated with splendid plates formerly attributed to Titian, but recently established as the work of one of Titian's students Jan Stephan van Calcar (ca. 1499-1546).

This was not the only book to contain masterpieces of graphic art illustrating the new science of anatomy; occasional masterpieces turned up when more or less unknown illustrators undertook to draw strictly educational material unaware that they were producing great art. Sculpture also was on the same high level as these illustrations. There are indeed many types of outstanding anatomical art produced during this period. In the first category come the educational books designed for artist, sculptor, doctor, and surgeon. Alongside Vesalius' book we could place *De Omnibus humani corporis interioribus membris anathomia* by Mondino de' Luzzi (Strasburg, 1513), *Spiegel der Artzney* by Laurentius Phryesen (Strasburg, 1529), *Isagogae breves perlucidae ac uberrimae in anatomiam humani corporis* by Jacopo Berengario da Carpi (Venice, 1535), *De Dissectione partium corporis humani libri tres* by Charles Estienne (Paris, 1545), and finally *De re anatomica, libri XV* by Realdo Colombo, published in Venice in 1559.

The second category includes anatomical models. In this group we can place the drawings, paintings, and sculptures depicting human bodies that have been entirely flayed. The most famous of these is the painting by Gerard David (d. 1523) in the Musée Communale, Bruges *The Flaying of the Unjust Judge.* Luca Signorelli also depicts bodies stripped of their epidermis in his *Last Judgment* (Orvieto cathedral). The artists of the sixteenth century appear to have been obsessed with flayed bodies, judging by the host of examples to be found. The quasi-scientific quality of these paintings and drawings may be better explained by the progress then being made in the field of anatomy, when these drawings were strictly utilitarian. Thus the flayed models that appear among the illustrations in Vesalius' book, depicted in various postures, display muscles stripped of the surface layers of skin. By the same token, the anonymous artists who illustrated Jacopo Berengario da Carpi's flayed bodies in his

book *Commentaria cum amplissimis additionibus super Anatomia Mundini,* published in Bologna in 1521, and those of Mondino de Luzzi (*Cy est l'anathomie de maistre Mundin boulonoys,* published in Paris in 1532) depicted the skin drawn aside in order to show the muscles and lay bare the organs beneath.

In the early days of this art form there was a self-conscious element in these utilitarian illustrations. The rather horrible flayed models were often placed in front of handsome pastoral scenes and elegant architecture.

Likewise the sculpture and modeling that treat the same subject in bronze, marble, ivory, wood, and terracotta often display a high degree of skill. We have, for example, an authentic masterpiece in the *Flayed Saint Bartholomew,* sculpted in marble in 1562 by Marco d'Agrate (b. ca. 1500) for the Cathedral of Milan. The saint carries his skin over his arm, folded like a scarf.

In tomb effigies we see the further development of scientific realism which was not limited to a study of the body but was equally concerned with the laws of gravity. Tomb effigies of the Middle Ages depicted the dead dressed in their best finery and stretched out on their monuments in idealized draperies that did not take into account the horizontal position of the models. The Renaissance was to flatten and spread out these folds as they are in real life. Furthermore, even if this patron were a prince, the Renaissance sculptor depicted dead bodies realistically, in decomposition or with bones piercing emaciated cadavers. The "light" of the Renaissance demanded an illumination of everything, even the physical horror of death. The most celebrated piece of this sort of sculpture is without a doubt that by the Lorraine artist Ligier Richier (1506-1567) done for the mausoleum of René de Châlons, Prince of Orange, in 1544 (Church of Saint-Pierre, Bar-le-Duc). And yet can we really call this a tomb sculpture, depicting a dead man, his flesh in shreds, ribcage quite visible, pulling himself out of his tomb in order to offer his heart to God? In other funerary effigies sculpted by Ligier Richier we can see a certain grandeur, albeit somewhat mannered. On the other hand, the statue of the second wife of René de Châlons, asleep at the feet of her husband and dressed in the habit of a nun of the order of St. Claire, is both realistic and anatomically correct.

Now we enter the domain of works of art that used medicine and surgery as subject matter to varying degrees.

The first "anatomy lessons" appeared during the sixteenth century. One of the most remarkable of these is to be seen in Rome in the Palazzo Borghese, depicting the Archangel Michael scalpel in hand, instructing students grouped around a flayed cadaver. The work is lively, detailed, and also well composed. It is tentatively attributed to Bartolommeo Passarotti (1529-1592). The Louvre

QUENTIN METSYS (1466?-1530)
Portrait of Doctor Paracelsus.

LOUVRE, PARIS

137

TOVRNELLES

While King Henry II of France is dying at the Hôtel des Tournelles in July, 1559, the queen is weeping at his bedside. To her left, the Mayor and the Cardinal of Lorraine; to her right, the child who will one day become Francis II. Doctors and surgeons are occupied around the table. At the far right of the engraving, the guards of the king's chambers. Through the window, we can see two surgeons and a physician on horseback, sent from Flanders by the King of Spain.

BIBLIOTHÈQUE NATIONALE, PARIS

has a sketch for this painting which is somewhat different in detail. Christoph Murer (1558-1614) also depicts a dissection scene at about the same time in a stained-glass window recounting the life of Leonhardt Thurneysser.

Some of the instructional books listed above contain, besides the illustrations of a practical nature that we have mentioned, a quality of their own, some boldly artistic engravings which did not shrink from depicting special medical data in detail. An example would be the *Feldtbuch der Wundartzney* by Hans von Gersdorff (Strassburg, 1529), depicting such a daring operation as the stitching of an intestine. These illustrations are so graceful and fresh in style and manner that the plates in the *Chirurgia e Graeco in Latinum conversa* by Guido Guidi are attributed to Primaticcio, as are the illustrations in the books of Ambroise Paré (Paris, 1564-1572), and those by Giovanni Andrea della Croce (*Chirurgiae universalis opus,* Venice, 1573) and Pietro Paolo Nogini (*Discorsi... intorna el sanguinar i corpo humani,* Rome, 1560). One of the most unusual examples is the very beautiful wood engraving, almost certainly executed by Gentile Bellini (ca. 1427-1507), to be found in the *Fasciculus Medicinae* by Johannes de Ketham (Venice, 1500). In this engraving, a doctor and his assistants are examining a victim of the plague—after having taken precautions against infection, the doctor with a sponge dipped in vinegar and spices placed under his nose, his assistants burning aromatics.

Apart from books, there is also an ample list of individual drawings, engravings, paintings, and sculpture that were inspired by medicine and surgery or from observation of physical ailments and diseases. In Barend Van Orley's (ca. 1493-1542) *Job's Friends* (Musée des Beaux Arts, Brussels), the wicked rich man is dying attended not only

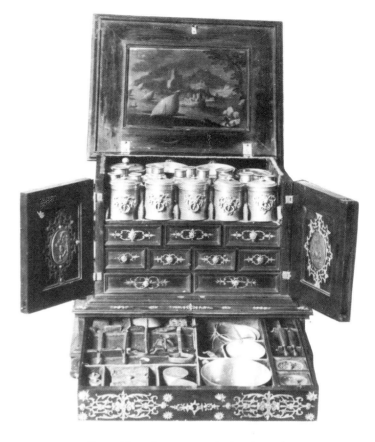

Portable pharmacy of the Renaissance

This splendid portable pharmacy of the Renaissance, dating from approximately 1600, is the work of an Augsburg master, whose signature H F has remained unidentified until this very day. German handicraft was at its zenith then, particularly in Augsburg where it produced veritable masterpieces. The ornaments, containers, and instruments of this little chest are of carved massive silver.

Bronze mortar, High Renaissance.
Southern Germany

The initials C. D. prove that this fine piece, created in 1555, is the work of the bell-maker Caspar Dietrich, of Ingolstadt, Bavaria. The cylindrical form, the clean lines on the edge, the body, and the foot, the dolphin-shaped handles, correspond to the characteristics of pharmaceutical mortars in the German Renaissance. The relief ornamentation on the trunk is superb; it shows a horseman fighting with a foot soldier, the muse Erato, and the Roman knight Marcus Curtius.

by his weeping wife but also by a doctor analyzing the patient's urine as if he had all day to spare. A pupil of Raphael's, Giulio Romano (1482-1546), has depicted in a drawing (a reproduction of which hangs in the Musée Fabre at Montpellier) a doctor in the process of cupping an invalid in bed, which incidentally shows that this method was already in use during the sixteenth century. At about the same time, an engraving by Arnold Jones (Collection of Dr. Clements C. Fry, New Haven, Connecticut) illustrates preparations for a Caesarian operation to be performed by a surgeon and four assistants. An engraving by the Flemish Joris David (1500-1566, Basel) gives us an idea of hospital life and charitable works by showing us three pious laymen lavishing their care on the patients.

Of course, humor often appears when medical instruments are used, particularly when the rectal syringe was the instrument in question, and when a Fleming was the artist. There could be no better example of such a work than the apothecary's sign in the Bruges Museum, a bas-

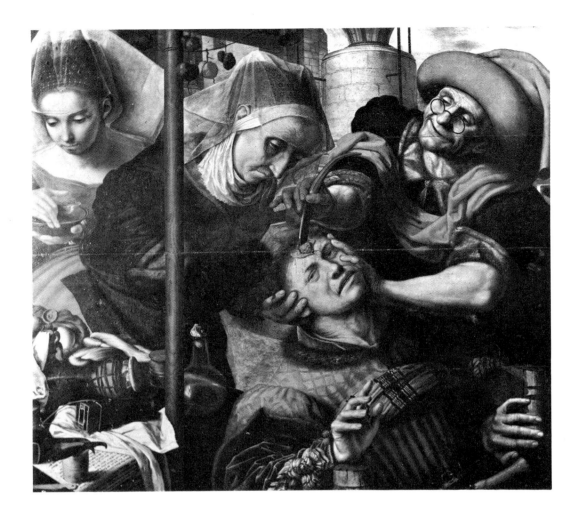

SANDERS HEMESSEN
(1500?-1566)

*The extraction of the
"Stone of madness"*

In those times, people believed that madmen had a stone
in their brain provoking the
disturbance of their reason.
The operation was often partially simulated by the "surgeon," who, at the last moment, exhibited a calcareous
object supposedly extracted
from the patient's skull.

PRADO, MADRID

relief sculptured out of wood and polychromed. Though
the style is still Gothic, the clothes and more particularly
the hats of the people depicted date from the sixteenth
century. An old lady is standing in the entrance of a
house with her skirts raised above her head, about to be
given an enema; the apothecary, holding the syringe, is
standing in the street. All this is taking place before a
man and two women who appear exceedingly interested
in the proceedings.

The picture by Louis Testelin (1615-1655) in Notre-
Dame de Bonne Nouvelle that depicts Louis XII—"father
of the people"— taking care of the sick is an example of
more serious work. In this noble, well-composed, and
highly realistic canvas, the king places his crown and
scepter at his feet; he holds the ulcerated leg of a poor
man over his knee, and assistants are handing him salves
and bandages. The fact that Louis XII is acting here as
the canonized Louis IX does not make the canvas any
less realistic.

Dwarfs, who were to be among Velásquez' favorite subjects during the seventeenth century, were already found
in the painting and sculpture of the sixteenth. Unlike
those painted by the Spanish school, the dwarf depicted
by the Fleming Antonis Moro (1519-1576) has normal
proportions. The presence of a dog standing next to him
that suggests his small stature and the lines of his face
are the only sign of his not being a child but a man; his
sumptuous clothes indicate that he was in the service of
a noble lord.

Similarly Holbein takes obesity as a secondary theme
in a drawing that can be seen in the Louvre, while two
great Flemish painters, Hieronymus Bosch and Pieter
Brueghel plunge into the world of madness and the most
diverse monstrosities. Bosch (1450?-1516) is a painter
who belongs both to the fifteenth and the sixteenth centuries. His visions are both delirious and acute, exceeding
even the audacity of the surrealists. In an engraving in
the Bibliothèque Nationale in Paris he depicts crowds of
cripples, noting minute details of deformities and natural
or accidental illnesses, all of which are rendered by a
clinical and cruel imagination. There are more cripples
to be seen in the extravagant canvas in the Gemäldega-

HIERONYMUS BOSCH
(1450 or 1460-1516)

The Ship of Fools

The delirious visions of Bosch
surpass the daring of the surrealists.

LOUVRE, PARIS

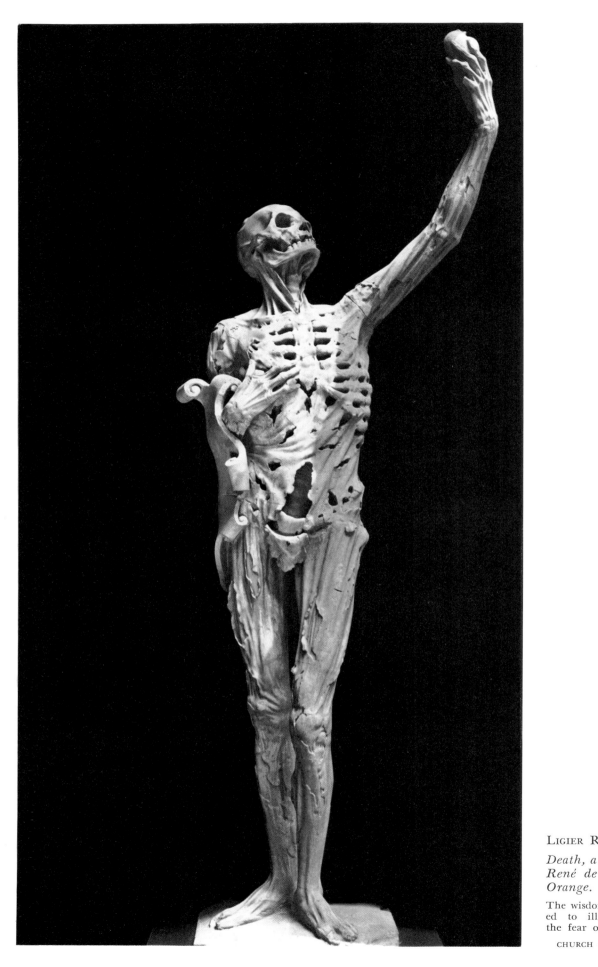

LIGIER RICHIER (1500?-1566)

Death, a statue on the tomb of René de Chalon, Prince of Orange.

The wisdom of the Renaissance wanted to illuminate everything, even the fear of death.

CHURCH OF SAINT-PIERRE, BAR LE-DUC

Drawing attributed to
PRIMATICCIO (1504-1570)

This expenditure of energy may have
some effect on what is probably a dislocated shoulder. It may even go
beyond its aim and cause a fracture
of the shoulder bone.

BIBLIOTHÈQUE NATIONALE, PARIS

lerie in Vienna, and yet it would appear that this time the subject is more of a "burlesque" between the "fat man" and the "thin man," while in his *Ship of Fools* (Louvre, Paris) madmen sail in a sea of dreams. Bosch, so different in his powerful and terrible imagination, so different from his cold and serious contemporaries like Hans Memling and Gerard David, was the first painter to be inspired by a superstition commonly held in his time, namely, the belief that a stone lodged in the brain of lunatics was responsible for their derangement. This superstition was so widespread that quacks did not hesitate to operate to extract the "stone." Happily, these operations were often faked. The surgeon would produce from his coat sleeve a piece of stone that he would adroitly cause to leap from the head of the patient at the right moment. We can see one of the "excisions" in a picture by Bosch in the Rijks-museum in Amsterdam. The quack is working on a

seated man, while the onlookers, stupified, are examining a stone the size of a cherry that apparently has just come out of the head of another patient who underwent the same operation, and whose head is being bandaged.

Pieter Brueghel the Elder (ca. 1530-1600)—also known as "Droll Pieter" on account of his lively and racy village scenes—also painted the quack operating on the "stone of folly." His style, often combining the burlesque and the fantastic, suits the subject perfectly. This can be seen best in a painting in the National Museum of Budapest. In this canvas, the cruel absurdity of the "excision" is rendered all the more horrifying by the stakes that appear to have been driven into the head of the patient. There is a similar engraving, dated 1585, and entitled *Amusing Scene* in the Museum at Bayeux. Many artists of the time turned their hand to this same subject, among them Jan Sanders van Hemessen (ca. 1500-1566) and an anony-

GÉRARD DAVID (1450?-1523)

The flaying of the corrupt judge

In the sixteenth century, there is a veritable flowering
of flayings.

MUSÉE COMMUNAL DES BEAUX ARTS, BRUGES

mous Dutchman, whose version in the Prado depicts the
quack wearing a funnel.

Brueghel also did other subjects of medical interest. For
example, in a drawing in the Albertina in Vienna, depicting the pilgrimage to Molenbeck, one can see men drag-
ging women afflicted by St. Vitus dance. He also painted
contemporary scenes of persecutions, criminals, highway
robbers, and punitive expeditions; and, as a form of
protest against the arbitrariness and cruelty of his time,
he added to the pictures as many cripples, beggars, and
blind men as he could fit in. Although these pictures
are primarily of interest on account of their satirical
content, their caricatural and symbolic execution, as well

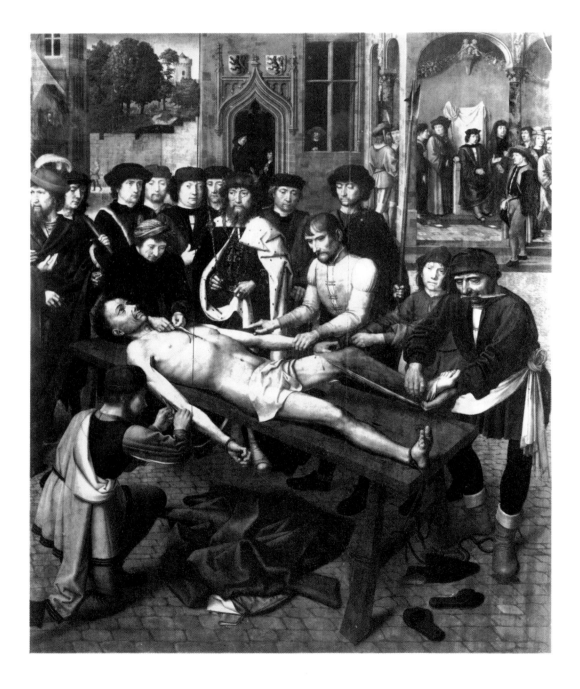

as their primitive and blunt style, they also have a medical
pertinence that can be seen in the suffering and sick
bodies that the artist observed in minute detail. The
Beggars of the Brotherhood of Ribaldry (Louvre, Paris)
and the *Parable of the Blind* in the Museo Nazionale,
Naples, spring to mind immediately when we consider this
period of Brueghel's work.

There is a tremendous volume of material in the art of
the sixteenth century that more or less systematically
makes fun of medicine and surgery. Undoubtedly there
was good reason for making jokes at the expense of medicine and doctors in a century when, despite the advances
made in the science of anatomy, curative methods were
still rudimentary. Yet there were two master healers at

this time, Paracelsus in the field of medicine and Pare
in surgery.

Paracelsus (1493-1541), whose real name was Philip
Aureolus Theophrastus Bombastus von Hohenheim, did
not become famous for any single major discovery. However, his views which caused considerable irritation to
his colleagues are still of value today. "Neither title nor
eloquence nor the knowledge of language should be of
importance to the doctor; rather, he should have a profound understanding of the secrets of nature; this science
surpasses all others." Why did he publicly condemn the
work of Galen and Avicenna who were the main source of
inspiration to his rivals? Paracelsus' motives in this matter
are unknown, but surely it was the spirit of the Renaissance

RAPHAEL SANZIO (1483-1520)

The Cripple

The anatomical precision of this scene of a miraculous
cure makes it a true medical document.

VATICAN MUSEUM, ROME

that prompted him—as it had prompted Leonardo da
Vinci—to penetrate the mysteries of matter hitherto considered sacred, regardless of the consequences.

One may say the same of Ambroise Paré (1510-1590)
who, although still expressing himself in a traditional
manner, scoffed at the idea that man could manage without the help of God. *Je le pansay. Dieu le guérit.* ("I
treated him. God healed him.") Like Paracelsus, he advocated an experimental and rational study of the human
body. He also refuted the ancients and their volumes on
medicine, despite the fact that he knew no Latin or Greek.
His reprimand launched at an eminent professor of the
Sorbonne, Etienne Gourmelon, is brief but most telling:
"Surgery is to be taught by using the eyes and the hands.
You, my little master, know absolutely nothing, except
how to mouth your jargon from the heights of a platform."

To these two famous names we must add another, that
of François Rabelais, undoubtedly one of the great French
writers. He was also a theologian, jurist, pedagogue,
philologist, sometime priest, and always a humanist.

Rabelais was also a doctor, something we tend to forget.
To quote Doctor Le Bouble, author of *Rabelais, Anato-
miste and Physiologiste* (published in 1899), Rabelais was
also a *good* doctor; and underneath the humorous, almost
burlesque façade of the writing, the anatomical descriptions to be found in Rabelais' *Quart Livre* were based
strictly on scientific fact. The sound knowledge that Rabelais had of his art is further attested to by his two
inventions: two pieces of apparatus to mend fractures
and wounds by tension, the "syringotome" and the "glot-
tomocon," reproductions of which can be be seen in the
*Sixth book of therapeutics or curative method by Claude
Galen, translated by Philatros,* Lyons, 1537, Philatros
being the pseudonym of Jean Canape, friend of Gargan-
tua's father.

Paracelsus, Paré, and Rabelais, three men of genius.
Their attacks on contemporary medicine were justified
since doctors so often hid their ignorance behind a flood
of unintelligible jargon and grotesque dress. Indeed it was
at times impossible for the ignorant patient to distinguish
between honest practitioners and astute quacks. Francis Bacon (1561-1626) wrote: "We can see that the stupidity and credulity of man is such that he more often than
not prefers a quack or a witch doctor to an experienced
physician." Surgery in those days was often confined to
barbers—since Pope Boniface VIII's decree excommunicat-
ing anyone who cut up a human body had not yet been
revoked. Dentistry, on the other hand, was practiced by
"tooth extractors" who operated at fairs with the assistance of musicians charged with the task of attracting
clients and then drowning out their screams and yells.
Of course the flowing robes and pig-Latin of these doctors

146

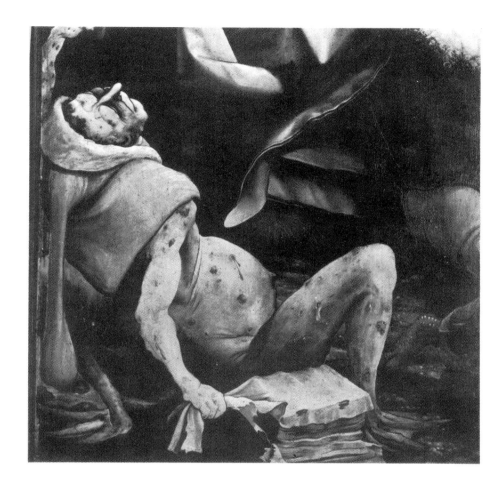

MATTHIAS GRÜNEWALD (1470-1528)

A man stricken with "St. Anthony's fire" (ergotism)

The Antonites of Isenheim, for whom the artist painted the huge polyptych, of which this is just a detail, tended the unfortunate who were struck down by this disease caused by moldy grain; direct, scientific observation was thus the inspirational source of Grünewald's masterpiece. Detail from "The Temptation of Saint Anthony".

MUSEUM OF COLMAR, FRANCE

were bound to stimulate the caricaturist's satirical activity.

One of the scenes most often depicted in caricatures of medicine during the sixteenth century was that of the extraction of teeth. The dentist is always jovial, and so are the spectators. As for the patient, he screams and writhes about but no one pays attention to him. An anonymous engraving dating back to the sixteenth century (Bibliothèque Nationale) shows in great detail the cruelly burlesque character of the dentist. Kneeling on a bench beside his patient, he is wielding a giant pair of pliers, heedless of the dog relieving himself over him, and a child doing the same thing on a table nearby.

As for the doctors, it was not unusual to see them depicted as monkeys (later, Goya would turn them into donkeys). In the *Collection of Facetious and Ludicrous Pieces from 1500 to 1600* (Bibliothèque Nationale, Paris), an anonymous engraving on leather shows them taking care of patients who have changed into chimpanzees or into gorillas. Their treatment ranges from bleeding to the extracting of teeth, and includes the dressing of wounds and the cutting of hair.

On the other hand, in the four satirical engravings executed at Haarlem in 1587 under the direction of Hendrick Goltzius (1588-1617), only the patients are made to look ridiculous, and the doctor is successively represented as God, an angel, and a devil—a transformation that symbolizes rather accurately the patient's change of attitude toward his doctor from the first call to the time when he has to pay the bill. There are also some very handsome engravings of this period in the Philadelphia Museum. These pictures are of distinct documentary interest because in the background of each print are some well-observed contemporary medical and surgical scenes.

The dreadful disease leprosy, which inflicted the cruelest ravages upon the Middle Ages, was for a long time a source of inspiration to artists. However, this interest waned when, by the middle of the sixteenth century, the disease was almost brought under control in Europe, although it was not until 1695 that the last leprosaria closed their doors in France.

Leprosy was also known as "ladrerie" in sixteenth-century France. The name was based on the story in the Gospel according to Luke in which the story is told of

PIETER BRUEGHEL, THE ELDER (c. 1525-1569)

The Parable of the Blind

Brueghel found his subjects in the real world of persecutions, poverty, plundering, and corporal punishment. His rigorous observation is always coupled with sarcastic protest.

MUSEUM OF NAPLES

the beggar Lazarus, known as "Ladre" by medieval Frenchmen. This Lazarus subsequently became the patron saint of the lepers. Most of the works of art showing Saint Ladre and victims of leprosy are late medieval: notably, the Flemish banner with its border made of lepers' bones, and the kneeling leper depicted in the fresco by Cosimo Rosselli (1430-1507) illustrating the Sermon on the Mount (Sistine Chapel, Rome). From the sixteenth century we have a painting in distemper, the ex-voto by Nicolas Manuel Deutsch (ca. 1484-1530) now in Basel, *Saint Anne between Saint James the Elder and Saint Roch,* showing a number of contagious diseases, including a fingerless man who symbolizes leprosy.

When the virulence of leprosy diminished in Europe, another disease appeared that was a pretext for a number of sarcastic and humorous works of art. This was syphilis. This pox owes its name to an Italian doctor called Girolamo Fracastoro (born in 1483), author of a poem entitled *Syphilis sive morbus gallicum,* which describes the deeds of a young shepherd called Syphilis, afflicted with a "terrifying evil" for having insulted Apollo. Fracastoro describes in verse and in detail the various phases of the disease and its cure with an ointment made essentially of mercury and guaiacum. We can understand the use of mercury which, under the name of Neapolitan ointment, remained a cure for venereal diseases; but we are completely at a loss with regard to the use of guaiacum.

With the end of the wars in Italy, syphilis invaded Europe. The Spaniards were also responsible for spreading it. Charles VIII's troops brought it back with them from the Peninsular campaign in 1495. The Swiss, who gave it the name of "gorre de Genève" were inflicted with it in 1496. The Dutch, who called it "lues Hispanica," declared that the courtiers in the suite of the Princess of Aragon (who had come to marry the archduke Philip) were responsible for bringing it into Holland, whereas the Germans accused Charles VIII's and Maximilian's lancers for having brought them the "scorra" or the "malum de Franzos." England experienced the ravages of what she called "morbus burgalensia." In Denmark it was called "pocken." Poland, Dalmatia, and Greece were also plagued with the disease. If the populace was terrified of it, the poets thought it very funny. Among them was Jean Droyn (1512):

> *Pour corriger mondains luxurieux*
> *S'est engendrée cette grosse verole..."*

and of course the artists followed suit. Thus we have an anonymous engraving entitled *The routing of the Spaniards from the city of Naples on the arrival of the Duc de Guise* (Bibliothèque Nationale, Paris), an allegory showing us the Spaniard sweating out his pox enclosed in a barrel and undergoing a mercury fumigation. Another engraving, *Venus wounded by thorns* by Giorgio Ghisi (1520-1582), depicts the misadventure with a certain amount of grace. Although there is no medical apparatus in an anonymous engraving dating from the end of the sixteenth century entitled *The Chariot of Love,* it is a satirical and moral story about the Rouen pox. Nicolas Manuel Deutsch (1484-1530), on the other hand, described the ravages of the disease in the most hideous fashion in his sketch now in the Basel Museum.

A drawing by Stradamus (Jan von der Straet 1523-1605) engraved by Jean Galle (Bibliothèque Nationale) is more instructive. In the right-hand corner we can see a guaiacum tree being chopped down and stacked; on the left lies a syphilitic patient attended by a doctor who is applying a salve extracted from the guaiacum.

Though this patient is anonymous, as were most of those depicted in the frontispieces of books devoted to the study and treatment of syphilis (among them *A mala Franczos* by Berth Steher and *Tractatus de Scorra* by Grünpeck), a large amount of publicity was given to the syphilis contracted by Francis I of France:

> *L'an mil cent quarante sept,*
> *François mourut a Rambouillet*
> *De la verole quil avait fait.*

There were also other epidemics that were a source of inspiration to the artist, and these were treated with much less humor. Among these of course was the plague. The plague is the subject of one of the enormous frescoes painted in 1518 in the Chapel of Saint Sebastian at Lanslevillard (Savoy). A surgeon is shown lancing or cauterizing a ganglion on the neck of a young lady; next to her are a man and a child holding their arms in the air so that we can see their boils also. Above them an angel is pointing from a nearby fresco in the direction of the tomb of Saint Sebastian. His gesture prevents a hideous demon from throwing his pustule-covered dart. There is no Saint Sebastian in the third fresco, but a portrait of Saint Roch, placed there in recognition of the successful occasions on which the saint intervened in time of plague. In this particular portrait he is shown with an invalid, Cromatius, prefect of Rome, whom he cured, if we are to believe the chronicles. In this picture, however, the prefect is asleep and appears terribly emaciated.

No saint intervenes in the illustrations made by Hans Weiditz for *Trost Spiegel im Glück und Unglück* (Augsburg, 1535). We do see the horrible ravages of the plague on two men and on various animals. This engraving shows us that in those days some precautions were taken against the epidemic: thus, the persons visiting the agonizing victim are holding cloths to their noses and mouths.

Four Engravings by HENDRIK GOLTZIUS (1558-1616)

Goltzius excud. N.º 87.

Dum ngris egrum prope Mors circumuolat alis,   Ο ΘΕΟΣ.   *Tum me promißis beat et domus omnis adorat,*
Funeſtamq, aciem iam fera iamq, parat.   *Tum vocat immenſum me venerata DEVM*

The physician is a god

excud.

igi Machaonia mgis et magis arte leuatus,   ΙΑΤΡΟΣ ΠΟΛΛΩΝ   *Ο HOMO, non fruſtra tantos ſubyſſe labores*
Cum ſedet ante focum, progreditur ue tripes.   ΑΝΤΑΞΙΟΣ ΑΛΛΩΝ.   *Noſces; quod reſtat tu modo tolle malum.*

The physician is a man

HS. exc.

Ast ego si penitus iam sanum præmia poscam, YBPIΣ ΤΕ ΚΑΙ ΠΛΗΓΗ *Cautior exemplo tu DVM DOLET ACCIPE,*
Ille Deus pridem mox CACODÆMON ero. ANTI ΣΩΣΤΡΩΝ. *Qui Medicæ exerces gnauiter artis opus.*

The physician is a devil

2. Htoltz. excud.

Paulùm vbi conualuit; paulùm de numine nostro Η ΤΟΥ ΘΕΟΥ ΧΕΙΡ *Tu cœlo nobis demissus es ANGELVS alto,*

The physician is an angel

HYACVM, ET LVES VENEREA.
Grauata morbo ab hocce membra mollia   Leuabit ista forpta coctio arboris

Preparing and taking a remedy (guaiacum)
against venereal disease.

Among the other sixteenth-century works of art devoted
to the plague is the fine canvas painted by Raphael in the
Uffizi in Florence *The Phrygian Plague.* In this picture,
human beings and animals, some indoors and some in the
streets, all afflicted with the terrible disease, are strewn
about in pathetic convulsions. There is a drawing in the
Louvre by B. Beham (1502-1540) reproducing the same
painting with a new variations. More faithful is the
engraving dated 1556 by S. Bernard in the Bibliothèque
Nationale. The relationship between art and medicine
obviously takes a less realistic turn in works of religious
inspiration, as, for example, in paintings depicting the
birth of Jesus. Biological and medical realism is generally
avoided, whether the Virgin is depicted in bed and already
in labor with the women busy around her (anonymous,
Musée Saint-Jean, Bruges) or when the artist has her
seated and fully dressed, her skirt barely raised by the
holy woman occupying herself with the delivery, as in
an anonymous painting reproduced in the obstetrical book
Der Swangern Frauwen und Hebammen Rosegarten by
Eucharius Roesslin, town physician of Worms, in 1513
(Strassburg).

Medical drawings depicting circumcisions, operations,
and cures of a miraculous nature are generally treated
without attention to detail, either through modesty or
ignorance, or because of a conformist respect for the
mystery. We shall never know whether, for example, in
the bas-relief by Tillman Riemenschneider that adorns the
tomb of Henry II (Bamberg cathedral)—showing a gall-
stone operation being performed on the naked emperor
by a monk—whether the king was able to sleep well
afterwards; or why the man seated at the foot of the bed, a
doctor no doubt, has turned his head away from the scene
with a profoundly anguished expression on his face. Was
it supposed to be a real operation, or a miracle intended
to prove the superiorty of Faith over science?

In any case, miraculous cures are certainly the subject of
such works as the *Miracles at Mariazell,* an anonymous
German engraving (Basel) in which we can see the child
Jesus putting an end to the sufferings of a woman shaken
by the spasms of childbirth. Then there is Titian's
(1477-1576) canvas inspired by the story of Saint Anthony
curing a young cripple, and the bas-relief by Tullio Lombardo (1455-1532) who depicted the same subject (Basilica
of Saint Anthony, Padua). No less miraculous is the curing
of the young man with contorted legs painted by Raphael
(Vatican) or the works by Quentin Massys (1466-1530)
and Pedro Berruguete (d. 1503-4), the two last-mentioned

152

choosing the same subject, namely, that of the blind recovering their sight. Massys also painted the curing of Tobias by his son, to whom the Archangel Raphael had given the advice of rubbing the eyes of his father with fish bile. Berruguete shows us an unknown blind man being led by a boy praying to Saint Thomas, or rather to his relics enclosed in a coffin, to cure his master.

Apart from the fish bile used by Tobias' father, the works of art we have just mentioned—painted or engraved by artists whose work spanned the fifteenth and sixteenth centuries—make no reference to healing and medicine in general; even though there may be a suggestion of the "light" of the Renaissance, it is only a stylistic one. The spirit is still that of the Middle Ages—a religious and mystical spirit.

In the meantime, there were many works of art in which the painter depicted the traditional religious themes that referred directly, sometimes with strange and often baroque allusions, to modern methods employed by doctors and apothecaries. An example of such a painting is to be found in a miniature adorning the *Chants Royaux du Puy de Rouen,* a manuscript written at the beginning

The Military Surgeon and his Assistant

Woodcut, printed by Nicolas Medelmann in Nürnberg. c. 1530 "I am known everywhere for my medicine for wounds and my noble salves taken from the 'Feldtbuch' (Book of military surgery) and which give proof of their effectiveness. Using them, I have made numerous soldiers hale and hearty again, though they had wounds deep into their bones. As soon as the battle was half over, I stayed up until all the soldiers who had been wounded by firearms were bandaged by me—no matter how serious their injuries—so that no misfortune befell them, and none of them died for want of treatment or comfort; and all this, whether or not they had silver or gold, and I did it for the honor of our flag."

BIBLIOTHÈQUE DES ARTS DÉCORATIFS, PARIS

The tooth puller
The artist shows the burlesque horror concerning the dentist "in this savage state."
From the "Recueil des pièces facétieuses and bouffon-nes." End of the sixteenth century.

BIBLIOTHÈQUE NATIONALE, PARIS

of the sixteenth century (Bibliothèque Nationale). In this illustration we can see Christ seated in an apothecary's shop making out a prescription for Adam and Eve, who are standing before him, quite naked, save for the usual fig leaf. There is also a Dutch engraving of the same period in which Jesus, with urinal in hand, is standing in the classical position of a doctor examining a specimen.

Anatomical and clinical observations of a detailed nature are also to be seen in the works of religious inspiration, as in the little wooden polychromes to be seen at the Musée Cluny, Paris, depicting the Virgin fainting, and the same theme in the statue by Ligier Richier in the church of his birthplace (Saint-Mihiel, Meuse). In the last-mentioned work of art, the muscular movement that accompanies Mary's fainting spell—as she is held in the arms of Saint John—could hardly have been more accurately depicted if the artist had looked at the human body with the same attention and the same experimental zeal as a Paracelsus or a Paré. As if out of respect for the Virgin, and the miraculous nature of her maternity, her pregnancy is treated in an allegorical manner in an anonymous Venetian bas-relief (Victoria and Albert Museum, London), by an anonymous Spaniard (wood statue, Amiens Library), and by enamelers from Limoges. On the other hand, an anonymous Hungarian painter (Budapest Museum) includes Mary's rounded stomach almost to the point of exaggeration, in rather the same way as did Raphael in a *Visitation* (Prado, Madrid) in which the sad expression on the face of Christ's Mother and the clinical roundness of her belly are treated with equal realism.

Henceforth even paintings of the Danse Macabre and the Last Judgment, in which completely or partially emaciated skeletons issue from the earth and sometimes form a circle around kings, princes, and bishops, owe something to

Goya was to depict physicians as donkeys. Here, the barbers and apothecaries are monkeys; as are their customers. From the "Recueil des pièces facétieuses et bouf-fones." End of the sixteenth century.

BIBLIOTHÈQUE NATIONALE, PARIS

154

medical observation. Thus, in the magnificent altarpiece painted in the 1510's by Matthias Grünewald (ca. 1455-1522) for the Convent of St. Anthony in Isenheim (Colmar Museum) the body of Jesus is depicted in a horrible state of swelling and putrefaction. The painter could have found models among the patients in the hospital run by the order of St. Anthony. Grünewald has painted at Jesus' feet a crouching man covered with terrible sores—the sores of St. Anthony's fire of ergotism, a disease induced by moldy grain.

One can find many other examples of these detailed paintings which, for purposes of edification depict rotting bodies. The macabre effigy that adorns a tomb in the cathedral of Moulins, the wooden sculpture in the church at Bures-en-Bray (a decomposed corpse, life-size, laid out in his coffin), *The Putrified Body* attributed to Germain Pilon (Louvre), and a painting by Bigarelli (Musée des Arts Decoratifs, Paris) are among the most horrible, but also the most detailed examples. It was in this manner, therefore, that the sixteenth century illustrated its feelings about death and the biological destruction of the body, a century that could so well exalt the beauty of living flesh, above all, feminine flesh. Whether dead or alive, healthy or deformed, intact or partially eaten by worms, one may say that the nude triumphed in the sixteenth century. But this triumph is above all a triumph of truth, of a realism based on careful, minute, scientific and specifically medical observation. One could cite a Leonardo drawing of a fetus (Royal Library, Windsor Castle, England) and his many sketches devoted to surgical operations, or the terrifying mask of facial paralysis, attributed to Nicholas Gerhardt of Leyden in the House Museum of Our Lady of Strassburg.

The beauty of the female sex was often caught by the painters of the sixteenth century, indeed so often that, by comparing portraits, we can determine an average type. The women were large-hipped, tall, with well-defined breasts and bellies. However, alongside paintings of these beautiful women, painters also depicted abnormalities and monstrosities, mental as well as physical. *The Adulterers,* a painting by Grünewald (Strassburg Museum), is not only a hideous allegory, but also a portrait of weary bodies—sunken eyes, drooping breasts, fleshless ribs, etc. The portrait of Lorenzo de' Medici by Giorgio Vasari (Uffizi, Florence) is an anatomical document of the first order, with its sunken nose, and the drooping mouth. Also interesting are the girl with a beard painted by Dominique Custod (Cabinet d'Estampes, Bibliothèque Nationale, Paris) or the *Branle des Fous* of Daniel Stoffer (Bibliothèque Nationale) in which all manner of mental peculiarities are represented.

Finally, during this century, in which man looked toward antiquity, not as a step backwards, but in order to get beyond the intricate Gothic age and bathe in the clear waters of the Mediterranean spirit, there was a preoccupation with the human body, with its preservation, and eventually with curing it with more care than in former epochs. Anonymous engravings, such as those of the *Schachtafeln der Gesuntheyt* of Strassburg (1533), and paintings, among them one by Hans Bock (Basel Museum) attest to this. These people bathed frequently, either in rivers or in tubs, or in thermal baths as did the Romans. There were baths in Germany as well as France.

> *Jehan l'avenu*
> *Va-t-en aux etuves*
> *Et te laves, nud...*

Hygiene, a prime requisite in medicine, was therefore not unknown. One may thumb through the *Histoires Prodigieuses* by Pierre Boaistuau (Paris, 1560) illustrated with portrayals of monstrously obese bathers or glance at the enormous canvas by Andrea del Sarto at the Uffizi in Florence, where we see the interior of a hospital where everything is clean and orderly. Yet despite increasing efforts for cleanliness in connection with either medicine or daily life itself, we are still a long way from the modern idea of hygiene, or from the modern use of antiseptics.

THE SEVENTEENTH CENTURY

The historic conditions underlying the seventeenth century were bound to have important effects upon the development of medicine, and, indirectly, on its representation in the plastic arts. The opening up of the New World, which had begun in an organized fashion during the sixteenth century, reached its climax in the seventeenth. The limited and insular ideas that had prevailed in the Western world until this point gave way to a broader view of life. The knowledge of new people,

GÉRARD DOU (1613-1675)

The dropsical woman

Starting with Gérard Dou, Dutch painting was more picturesque than realistic. Even if the professional attitude of the "doctor analyzing urine,"—a subject that inspired quantities of paintings—is extremely well captured, this physician is first and foremost a pretext for a rich effect of drapery.

LOUVRE, PARIS

new languages, and new social customs was paralleled by new strides in science—particularly in mathematics, optics, and astronomy, all of which were so necessary to the expanding interest in exploration.

But to the degree that the humanism of the Renaissance and its insistence on man as the center of the universe gave way to a broader conception of a world of infinite size rather than a world revolving around the earth and its relatively small concerns, the concern with the development of human anatomy, for example, was less visible as an organized effort in the seventeenth century than it had been earlier. Where the seventeenth century developed ideas and biological science, it seemed to deal equally with systems rather than with isolated elements, as in the case of the most celebrated discovery of that period, the circulation of the blood. Equally interesting in the development of biological knowledge was the invention of the microscope by Leeuwenhoek, opening to the eyes of mankind the microscopic world

157

at the extreme end of the scale, at the opposite end of which the earliest discoveries of Copernicus had opened the heavens to mankind.

In spite of whatever discoveries were made in seventeenth-century medicine, the profession as a whole still remained very much attached to the tradition of Galen, which in turn constituted the main body of medieval medical doctrine. Yet several very important discoveries were made, notably that of William Harvey concerning the systolic contraction that forces the blood from the heart into the pulmonary artery and back again (*Exercitatio de motu cordis et sanguinis in animalibus*, Frankfurt, 1628) and Marcello Malpighi's later discovery concerning capillaries. However, these discoveries were not enough to persuade the medical profession to divest itself of its medieval trappings. Nor did the progress made by Thomas Sydenham in the field of therapeutics (he invented the formula for laudanum, prescribed quinine in cases of fever, and a mixture, the base of which was a compound of gum of Araby, for the cure of diarrhea) have any effect on the profession. The majority of doctors did not agree. There was even a doctor of considerable repute called Jean Riolon, physician to Marie de Médicis and her son Louis XIII, who, in order to discredit William Harvey, brought forward this ingenious notion: according to Galen, nature modified anatomy: the discovery of the mechanism of circulation only proves this modification; it does not prove that Galen was wrong. As Jean Fauvet wrote: "It is rather disconcerting that the Renaissance did not give medicine the free reign that one might have hoped for. Of course, anatomy and surgery were greatly stimulated by the work of two men, Vesalius and Paré. But all medicine really learned was a better understanding of the Greeks and Romans without managing to detach itself from the grip of the latter. Only one or two people managed to raise the leaden lid of medieval conformity, and they appear as revolutionaries. By preferring erudition to research, the evolution that one might have hoped for was quickly halted; it was not a Renaissance; it was rather an exhumation."

This lamentable condition of medicine during the seventeenth century did not prevent the artists from using medical subjects. Often they treated medicine with indulgence, but they also ridiculed it, even avenged themselves on its shortcomings. At the end of the chapter we shall discuss certain specific subjects. For the present let us examine country by country the artistic production that developed through a relationship with medicine. This classification will help review the art of each country which in the seventeenth century found its individual national character despite the universal Italian influence.

158

REMBRANDT VAN RIJN (1606-1669)
Woman ill in bed
Presumably a portrait of Saskia, the artist's wife.
MUSÉE DU PETIT PALAIS, PARIS

The Dutch

This national personality is particularly manifest in Dutch painting. While Flanders still remained under foreign domination and the power of the Catholic Church, Holland was now independent and Protestant. Holland was a rich country, and the Dutch had won their prosperity through stubborn hard work, struggling against the elements as much as against their rivals. Dutch ports were full of foreign ships, and all over the world their agencies flourished. A secure and comfort-loving bourgeoisie, fond of good food and a joke, with a taste for fine furniture and white linens, ruled a flat country literally won from the sea. They needed no prompting to mount a parade with soldiers in full-dress uniform, and yet as a people, the Dutch preferred to keep their feet warm in their comfortable homes among their mirrors and copperware, their tapestries and potted plants. At the same time they demonstrated their generosity in public charities. Burghers and their wives in lace collars founded hospitals, orphanages, homes for the aged and lay convents, subsidized academies in which the art of medicine and of surgery were to be practiced with funds derived from penny-pinching, though largely prompted by an "obscurant" respect for the sacred mystery of the human body. As a result, the Dutch were noble in appearance, hierarchical, and severe, whether counting gold coins on a damask cloth or watching over the cleanliness of a hospital parlor. Of course they wanted posterity to know who they were and what they had done; so they called on painters, and looked favorably upon paintings that depicted them to their best advantage. One of the most unusual evidences of this aspect of Dutch life is to be found in a special category of hospital pictures showing not the act of curing or even examining, but rather the assembling of the directors of a hospital and other charitable institutions (such as homes for the aged), as seen in some of the paintings by Frans Hals. Works of this kind reflect not only the character of the gentlemen and ladies involved, but also a great awareness on the part of the Dutch public for the need to exercise this function. A curious subdivision of this category is to be found in a number of examples showing the directors of a leprosarium (or leper hospital) with a suffering patient being presented to these gentlemen for their charity, e.g., in the works of Jan de Bray. Although leprosy had obviously existed as far back as the Middle Ages (as indicated in earlier chapters), it is apparently only in Dutch art of the seventeenth century that the leper as such emerges again as a theme. One may readily conjecture that the interests of the Dutch in the Far East during this period—centered in the Dutch East India Company—may well have had something to do with this.

Dutch art of the seventeenth century, therefore, will reflect Holland itself and give a picture of Dutch life. It was in proportion to his respect for Dutch reality that the giant of his period, Rembrandt (1606-1669), was able to command the valuable patronage of his fellow citizens of Amsterdam. It was in proportion to his separation from it all that he became an outcast whose funeral had to be paid out of public funds.

Rembrandt never visited Italy, but he learned about Roman civilization at the University of Leyden where he completed his studies. He certainly did not ignore the Renaissance in Italy. His art collection, sold by court order fifteen years before his death, contained canvases by Guido Reni, the Carracci, all the engravings by Mantegna, and all the engravings done of the work of Michelangelo and Raphael. He was even familiar with Caravaggio's *chiaroscuro*, which influenced a number of works painted in the Low Countries.

When considering the subject of medicine in Rembrandt's work, the first canvas that comes to mind is one of his anatomy lessons. *Professor Tulp's Anatomy Lesson*

REMBRANDT VAN RIJN (1606-1669)
Servant at a patient's bedside

A moment of respite in the melodramatic works of Rembrandt. On the general level of Dutch life.

SCHLOSSMUSEUM, WEIMAR, GERMANY

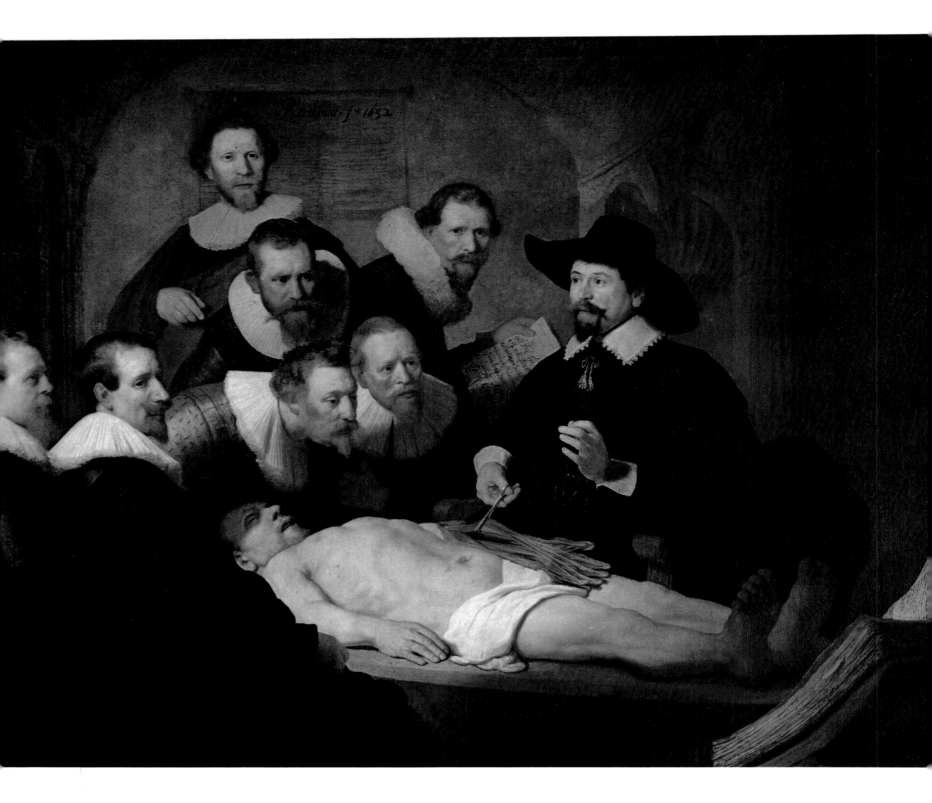

Rembrandt van Rijn (1606-1669)

Professor Tulp's Anatomy Lesson

Like most "anatomy lessons" painted in the seventeenth
century—and many were painted now that the study
of anatomy was allowed—this painting, which Rembrandt finished in 1632 at the age of twenty-six, is
more than anything a collective portrait of an eminent
surgeon and his pupils, all of whom are anxious to
let posterity see them from their best side.

MAURITSHUIS MUSEUM, THE HAGUE

160

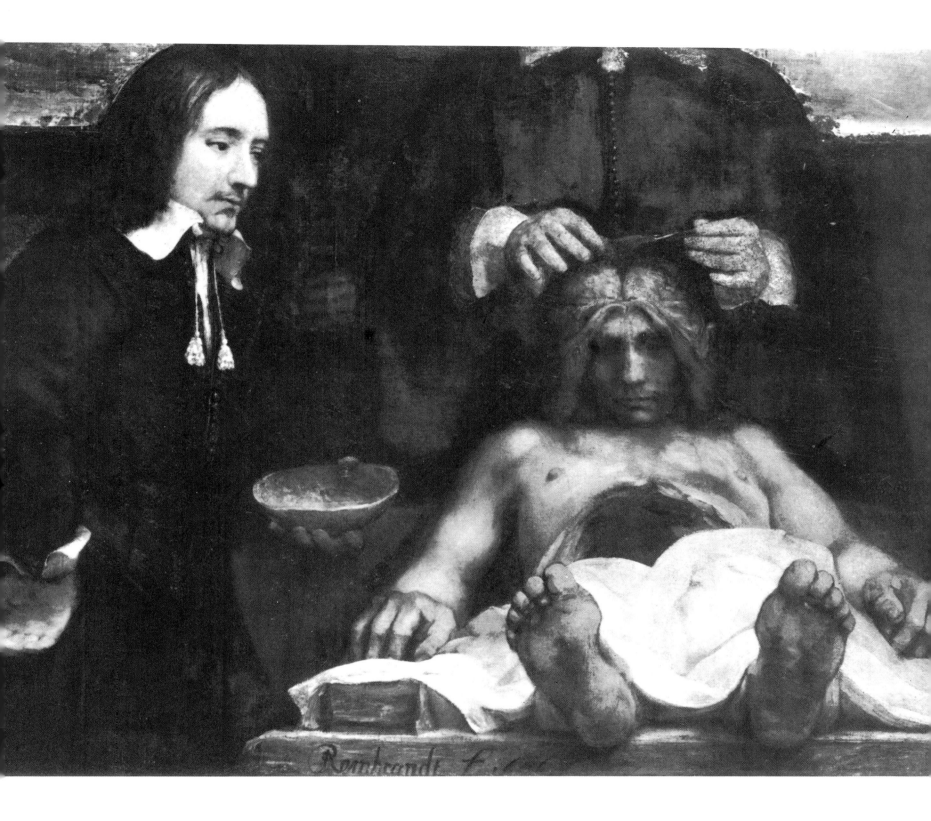

REMBRANDT VAN RIJN (1606-1669)

Doctor Deyman's Anatomy Lesson

This is the most tragic and the most realistic of Rembrandt's "anatomy lessons." The dark chest cavity, the dramatic expression of the corpse, the attentive seriousness of the assistant are exceptionally moving and true-to-life.

RIJKSMUSEUM, AMSTERDAM

161

CORNELIS DUSART (1660-1704)

The Charlatan

Halfway between caricature and realism. The barber-surgeon-bonesetter played an important role in society.

BIBLIOTHÈQUE NATIONALE, PARIS

GABRIEL METSU (1629-1667)

The Sick Child

The blank eyes, the failing body, the doleful expression of the child are all "clinical" details that turn this admirable painting into a true medical document.

RIJKSMUSEUM, AMSTERDAM

(Mauritshuis, The Hague) is the best example of picturing the social milieu, honored to a hitherto unknown extent by the Dutch. Here Rembrandt applied himself (taking the word in every sense that it implies, for the painting itself is not without a certain stiffness) to depicting a dissection scene but, even more so, to turning out ideal portraits—that is to say, to painting his models, Professor Tulp and his companions, as they would have liked to be painted. So concerned with these portraits was Rembrandt that the corpse, with all the veins open in the forearm, was granted less pictorial prominence than the face of the surgeon who, holding his pincers in a somewhat distracted manner, seems bent on posing for posterity. On the other hand *Professor Deyman's Anatomy Lesson* (Rijksmuseum, Amsterdam) accentuates the corpse that is in the process of being dissected. The picture, partly damaged, consists of a man spread out, arms apart, his feet placed in the foreground, in a foreshortening that has nothing to do with academic respect for the laws of perspective, but which certainly displays a flair for the dramatic. The professor stands behind the body and is in the process of examining the cranium. Even more impressive is the enormous cavity that has been opened in the thorax. Though the faces of the assistants in Professor Tulp's lesson bear an expression of rapt interest, there is in the expression of the young man placed to the right of the cadaver in this second painting a look of deep thought, of almost serious compassion, harmonizing with the dark anguish with which we ourselves witness this picture of flesh and bones being explored by the surgeon. The first scene was painted in 1632 by the twenty-six-year-old Rembrandt. The second, in 1656, when he was in his fifties and had removed himself from society, having decided to "paint for himself" and no longer for others, even if commissioned. He had accepted loneliness and poverty. And yet this change of heart did not prevent Rembrandt from painting one of the most detailed documents that one could wish to have on the art of dissection in the seventeenth century, painting at the same time one of the finest works of art that surgery has ever inspired in an artist.

A number of Dutch painters, after Rembrandt, painted their anatomy lessons. That of Thomas de Keyser (1595-1679) (Rijksmuseum, Amsterdam) is a gallery of portraits as much as it is a medical scene; also, the anatomical study in question is of a skeleton rather than corpse. In that of Jan Van Neck (1683, Rijksmuseum) a dissection is being conducted on a newborn child still attached to the placenta by the umbilical cord that is being held by one of the students. A rather curious detail in this picture is the presence of a boy about twelve years old holding in his hand the skeleton of a small child. One may well ask

163

why the artist included this figure when, as in the case of most of these studies at the time, the picture was intended to be a collection of portraits, the center of the group here being Professor Fredrik Ruysch. This doctor probably enjoyed being painted, for there is another canvas in which he is the principal character, painted by Adriaen Backer (1670, Rijksmuseum). This time he is operating on a male cadaver lying on its back, still intact, foreshortened, with a fine effect of perspective.

Rembrandt and the other Dutch painters who looked to the field of medicine and doctors for subject matter did not limit themselves to painting anatomy lessons. In hundreds of drawings, Rembrandt has illustrated intimate studies of sick persons, surrounded by their relatives and attended by their doctors, their surgeons, and people praying at their bedside, etc.; or being assisted by an angel if a miraculous operation was being performed, like that of Tobias (Copenhagen), or as in such pictures as *Delivery Room, A Sick Person Kneeling by a Cavalier in Armor* (Besançon), *Operation for Cataract* (Stockholm) or *Saskia* (Weimar), in which he depicts all sorts of medical and surgical operations.

Frans Hals (1580-1666), who painted so many splendid burghers, was on occasion interested in less lofty personages, and made observations that have to do with the subject at hand. His *Malle Bobbe* (Berlin), witch and fishwife, is an excellent document of the ravages of alcohol, and his *Idiot* (Rothschild Collection) a perfect study of the idiot's grin.

One of the masterpieces of medical painting is *A Sick Child* (Amsterdam) by Gabriel Metsu (1629-1667). The abandon of the young and feverish body, the complete relaxation of the muscles and the tragic expression on his face are amazingly effective. Not only is this a good and compassionate painting, but a clinical document of the first order.

Jan Steen (1626-1679) on the other hand, in his picture entitled *The Invalid,* only intended to paint an elegant picture. This beautiful languorous young lady whose doctor is taking her pulse is not really sick. The inscription gives us a hint: *Medicine is of no use; she is suffering from the pangs of love.* Gerard Dou's (1613-1675) *The Dropsical Woman,* is more accurate, although the artist has dressed the visible and no less justifiable anxiety of the poor woman in elegance and luxury.

The subject of urine examinations was treated by many Dutch painters. Adriaen Van Ostade (1610-1685) excelled in this subject matter. His amusement in the scene is coupled with the most minute observation. Gabriel Metsu and Gerard Terborch are equally as good in this altogether classic examination.

ADRIAEN VON OSTADE (1610-1685)
A healer praising his wares
BIBLIOTHÈQUE NATIONALE, PARIS

JAN STEEN (1626-1679)
The Sick Girl
Sacha Guitry chose this painting for his imaginary museum, which he called "The hundred miracles."
MAURITSHUIS MUSEUM, THE HAGUE

164

It is difficult to mention all the paintings depicting medical subjects produced in the Low Countries during the seventeenth century. "I do not think there are so many good painters elsewhere," wrote Parival in 1651. He might well have added: "And as many good paintings inspired by the same subject matter." The Dutch had everything they wanted to take good care of themselves, even if all the illness required was a good rest in pleasant surroundings. It would be foolish to try to enumerate all the canvases depicting "consultations," the scene the Amsterdam bourgeois liked best. Ferdinand Bol and

Govaert Flinck, those good pupils of Rembrandt, painted doctors taking pulses with as much success as Jan Steen and Van Ostade had in painting the administration of enemas, urine inspections and delousing.

All these paintings have the same quality of luminosity and tenderness. The interiors glow with cleanliness; four-poster beds, beautiful objects placed on the canvas according to the laws of perspective. Despite their utilitarian character, these objects seem to belong to all times and to have been invented in order to serve as a frame and background for a doctor in a long robe. With the same

THOMAS DE KEYSER (1596?-1667)

The Anatomy Lesson

A good excuse for a portrait of the professor and his pupils.

RIJKSMUSEUM, AMSTERDAM

JAN STEEN (1626-1679)
A patient in bed and his doctor
MAURITSHUIS MUSEUM, THE HAGUE

attention to detail, the painter depicts the doctor as he massages an invalid's hand (the patient is usually female) or examines a tongue. Often, the patient is seated or lying down, languorous, even fainting, or with a gentle look on her face that matches those of the people around her. However, there are times when the artist fails to respect the tradition of these scenes, and instead of depicting their somewhat sickly intimate quality, exaggerates the expression on the doctor's or patient's face, and here we have the medical caricature.

This desire to caricature medicine can also be seen, although only hinted at, in works of art that are not medical scenes, but portraits of people with anatomical problems. Thus, we have the *Portrait of Andries Bicker* by Bartholomeus van der Helst (1613-1670) (Rijksmuseum, Amsterdam) showing a gentleman of considerable obesity. Jan Steen and Van Ostade amused themselves by painting the tooth-pullers plying their trade in the market place, and depicting the agony of their patients. One might finally mention the interest in surgery shared by Jan Steen

167

(Rotterdam Museum) and his colleague David Teniers, the Younger (National Gallery, Prado, Amiens, Budapest, Kassel).

The Flemish School

In the same way as the Dutch School was dominated during the seventeenth century by Rembrandt, that of Flanders was dominated, during the same period, by Peter Paul Rubens (1577-1640). This great pagan poet of the flesh, a cultivated man who spoke seven languages, a far-ranging traveler who studied Italian painting in Italy for eight years, travelled to France and Spain and England to study those cultures in the course of his work as ambassador, this man was able to blend his personal and national genius into the framework of seventeenth-century Baroque civilization. Rubens, full of health and vitality as he was, naturally expressed a joyous and outgoing viewpoint rather than any interest in morbid or even sick ideas. At the same time, he did not gloss over the torture, executions and butchery as perpetrated by the Spaniards during their occupation of Flanders. When depicting subjects both religious and profane, or a human being wracked with pain, or simply dying, he demonstrates a power of medical observation. One thinks of the *Coup de Lance* (Musée Royal des Beaux-Arts, Antwerp) and the way the painter depicted the lance entering the flesh—the skin being lifted by the metal trying to penetrate deeper—the elongation of the arms and legs of Christ, or again the convulsions of the two thieves with their legs hanging freely, arms outstretched and whose weight is supported by the nape of their neck and shoulders. And again, one thinks of the *Last Communion of Saint Francis of Assisi* (Musée Royal des Beaux-Arts, Antwerp) in which the dying man on his knees is painted with exemplary anatomical detail. And it would be impossible to forget *Saint Ignatius Healing the Possessed* (Kunsthistorisches Museum, Vienna), especially since Rubens painted this subject seven times. For a painter obsessed with the human body, patients in a hysterical trance yielded valuable material. If he paints a pleasing subject, Rubens shows a definite knowledge of anatomy, whether it be the emphasis of the torso of a beautiful girl, or painting of the fold of a neck. In indicating the obesity of the drunken Silenus and the posture of the fauness giving milk in his famous *Bacchanale* (Kunsthistorisches Museum, Vienna), everything is the result of meticulous observation and at the same time an expression of tremendous vitality.

Jakob Jordaens (1593-1678), a distinguished follower of Rubens, was also interested in possessed people, as in his *Saint Martin Healing the Possessed* (Musée Royal des Beaux-Arts, Antwerp); allegorical monsters, as in *The Peasant and the Satyr* (Kassel); and in such lusty themes as the *Fecundity* (Brussels), which from our point of view is a document of tremendous strength. A man who was quite willing to look at the joyful things in life as well as pain and death, Jordaens nevertheless looked for pretexts in order to paint health and well-being rather than disease.

After Rubens, Jordaens and Van Dyck (the great masters of seventeenth-century Flemish painting) one could

DAVID TENIERS, THE YOUNGER (1610-1690)
Surgical Operation
Neither anesthesia nor hygiene had as yet been invented.

PRADO, MADRID

DAVID TENIERS, THE YOUNGER (1610-1690)

The Village Doctor.

The classical theme of a urine analysis gave Teniers the chance of painting one of his most delightful works. The serious attitude of the doctor and the terror of the patient have something touching about them.

DAVID RYCKAERT III (1612-1661)

The Surgeon

This is evidently a village barber. On occasion, the prophylactic means and precautions were less rudimentary in hospitals. The hour was yet to come when surgery would finally be an art and its exercise seriously regulated.

MUSÉE DES BEAUX-ARTS, VALENCIENNES

cite many other painters who drew their subject matter directly from medicine and surgery. David Teniers (1610-1694), who has already been mentioned, would not be the least of these. Nor would Adriaen Brouwer (1605-1638), who painted a magnificent *Surgeon* (Munich), executed in an altogether different manner. In this picture we have a village surgeon in the process of repairing, though not with much success, the arm of a young man who obviously is in more pain than he was a few minutes ago. We have come a long way from Rembrandt's famous dignified doctors. Here in Flanders the quack, rather than the

physician, does the business. Is it a question of money or social position? More probably it can be explained by the fact that Flanders was Catholic, pillaged by Spain, not free, poor, and to a certain extent not as progressive as Holland.

The tooth-extractor also is of great interest to the realistic painters, and there are many during that period who depict this subject—Theodore Rombouts (1597-1637), Cornelis Dusart (1660-1704), to mention only a few of the artists who found in dentistry material for their sense of humor.

JACOB JORDAENS (1593-1678)
The Sisters of Charity of Antwerp
ROYAL MUSEUM OF FINE ARTS, ANTWERP

Spain

From a medical-artistic point of view, moving from Dutch to Spanish painting of the seventeenth century is like moving from one world into another. This can be explained by the singular nature of the Spanish people, which is both mystical and cruel, with a love of death and a taste for violence. If the Spanish painters of the period often depicted cripples, dwarfs, madmen and people who were more or less deformed, it was neither out of medical curiosity nor out of a desire to be realistic. Rather, because the depicting of these unfortunates, of whom there were so many in that miserable country, where they received little pity or help, allowed the artists to express their pathetic and somewhat melancholy conception of life. So much so that many of their works of art, because of their naturalistic exaggerations, are medical documents of real value. The celebrated picture by José Ribera (1591-1652) entitled *The Clubfoot* (Louvre, Paris) comes to mind, though it does not exactly correspond to its title since, though the child represented is afflicted with a club-foot, he also has a deformed hand. In fact his is a case of infantile hemiplegia, obviously obstetric, with a retraction of paralyzed muscles in the right side. Of course Ribera had many excuses for ignoring all this, had he wished; yet, he has shown us, though certainly inadvertently, an example of a known disease.

In the same way, Diego Rodriguez da Velásquez y Silva, known as Velásquez (1599-1660), who is less of a mystic than a naturalist, seemed to have more of an obsession for dwarfs than most, not only as anatomical examples, but also as particularly picturesque figures. By the sixteenth century it was already fashionable for important people to be surrounded by dwarfs who played the roles of foil and buffoon. They became even more popular in the seventeenth century, and Velásquez must have seen many of them at court, where they were the only people allowed to behave in a familiar manner to the monarch.

Since the causes of this affliction are unknown to the average person, it may be mentioned that the most frequent cause of dwarfism is achondroplastic, that is to say that the cartilages ossify prematurely. As a result, the dwarf's arms and legs are short, whereas his trunk and head develop normally. One particular type of dwarf is the myxoedematic, due to insufficient functioning of the thyroid; this type of dwarf is obese and not very intelligent. Velásquez depicted such a creature in minute detail, enabling us to make a positive diagnosis of the origin and nature of its deformity. The names of the dwarfs depicted are also mentioned, a fact adding to our certain knowledge that these abnormalities were not imaginary.

Velásquez's two most famous dwarfs are those he included in his masterpiece *Las Meninas* (Prado, Madrid). One of them is Nicolasito Petusato, who, with his foot planted upon a sleeping dog, appears relatively well proportioned, whereas Barbola, the little woman, afflicted with short arms and legs, is obese, deformed and has an enormous head. But the list of dwarfs and other monsters that Velásquez painted is far greater; it runs from d'Antonio el Inglés, an obscene little dwarf whose small stature is established by his being placed next to a dog and a book (Prado, Madrid), to Don Sebastiano de Morra, a complex pathological case of a dwarf with a club foot (Prado, Madrid), the *Idiot of Corria* (Kunsthistorisches Museum, Vienna) with a stupid smile on his face and a bunch of flowers in his hand, and *Il Bimbo de Vallecas* (Prado, Madrid), a one-eyed idiot. Once again, Velásquez's familiarity with short people, hideous and nightmarish, has sociological and psychological implications; these people were to be found on street corners, where they were either sources of amusement or objects of horror. They were something dramatic and amusing, a species no one would probably have had any dealings with had the Spanish built hospitals for them, or at least taken care of them in some way.

All Velásquez had to do in order to enlarge this museum of the abnormal was to paint, with the same naturalism, a certain number of royal personages whose sparkling decorations and heavy court dresses failed to hide their ugliness. The *infantas* in particular were not blessed with good looks. Velásquez painted these girls as he saw them—prognathismatic, lymphatic and cross-eyed; he was hardly flattering. In Philip IV with his pouting lip and fish-like face, he seems to have formed the archetype of the abnormal.

Twenty years younger than Velásquez and protégé of the master was Bartolomé Esteban Murillo (1618-1682) who did not try his hand at painting abnormalities. At the most, one could cite the portrait of a club-footed dwarf (Louvre, Paris) who is leaning against a long cane and holding a bowl. This famous little boy, standing near a pitcher of water and a basket of apples and looking for fleas, can only be cited as a representation of a sociological problem involving hygiene, rather than as a genuine example of medical art.

DIEGO VELASQUEZ (1599-1660)

Presumably a portrait of the dwarf Sebastiano de Morra

PRADO, MADRID

Italy

During the seventeenth century, the artists of this country who, in the field of art served as guides to the rest of Europe, and whose role as artistic innovators was far from being over, were on the whole oriented toward the Baroque and the emotional. In statues and religious paintings, religious feeling was their main source of inspiration; gestures thus became exaggerated, eyes rolled backwards, with the whites showing. Painters and sculptors for the most part were not interested in medical or anatomical subjects that had inspired their great forebears during the Renaissance.

Among the exceptions are the canvases and engravings that depicted the plague. One could also cite a drawing by Guercino (1591-1666) depicting a blood-letting that could also be an operation involving the incision of an abscess. Vaguely bordering on medicine is the canvas by Francisco Albani (1578-1660) entitled *Salmacis and Hermaphrodite* (Louvre, Paris).

Related to medicine from a more modern, even Freudian, view is the group by the sculptor Gianlorenzo Bernini (1598-1680) entitled *The Ecstasy of Saint Teresa* (S. Maria della Vittoria, Rome). The expression of her so-called ecstasy has a marked resemblance to a fainting spell which could be called voluptuous in a mystical, almost obsessive sense.

France

Two famous names come to mind when thinking of the relationship between art and medicine in France during the seventeenth century. The first of these is that of Jacques Callot (1592-1635), painter and engraver of the horrors and miseries of his time. The second is that of Molière, who, though neither engraver or painter, through his satires on medicine gave painters subjects for many caricatures.

The "Cours de Miracles," those stinking dens of vice and misery that by the late Middle Ages had spread through the heart of Paris and other large cities, had become a formidable problem by the reign of Louis XIV. The unending wars, the resulting famines, mutilations, looting, and attacks from so many armies were the background of these hell-holes. It was literally impossible to count the lame, the blind and the mutilated. Within these infernos prospered the "schools," which the beggars formed into associations with picturesque names such as the "Morcandiers," "Abouleux," "Coquillards" in order to teach their kind how to abuse the credulity of the

174

JOSÉ DE RIBERA (1588-1656)

The Club foot

The title under which this painting is known is medically inexact. The arm actually shows the same retraction as the foot. It is consequently a hemiplegia of probably obstetrical origin.

LOUVRE, PARIS

175

JACQUES CALLOT (1592-1635)

Crippled Beggar

Callot found his subject matter in the mournful reality
of his time: wars, punitive expeditions, and mutilations.

BIBLIOTHÈQUE NATIONALE, PARIS

176

public. Jacques Callot, in his series of etchings entitled *Vagabonds,* devoted himself to depicting these miserable people with a striking naturalism that reminds one of Pieter Brueghel, the Elder, and also heralds the arrival of Goya. Some of the pictures depict the sick, their faces reflecting their privations; others show men and women publicly exhibiting their sores in order to attract sympathy and alms. Apart from this crowd of sordid beggars in whom the physician can trace an extensive repertoire of the deformities and pathological stigmata of the time, Jacques Callot depicted, just as naturalistically but poignantly and scientifically at the same time, the miserable crowd of amputees, cripples and tramps who came back from the "glorious wars." Not only the doctor but the historian as well can find pertinent material here, since Callot was a great expert in this area and worked directly from life.

Callot was equally interested in gypsy life. He was well acquainted with these people since they had adopted him when he was a small child after he had run away from his parents. The documentary character of this part of his work can be seen in a medical context, in the engraving entitled, *The Birth of a Child in a Gypsy Camp* in which a young girl of the tribe leans against a tree, supported by two friends. A midwife is looking for the child under skirts that are barely raised, while all around her, men and women calmly proceed with their daily tasks.

Molière, whose jokes at the expense of the medical profession were not quite as mean as they appeared to be— he could very well have blasted the profession but was satisfied with ridiculing it—had two good doctor friends in Mauvilain and Liénard, who gave him all the information about their work that he needed. As for the costume and general apparel affected by doctors at this time, all Molière had to do was simply to look at it to find some hilarity therein.

In two engravings by Nicolas de Larmessin (1636-1694) (Bibliothèque Nationale) we can see two doctors who obviously have no idea how to cure their patient. After interrogating his patient, the doctor still undertakes his cursory examination: he feels the pulse, examines both tongue and urine. Then he pronounces his diagnosis, at the same time taking into consideration the astrological positions, the humors and temperament of his patient, and finally draws up a prescription in Latin that invariably includes the words: "Saignare, purgare, clysterium donare" (bleed, purge and give an enema). This treatment could hardly have done any harm to the members of high society who spent most of the day abusing their stomachs. However, it was unfortunate when the same treatment was applied to some poor starving per-

NICOLAS POUSSIN (1594-1665)
The Philistines Stricken with the Plague
LOUVRE, PARIS

Au bout du comte ils treuuent pour destin
Qu'ils sont uenus d'Aegipte a ce festin.

JACQUES CALLOT (1592-1635)
Childbirth in a Gypsy camp
BIBLIOTHÈQUE NATIONALE, PARIS

son, or to a case of pleurisy, or to a wounded person who had already lost a lot of blood, in short to all sorts of illnesses that had nothing to do with the circulatory or digestive systems. It is more than surprising to learn that Bouvart, personal physician of Louis XIII, prescribed two hundred and fifteen medicines to his royal client, and bled him thirty-seven times. Even more amazing is to read in *The Journal of the King's Illnesses,* compiled daily by his doctors Vallot, Daquin and Fagon, that Louis XIV, was bled thirty-eight times, purged about two thousand times, and that he absorbed several litres of quinine, a fact that brings us to the pharmaceutical practices of the time. The extravagances of the medical profession in this field are beyond the imagination. The basis of the medicines more currently prescribed were wood-lice, earth worms, lizards, toads and vipers, while the famous "Catholicon"

used by Madame de Sevigné in the form of drops for the vapours was nothing but essence of urine.

As one can see, critics like Molière had splendid material at their disposal. Molière was not, however, the first to attack the doctors. After Guy Patin, a celebrated doctor of the time, published a paper in which he declared William Harvey's new thesis on the circulation of the blood to be "paradoxical, useless, false, impossible, absurd and harmful," Boileau and a friend of his, François Bernier, published their own paper, in which they said the following:

> "The court orders the chyle to go straight to the liver without going through the heart, and once there to forbid the blood from being such a vagrant as to circulate through the body, under pain of being delivered and abandoned to the Faculty of Medicine."

However, Guy Patin's sublime stupidity did not prevent
him from lampooning the stupidities of others, as can
be seen in his pamphlet against Mazarin's doctors, and
from which Molière drew inspiration for the consultation
scene in his play *Amour Medecin:*

"Yesterday at ten o'clock in the Bois de Vincennes,
four of his doctors, Guenot, Vallot, Brayer and Béda
des Fougarais, were arguing together, and could not
agree as to the nature of the disease the patient was
dying from. Brayer says the spleen is spoilt; Guenot
says it's the liver; Vallot says it's the lungs, and that
there's no water in the chest; des Fougarais says it's an
abscess of the mesentery. Clever bunch, aren't they?"

As for the poor who happened to be ill, the situation
was even more complicated because of the large number
of quacks. The latter carried on their practice in the area
of the Pont-Neuf. Opposite Rue Guenégaud, Marchisédec
Bary had his consulting rooms. He had cured "a white
elephant of Siam of a nervous tic, the wife of the ruler of
Ragusa of a cancer of the right breast, and the Grand

179

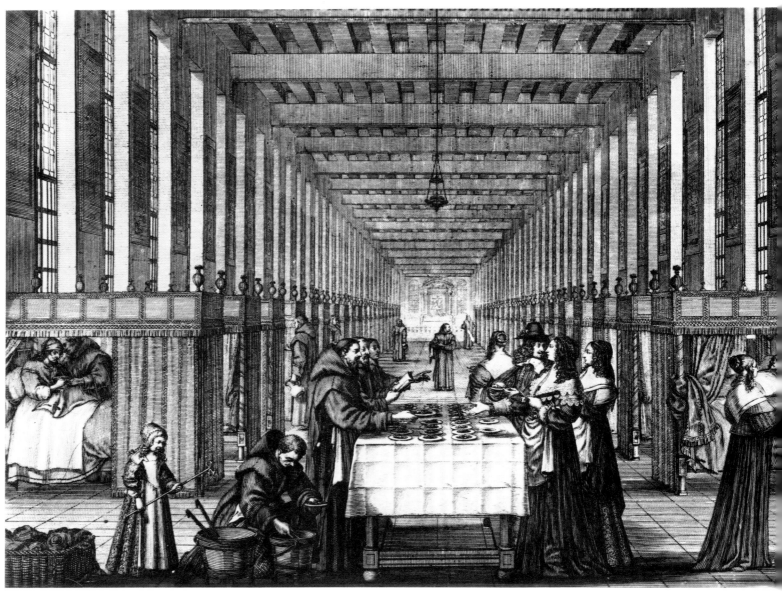

ABRAHAM BOSSE (1602-1676)

Anne of Austria visiting the great hospital ward of
the Charité c. 1640.

Mogul of his last little case of the pox." How could one
not have confidence in a man with such magnificent
references? In the same neighborhood, Carmelino pulled
teeth with his thumb and index finger. In the earlier
days, the quacks were confined to the Pont-Neuf district.
Numbers of them were actually doctors and surgeons who
hardly merited those titles. Here, for example, is the
way Martin de la Martinière, Surgeon and Physician-
Chemist to the King, presents himself in his work, *The
Ingenious Surgeon*: "God, having given me the talent to
cure, I feel that I can tell you that I have the ability

to cut the stone, and that with the probe I can judge the
various reasons for the retention of the urine, give a
perfect diagnosis as to whether the patient has kidney
stones, phlegms, gravel in the kidney, gallstones, and many
other illnesses for all of which I have a full cure." Martin
goes on for a long time in this vein, listing a large number
of things he can presumably accomplish, removing all
human disabilities from harelip to cataract.

The empiricists were no less harmful, despite their
being of good faith and often disinterested. At the top
of the list one would have to place the King of France,

PHILIPPE DE CHAMPAIGNE (1602-1674)
The Sick Child

MUSÉE DES BEAUX-ARTS, BESANÇON

who had by Divine Right the faculty of curing scrofula by simply laying his hands over the patient. There is an anonymous engraving to be found in the Bibliothèque Nationale depicting Henri IV in this scene. It shows the king, in the midst of many assistants, most of whom were policemen and churchmen, walking past a row of kneeling invalids, touching them on the forehead and pronouncing the ritual words: "The King touches you, God cures you."

There were also empiricists among aristocrats and priests. The Prior of Cabrières gave a formula to Louis XVI for the treatment of giddiness and hernia. With the assistance of his first *valet de chambre* he did not hesitate to compound the drug with his own hands. Madame de Sablé recommended viper powder. Monsieur de Fossé "linden tea against quinsy, toads against the plague, birch-wood water against colic." Finally everyone agreed

on the universal and wonderful effect of being bled and purged. Everyone, that is, except the caricaturists and writers of epigrams. A proof of this is a fine engraving by Guerard (Bouvet Collection) entitled: *Everything as a Precaution.* The following inscription accompanies the engraving:

"Do you have the quatraine fever,
Corns on your feet, or migraine,
Are you unhappy, or are you sick,
Ill inside, or outside,
Purge, bleed, do your work, oh Syringe,
You'll either die, or survive."

Medicine to laugh at - serious medicine

One would have to write a separate book about the works of art depicting the ridiculing of doctors and medicine during the seventeenth century. Why are there so many? Because medicine was beginning to become part of daily life and was in the process of losing the mysterious, almost sacred character that had been its hallmark. In the early years of the century, to lampoon medicine was to recognize its importance. Besides, the many charges that were levelled against it did not prevent medicine from developing, or from taking on a more and more important role in social life. Indeed, so much so that man was roused from his medieval concept of death and from his mistrust of life on earth, to go as far as to see a new religion in this science, the objective of which was the conservation and prolongation of life; in other words, medicine was on the way to becoming humanity's most precious gift.

Earlier there have been mentioned medical satires that were drawn, painted or engraved. Here are some others, part of which belong to what one could call genre scenes and others to caricature. Examples would be the "curers" and "tooth-pullers" that the Dutchman Adriaen Van Ostade painted so successfully, as did his colleagues. Others, more easily classifiable as caricatures, include such works as the engraving by a Dutchman, after a drawing by Cornelis Dusart, depicting an imaginary barber bleeding an unwilling patient. Also, there is the engraving by the Strasburg master, Mathias Greuter (1564-1638), entitled *The Doctor Curing a Phantasy*—very much in the caricature tradition—and where we can see a "possessed person" in the foreground being placed in an oven in order to dry out the spirits from his body. And then there is that of Jacques Lagniet, taken from his *Collec-*

PIERRE PUGET (1620-1694)

The Plague in Marseilles

MUSEUM OF FINE ARTS, MARSEILLES

tion of Famous Proverbs (1657), an illustration of the old saying: "The mad always recognize each other."

The beautiful anonymous French engraving entitled *The World's Three Snares* (1650?) is both a caricature and a drawing with a moral, but it is the patient rather than the doctor who is being caricatured, the artist pointing to the bordello, the cabaret and general wickedness as the great suppliers of patients. On the other hand, there are also anonymous French engravings that ridiculed the surgeon Habicot and Doctor Fagon, "the king's acolyte," by depicting their apparatus, medicines, etc., or the futility of their attentions when it was already too late.

One can move on from these works of art that are really caricatures (they were surpassed in ferociousness only by the drawings of William Hogarth in the eighteenth century) to the artists who were inspired by the work of serious physicians—there were a few! Abounding in detail, their paintings are real medical documents. Thanks to them, we know practically everything about medical practices of the period, whether child birth, bleeding, or the administration of enemas. We also have to thank Abraham Bosse (1602-1676) for having painted, in his usual luminous and neat manner, a hospital, the one in question being that of the Sisters of Charity, whose establishment, La Charité, reserved for men and more particularly for contagious diseases, was a model at the time. There exists an engraving (a gouache of which is to be found in the Musée Carnavalet, Paris) inspired by the visit of Anne of Austria and the Dauphin to the patients of the establishment in 1640. To be more precise, the picture depicts the main ward, which appears to be divided into private rooms by the drawing of curtains around each bed, a complete innovation which put an end to the medical promiscuity among patients during the Middle Ages.

A picture by a Madeleine de Boulogne (Musée de Versailles) shows, in the same realistic style, how the nuns of Port Royal tended the sick, and there is another work very much in the same vein at the Bibliothèque Nationale, entitled, *The Sisters of the Hotel Dieu Feeding the Patients.* Let us examine this picture for a moment, because it conforms to everything we know about hospitalized patients at the time. Above each bed is a tablet and various utensils used by the patient. We can also see an earthenware pot, into which a sister poured a half litre of wine at regular intervals, a goblet and a wooden spoon and bowl. One needs very little imagination to be able to visualize meal time, when, at eleven and six o'clock, the bells for meals were rung, and all the patients would sit up in bed and seize their spoons and bowls, and wait for the sister in her pointed hat to pass by with food.

There is another picture of documentary interest in the anonymous frontispiece to *Ars curandi morbos expectatione* by the English surgeon Gideon Harvey printed in Amsterdam in 1695. It depicts a patient lying in bed. He appears to be alarmed by both the rather sanguine "wait and see" expression on the face of Dr. Harvey and the apothecary's syringe.

Several pictures depicting medical subjects appear to have been commissioned, because they are great masterpieces. One of these is a canvas by Philippe de Champagne (1602-1674) depicting a sick child (Besançon Museum), a work of art the moving realism of which can perhaps be explained by the Brussels origin of the painter who owed his classic training to the influence of Nicolas Poussin. Also, we have the *Joueur de vielle aveugle,* a very detailed painting by Georges de La Tour (1593-1652), one of the prized possessions of the museum at Nantes.

Epidemics and miracles

The epidemics that swept through Europe during the seventeenth century made a strong impression on all classes. It was inevitable that they should furnish artists of all countries with a common theme, and to such an extent that special consideration must be given to this aspect of the medical art of the period. It is thanks to these painters that we are able to conceive of the nightmare aspects of a town completely silenced by the plague, or some other contagious disease. All the houses shut and locked their doors and windows; those that had been struck by the plague had a white cross on the door. In the streets, monks and nuns draped in hoods made of oiled cloth were about the only people circulating. They were gloved, holding sponges doused in vinegar under their noses, beating off people who approached them as they carried around their necks ciboriums containing hosts. Their main task was also that of administering to the dying. Doctors and surgeons were clothed in outfits designed for them by Charles Delorme, court physician to Louis XIII. These consisted of shirt and trouser made of skins, high boots, long robes made of morocco, the sleeves of which were gathered at the wrist, and kid gloves. The sealed-in effect of this outfit protected them from fleabites—doctors had in fact come to understand that fleas carried germs. The most picturesque part of

PEDRO GAETANO
The Plague
Late seventeenth century.

MUSEO NAZIONALE, FLORENCE

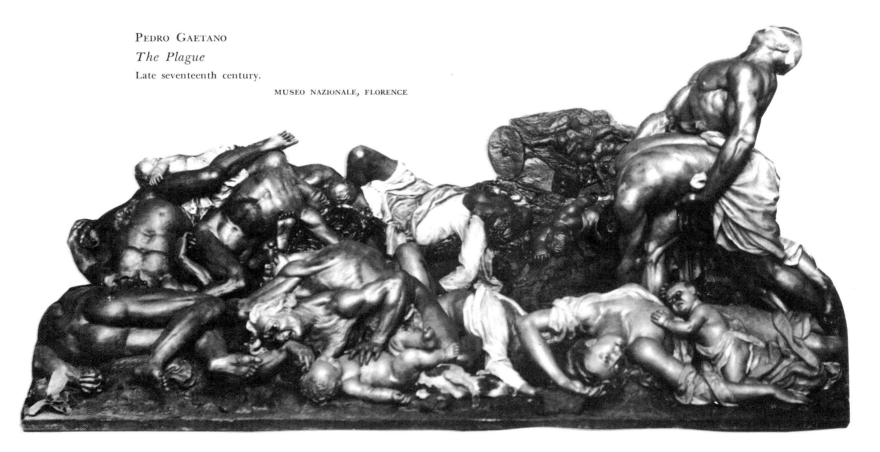

WOLFGANG HEIMBACH (1613?-1678)
The Sick Man

this garment, however, consisted of a mask that covered the head, with crystal eyes and a long nose with a filter containing perfume, giving the wearer the appearance of some sort of Egyptian divinity, with a human body and a bird's head. Although one can smile at this extraordinary get-up, it does prove the birth of serious ideas about hygiene that had been started by Girolamo Fracastoro in 1546 with his book *De contagione et contagiosis morbis*. We are a long way in any case from the time when the massacre of fifty thousand Jews—who were made responsible for the plague in the XIVth century— was allowed to occur.

To come back to the historical-medical picture of the plague, most elements of which are supplied for us by the artists, armed patrols constantly circulated to enforce the execution of sanitary measures. The laws were strictly enforced. Anyone picked up in the streets with the plague was immediately killed; all people in danger of contamination (that is, those involved in administering to the dying) had to carry a white stick, otherwise they were conducted to the pillory and exposed. Finally the stranger who managed to enter the city without a sanitary passport and the thief caught rifling houses and corpses were hanged from the nearest gibbet. A silence of the dead fell on the city, only to be interrupted by the rumbling of carts laden with corpses and led by men known as crows to ditches hastily dug outside the city limits.

More horrible still than the spectacle in the streets was that in the hospitals, that, only able to hold a certain number of patients, had to receive thousands. These were crammed four and five to a bed; a barber making incisions into boils and a lawyer charged with making out a will were perhaps the only people to penetrate these halls of the dead.

Although in the seventeenth century people began to acknowledge that the origins of the plague could be found in rodents and invisible microbes, the notion of divine displeasure, always linked with this disease in the past, was still predominant, not only among the people, but also among artists as well. This certainly might explain their quasi-obsession with this shocking subject, and even an enlightened man like Rubens is among them. There is a master composition in the Munich Pinakothek that depicts people afflicted with the plague lying in wretched condition on the ground while several nurses are trying to attract the attention of Saint Anthony flying above in the sky.

In Italy, Gorgiullo (1612-1679) attacked the same subject in an impressive canvas (Museo Nazionale, Naples) that depicts a veritable pile of dead and dying that are being brought outside the gates of the city, and one can

Ie suis ce Medecin qui voit dans les vrines,
Les effetz merueilleux contre nature faits;
Et purgeant les esprits de leurs humeures malirice,
Ie fait de mes secrets sortir de bons effects.

Aux vns par L'alembic ic purge la ceruelle,
Aux autres l'intestin par vn gros robinet,
Ainsi de cés vapeures par ma mode nouuelle
Ie rends de tous ces fous l'esprit, et le corps n.

"Fools make themselves known in all times"

From a collection of the best-known proverbs divided into three illustrated books by Logniet, c. 1675.

BIBLIOTHÈQUE NATIONALE, PARIS

see the same pile of dead and dying in a waxwork by Pedro Gaetano (National Museum, Florence).

French artists of the seventeenth century were also inspired by the abominations of the plague. Faithful to classicism, Nicolas Poussin (1594-1665) depicted them in a classical manner. He painted three pictures of the epidemic that felled the Philistines. Two of the compositions are very different from the third and belong to the Louvre. They both show the usual pile of corpses in a background of classical temples. In the foreground, people dash madly in all directions and enormous rats run down the steps of one of the temples; their association with the plague had already been guessed. The third of these works (Cook Collection, Richmond) is somewhat like the others, but has

less movement. The dead lie about on the ground, but the survivors seem to have kept control of their senses.

In a similar classical background the sculptor Pierre Puget (1622-1694) created a scene of great excitement, the inspiration of which was the epidemic of the plague which broke out in Marseilles (his home town). In this marble bas-relief (Musée des Beaux-Arts, Marseilles) we can see the carts drawing off the dead, the real tears of the living, and the supplications they are offering to a sky peopled with angels.

Nicolas Mignard (1606-1668), painting the same scene, twice created works of art that are of historical-medical value. He also depicted the scene in a classical background, showing what a hard time the art of Rome had

185

POUR LE MAL DE DENTS prenez
medecine, car selon hippocrate et gallien
Ce capricieux mal a plusieurs causes et tou
tes ces causes une mesme fin qui est la
douleur. dou je conclus que la medecin
ayant aussy sa fin principalle qui est
la sante elle doit non seulement ba
layer nettoyer expulser toutes ordures
corruptions cathares et defluctions
mais doit aussy rafermir consolider
les gensius et renchasser les dents
Ebranlee

POUR LES ANGELEURES
Aux doibts prenez des lavements
Car cest aux intestins quil faut
aller recta. Ce mal netant cause que
par des esprits nitreux qui seshale des
Entrailles lors que le ventre est paresseux. Ergo clistere amollian
Ex bong pour abaisser les fumee du ventricule qui montent
Aux doibts Circulando

Remedies for all ailments

"Are you suffering from quartan ague,
A mental ill or a physical ill,
An outside ill or an inside ill?
Be purged, and bled, take many enemas:
You'll either die, or else you'll be all right."

BIBLIOTHÈQUE NATIONALE, PARIS

in France, despite the "modern" classicism of Charles Le-brun. The first of these pictures is very different from the usual gracious and flattering style of the portrait painter of Louis XIV. It is called *The Plague of Aegina*. The best description of this painting was that made by Gerard Audran when he said: "As always, it is the dying, the dead and various spectators who form the essential action, but in this case the heavens are not unaware of the situation and Juno is sending down poisonous vapors." The second picture showed *Charles Giving Communion to the Sick Struck by the Plague*. This picture has unfortunately disappeared, and we would have known nothing about it except that an engraving by Poilly has been preserved.

In the seventeenth century we still find a number of paintings or engravings which, although religious in subject matter, are nevertheless related to medicine. First let us look at those representing miraculous cures. We may name as examples of this category in France *Christ Curing the Dropsical Man*, engraved by Charles Vignon, and *The Wounded Saint Sebastien Tended by Holy Women*, engraved by Georges de La Tour (Musée de Rouen), where the women try with extreme care to remove an arrow from the Saint's thigh. In this same category is the painting by Poussin entitled *Christ Curing the Blind at Jericho* (Louvre).

Other schools are also "full of miracles." In a magnificent canvas by Rubens, *Saint Francis Triumphing Over Satan*, at Saint Francis' call the sick arise and the blind recover their sight. In a painting by Gaspard de Witte (1624-1681) where landscape occupies a major part of the picture, Jesus Himself is shown restoring sight to a blind man. In the print room at Einsiedzen, the Swiss have a fine engraving by Pierre Fierens showing Saint Catherine curing a "possessed person," a scene which looks more like an ordinary case of hysteria.

Illustrated Medical Books

Illustrations of medical works published in the seventeenth century are often real works of art, even when they have a primarily didactic purpose. Among the most frequently engraved subjects we find "anatomy lessons" which recall the great Dutch compositions. The frontispiece of the *Œuvres anatomiques de M. Jean Rioland* (Paris, 1628) and of the *Opera Omnia* by André Laurens (Paris, 1628) represent the corpse stretched out and the belly open with someone in the process of explaining anatomical facts to a group of students. It is pictures of this kind which illustrate the *Primitiae anatomicae de humani corporis ossibus* by Pieter Paaw (1615), *Anatomia practica rationalis* by Stephen Blancard (1688), *Vade Mecum Anatomicum sive Clavis Medicinae* by Jean de Muralto (Zurich, 1677), and many other similar works.

The anatomical plates which represent, more or less accurately, the relation of muscles and bones or of vessels and nerves must also be discussed. Several of them have an undeniable artistic quality, among them the *Tabulae anatomicae* which Bucrotius engraved to illustrate the *De humani corporis fabrica* of Spieghel; or the plates which were engraved by A. Blooteling and by the Van Gvust brothers after designs by Gerard de Lairesse to illustrate *Anatoma humani corporis* by Godfried Bidloo (Amsterdam, 1685).

Books of surgical technique also contain illustrations which often rise to the level of indisputable art. If there is no work in the seventeenth century to compare with the engravings in Ambroise Pare's works, the *Observationum et curationum chirurgicarum centuriae* by Fabricus von Hiden (Lyon, 1641) nevertheless contains some remarkable early prints, and the *l'Armamentarium chirurgicum* of Jean Sculet (Ulm, 1655) is also full of notable engravings representing instruments, reductions of fractures, trepannings, and other surgical operations.

Illustrated theses are also part of medical iconography, although in a most peripheral fashion. When Thomas Dialvivoc wanted to pay court to Angelica and offered her his thesis, which the girl refused, the clever Toinette took it, quickly saying: " Let's have it. Let's have it. It is always good to take the pictures out of it. It will help to decorate our room." Thus the custom was apparently established in the seventeenth century that future doctors, if they had the means, had their theses illustrated. But, curiously enough, these illustrations for medical theses had very little to do with medicine. They often represented the coat of arms of the noble personage to whom the thesis was dedicated. More often they symbolized the necessary virtues which a respectable man was supposed to possess: prudence, justice, etc.—the latter represented by nude women generally shown with the serpent of the Caduceus. Occasionally these often charming pictures were completed by the portrait of the eminent protector.

GASPARE TRAVERSI (1732-1769)

The Injured Man

The injury isn't serious, and this genre painting is charming.

GALLERIA DELL'ACCADEMIA, VENICE

THE EIGHTEENTH CENTURY

During the eighteenth century, art and medicine were to influence each other in the same manner as they had in the previous century, yet these relationships were to grow less and less frequent. However, looking at the philosophical, scientific and social structure within which they established their interrelationship will help us to understand their gradual separation and their change of character.

With the eighteenth century, there comes a considerable increase of interest in philosophical ideas. Although Diderot's *Encyclopedia* appeared in France (and that monumental work will be referred to again since the chapters in it devoted to medicine and anatomy contain superb illustrations), the ideas brought forward in the book were not exclusively of French origin. For example, *An essay concerning human understanding,* published in 1690, exercised a considerable influence. The author, the Englishman John Locke, was a philosopher who doubled as mathematician and student of natural history. While Diderot made the now classic remark: "There is nothing

ordinary about the chain of causes; the idea of a human being situated outside the universe is inconceivable," Voltaire was carving his sarcastic rationalism into the European conscience. He was also bringing to France the German treatises of Gottfried Wilhelm Leibniz concerning Cartesian "Dynamism," as well as Kant's lengthy works—books whose influence was to be felt in the nineteenth century, and even in our own. In the meantime, the Scottish philosopher David Hume (later Secretary at the Embassy in Paris) came under the influence of Jean-Jacques Rousseau and caused a considerable stir with his essays on human nature. From Italy, which had its Voltaire in Cesare Beccaria; to Russia, where the Empress set about educating the serfs; to Spain, where by royal command the Jesuits were expelled from the country, the idea that man was bound by his metaphysical condition was either totally, partially, or more or less immediately accepted.

One must admit, however, that the doctors were to have difficulty in making this gospel a basic part of their ap-

PIETRO LONGHI (1702-1785)
The Tooth Puller

BRERA, MILAN

The surgeon is wearing an elevatory as his headpiece. In his right hand, he is holding a pan
for making salves, and in his left hand a pot.
In his belt, there are a saw and a drill for
bones, a trepan, an elevatory to be used in
trepanations, and on his shoulders: scissors, ra-
zors, and combs. A barber's plate is hanging on
a large cord from his neck, from which a glass
for throwing water is suspended. Beneath his
left arm, he is holding a barber's bag.

LIBRARY OF DECORATIVE ARTS, PARIS

The surgeon's wife is holding a barber's plate
in her left hand. A barber's bag is slung over
her shoulder, and on her shoulder there is linen
for shaving.

LIBRARY OF DECORATIVE ARTS, PARIS

190

proach. The influence stemming from the seventeenth century, coupled with the superstitious and empirical tradition that was late in dying under the scalpel of reason, still weighed heavily on them. Thus we observe Georg Ernst Stahl studying medicine at Iena and violently opposed to Friedrich Hoffmann's thesis, inspired by Leibniz, concerning organic dynamism. Stahl also negates the usefulness of the theoretical study of anatomy and physiology, refusing to acknowledge the use of quinine and opium in therapeutics. Finally, he still insists that bleeding is the natural remedy employed by the soul in order to rid the organism of pain and sickness.

On the other hand, surgery took great leaps ahead. This was helped along in France by the founding of the Royal Academy of Surgery in 1731, while the declaration of 1743 forever separated surgeons from the company of barbers, giving them special rights and privileges, and thus chartered their profession. In addition, the wars of the period were to give surgery a chance to perfect its techniques, although in this process many surgeons were to perish. At one point in eighteen months six hundred surgeons died either in combat or in the hospitals. Finally, when a decree of the Revolution put an end to the Academy, surgery crossed the Channel, where John Hunter and his followers laid the foundations of English surgery.

During this period in France, more than elsewhere (though it was perceptible all over Europe), it was felt that something was wrong with the social order, that something was in the process of collapsing. Nothing was done to stem this feeling of impending doom; in fact it appears to have been encouraged, particularly by French gentlemen of letters—or even by the King of Prussia—who spent their time composing Voltairean treatises. Although it did not appear on the surface, people began to grow weary of Divine Right. As a kind or reaction, they escaped into a world of charm with *trompe-l'oeils,* elegant mythologies and *fêtes champêtres.* Bad taste was on the way in. No single period in history fostered it as much as did that of Louis XV. For the élite, the feasting went on as usual, but it was now masked. François Hubert Drouais dipicting Madame du Barry as Flora is as "realistic" as Giovanni Battista Tiepolo or Francisco Guardi painting in Venice scenes of men and women, including monks and nuns, who do not step out without masks or

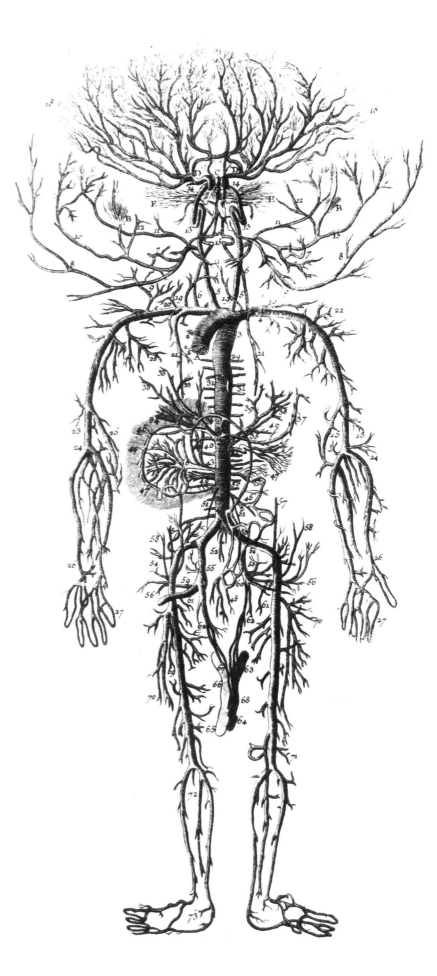

The Arterial System

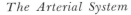

Engraving based on Roberg (1745). This is one of the 111 plates illustrating the monumental *Encyclopedia* of Diderot and d'Alembert.

hoods covering their faces. The French and Italians reflect the same desire that was felt by their contemporaries elsewhere, to forget momentarily that their world was in the process of crumbling. Masks, false noses and garlands of roses merely served to hide thoughts of death. One could say the same for Watteau's silks, moonlights and wooded copses, for one side of his personality was fluid, lyrical light that dictated a tone of good health; and the other side was the languorous gloom of the consumptive (for he died of tuberculosis) and the saddening elegance of the gallant: ladies and gentlemen were in a world of weariness and pretence.

After Watteau there occurred, in the heroic and virtuous climate that followed the successful philosophical revolution, an era in which eighteenth-century art in France became nothing but a fabrication of "objets" without lyricism and realism, made to adorn the corners of charming salons, to accommodate the brilliant and luxury-loving men and women of that day who were primarily concerned with appearances. They and their art were incapable of being interested in the "great subjects"—suffering, misery, passion, death—that inspired great works of art. These great subjects (among them medicine—with its double role of scientist and giver of charity) were foreign to this foolish generation. It avoided the serious, preferring scenes in alcoves where love is a game, or pastoral scenes with nature acting as a backdrop. If anyone dares suggest illness or medicine in this period, it is in a genre picture of cunning licentiousness, or in a caricature. There is no place for the serious painter. Above all, one has to be light in touch, spiritual, charming, cynical and naughty. The style of the paintings corresponds to the subjects; graceful, without depth, and without any real resemblance to flesh. The one miraculous exception was Jean Baptiste Simeon Chardin, who painted what he saw in his own manner. Without him, the painting of this period in which life revolved around the "salon" would have to be qualified as minor. Since the great subjects which we spoke of above cannot be depicted except realistically, nor without "religion" in the ethnological and social sense of the term, these subjects were not treated in England, where the painters were men of the world, or in Italy, where life was a carnival and anarchic, or in Germany, where music was the main preoccupation, or in Spain, where all life was stifled by the church and the executioner, or finally were they treated in Holland, where the creative arts were smothered under eiderdowns of comfort. At least during the first half of the century, in countries like France artifice and emptiness were to be the keyword in a style of painting whose main intent was to please, and which closed its eyes to the real role that painting should play in the arts. In order for this art form to again discover its strength, to become serious, to

return to subject matter worthy of its efforts, one would have to wait for the whole of Europe to become civic minded again; for the surge of the neo-classical movement in which André Chenier in poetry and Jacques-Louis David in painting would set the tone. One would also have to wait for the new Romanticism and for the return of a true appreciation of nature, of men, and of objects to take the place of powdered wigs and geometric gardens.

In the meantime, people were content with dressing elaborately, being pompous and ribald and merely amusing themselves. The painter or the sculptor, at least in France, was little more than an artisan in the service of the aristocracy. As seen above, there was one Chardin who insisted on painting what he wanted to paint; his family, his modest home, the kitchen range, an urchin amusing himself with a penny top, home-made brioches, cloth woven by a grandmother. Chardin did not venture into the salon; he left that to Jean Baptiste Greuze, Jean Marc Nattier, François Boucher and Honoré Fragonard. He did not want any part of this profitable market. He was a genius, comparable to Jan Vermeer and akin to him in sensitivity and tenderness. This man of the people who refused to pay court to a dying aristocracy represents the triumph of a new esthetic, a human and a free art, one which was no longer merely worldly and frivolous, a triumph that ran parallel to victory of the Third Estate.

Genre painting

As mentioned earlier, at the very end of the eighteenth century, Jacques-Louis David was to rediscover lyricism and grandeur, not without falling victim to a new formula, that of the antique. Yet the people he painted were real human beings with flesh and bones, whose blood flowed red when they were wounded. Among the works of art vaguely connected with medicine we may place David's *The Death of Marat* (Musée Royale des Beaux-Arts, Brussels); the subject is shown dying in his bath, Charlotte Corday having just stabbed him in the chest. His posture is a realistic one, which the artist could only have rendered by direct observation of a dying person. This dramatic canvas is also a documentary for the tedious bathing process used in the care of skin diseases during the eighteenth

PIETRO LONGHI (1702-1785)

The Apothecary

The aloes in the foreground is placed there no doubt to remind us of its blood-cleansing powers.

GALLERIA DELL'ACCADEMIA, VENICE

192

SÉBASTIEN LE CLERC (1637-1714)

Dissection Experiment

BIBLIOTHÈQUE NATIONALE, PARIS

century. We know that the "friend of the people" got little relief from his itching skin from the hours he spent in his bath.

But David belongs to the late eighteenth century, and even at that point it is one of the rare exceptions in a century dominated by the light touch. This light touch was to become even more intense in contrast to David's *Marat*. Indeed, before the arrival of David, paintings occasionally conceived with the intention of creating great works of art rarely got beyond the level of charming genre painting, even if their subject happened to be as tragic as an epidemic.

Antoine Coypel (1661-1722), a painter who straddles the seventeenth and eighteenth centuries, abundantly illustrates this point with his gracefully treated mythological scene entitled, *Esther in the Presence of Ahasuerus* (Louvre). The theme in this case is fainting. Fainting inspired several artists, especially towards the end of the Middle Ages, when they represented the Virgin in a fainting spell. Coypel treated the subject according to the fashion of his day, that is to say by placing the scene in an antique décor, complete with precious carpet. In the center of the picture we see Esther, clothed in rich brocades and collapsing with eyes upturned into the arms of three attendants, including Ahasuerus, but without losing any of her exquisite shape as she does so. Ahasuerus is support-

ing her to the best of his ability. In the foreground an old man, obviously a priest, is staring at the proceedings with astonishment.

Also charming, though the subject is far from attractive, is the style of *Fruits of Secret Love,* an engraving by François Voyez (b. 1746) after Pierre Antoine Baudoin (1723-1769). Though this work has small bearing on medicine, it is a social comment of the time. A young girl who has just given birth to a child is shown holding the hand of her lover without even looking at the illegitimate child, whom a servant is taking away. Among other genre pictures of a medical nature there is the handsome engraving by Saint-Non entitled *The Sick Woman* (Bibliothèque Nationale) that offers the everyday subject of a woman in bed talking to friends who have come to pay a visit.

Jean Baptiste Greuze (1725-1895) achieved considerable fame during his lifetime. His vogue, to which Diderot contributed on account of his enthusiastic comments in his *Salons*, was a contemporary of the *Nouvelle Héloise* of Jean-Jacques Rousseau, in which the author exalted the virtues of family life, piety, good masters, faithful servants, respectful children and faithful couples. Greuze exhibited paintings depicting such subjects at every salon: *The Paternal Curse, The Broken Pitcher, The Country Wife* and *The Young Girl and the Dead Bird*. It is hardly sur-

194

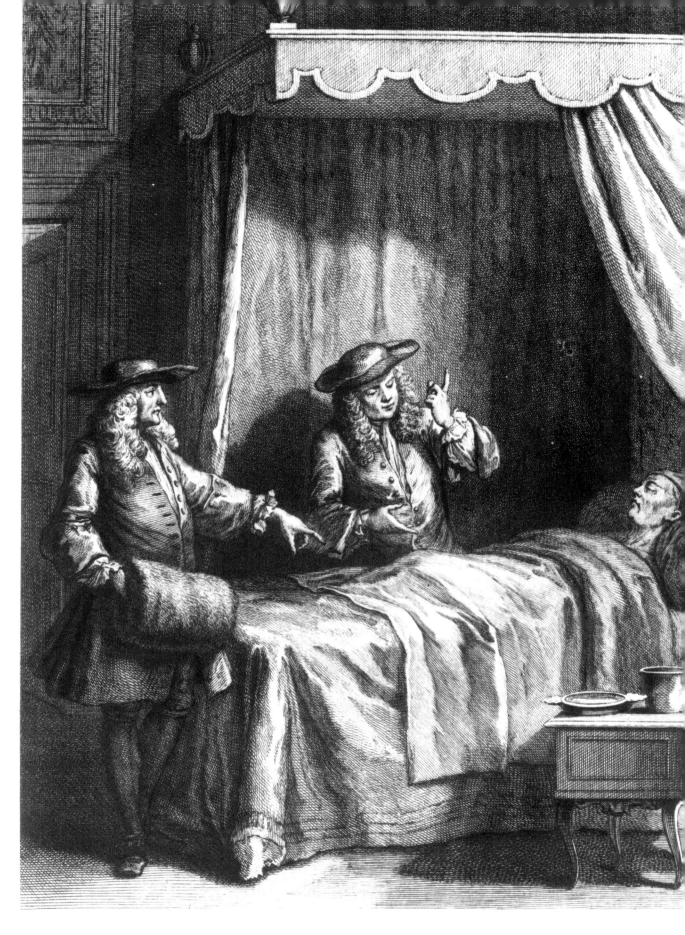

GIOVANNI-BATTISTA TIEPOLO

The Charlatan

prising to learn that he also chose medical subjects, with the purpose of touching the sensibility of his public. Although in his bust of a paralytic (Musée Fabre, Montpellier) we can see no reference whatsoever to the illness in question (it is just *there;* the emaciated head, wrapped in a scarf), more typical of a medical-sentimental picture is that in the Lyon Museum entitled *The Paralytic Visited by a Charitable Lady*. This canvas is a compendium of all the virtues from resignation to generosity, but at the same time is a realistic portrait of paralysis.

Much less well known than Greuze was Etienne Jeaurat (1699-1789), who has left us a pleasant canvas that belongs to the Cognacq-Jay Museum (Paris) entitled *The Quack*, or *The Orvietan Merchant*. Orvietan was an elixir concocted of from nine to fifty-four exotic elements, invented by one Ferrante d'Orvieto. During the eighteenth century, quacks made ample use of this medicine, and the public thought very highly of its inventor. The picture by Jeaurat shows the quack doctor at work. He is on his knees with a hamper-full of the cure-all medicine, trying hard to convince a rather embarrassed invalid of the efficacy of his product. The young wife of the sick man is raising her hands in an expression of scepticism. We shall never know if the Orvietan saved her husband, but the canvas is spiritual and successful. By the same token, one appreciates the quality as well as the documentary value of an engraving by Simon Charles Miger (1747-1805),

after Jean Touzé (1747-1809), to be found in the Bibliothèque Nationale, entitled *The Charlatan,* where several quacks are surrounded by passers-by, among them a sick dwarf.

The classic theme of fainting spells is represented by an aggreable canvas by a "petit-maître" Jacques Gamelin (1738-1803). The scene depicted is a poor interior in which a man, doubtless the *paterfamilias*, is shown pushing before him a young girl whose waistline is somewhat enlarged. A woman, probably the mother of the guilty girl, is pointing in her direction and fainting into a chair. Other women, a child and a man wearing a Bonaparte hat stand around the mother, in a scene reminiscent of Greuze, and painted with vigor and realism.

A picture painted by Charles Amédée Van Loo (1705-1765) may be considered as having medical overtones, because of the presence of a eunuch standing in a large doorway. The picture is entitled *The Sultana Commissioning Work from the Odalisques*. We know that eunuchs, brutally deprived of their virility, often became fat and lost their secondary sex characteristics—hair, voice, musculature. The eunuch depicted here is rather slim, doubtless because the artist was not entirely sure what a eunuch looked like.

In the seventeenth century the artists of the Low Countries produced a great many paintings depicting medical subjects. Although this did not occur in the

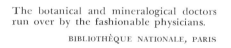

The botanical and mineralogical doctors run over by the fashionable physicians.

PIERRE-ANTOINE BAUDOIN (1723-1769)
The Young Mother or The Fruit of Secret Love

eighteenth century, an Italian, Pietro Falca, known as Pietro Longhi (1702-1785) returned to this earlier tradition and made it his own. His *Apothecary in His Shop* (Accademia di Belle Arti, Venice) could have been painted in Flanders during the previous century. This picture portrays a young prostitute. She is showing the apothecary her infected syphilitic sores. The scene takes place in the classical pharmacy decor among flagons, pots, phials, mortars and pestles. An assistant is seated at a table filling out a prescription while two clients await their turn on a bench. In a corner, a young assistant is working at a stove, doubtless heating a cauterizing-iron. In the Brera (Milan) there is another painting by the same artist entitled *The Tooth Extractor*. The people in this canvas are painted very much in the mood of the Flemish masters, but the style is Venetian. Standing on a rough trestle-table, the dentist is showing his assistant a tooth he has just removed from an adolescent who is seated, a handkerchief over his mouth. All around are children holding teeth that have doubtless just been extracted. In the foreground a dwarf woman is begging from passers-by, among whom are four classically masked figures wearing tricorns and draped in large black capes.

Another Italian artist already mentioned here, Giovanni Battista Tiepolo (1698-1770), painted a picture of a charlatan, another subject dear to the Dutch masters, but the picture is no more Italian than the one just mentioned above. In the middle of this canvas (Palazzo Papadopoli, Venice) a charlatan is mounted on a stage with his back to us, but we can see his face and wigs reflected on a banner placed behind him and facing us. The crowd is composed mainly of Venetian masked types and people with black capes and tricorns; some wear wolf's heads, others long cardboard noses. In the foreground, a young woman, dressed in a hoop skirt showing her ankles, appears to be refusing the advances of a particularly insistent gentleman. In the background is a terrace from which several people are watching the spectacle.

Another medical scene is by the Neapolitan artist Gaspare Traversi (1732-1798) entitled *The Wounded Man* (Accademia di Belle Arti, Venice). The man's wound is so slight that it was obviously an excuse for a genre painting. Wearing an elaborate uniform, his elbow leaning on a table, he has placed his head on the shoulder of a young girl who is supporting his head from behind. His shirt, pulled up slightly, exposes a naked area near his right hip. The surgeon is opening the linen, making a close examination, but we cannot see the nature of the wound. Behind the surgeon is an old man who is very interested in the proceedings, while a young assistant, obviously somewhat overcome, has turned his head away.

Genre paintings that were more or less inspired by

NICOLAS LAVREINCE (1737-1807)

The Unseasonable Arrival

Until the nineteenth century, the enema was the domain of humorists. It did not always inspire works as elegant as this one.

BIBLIOTHÈQUE NATIONALE, PARIS

JEAN-HONORÉ FRAGONARD (1732-1806)

The Remedy

The traditional enema adapted to the *style galant* of a painter and an epoch.

BIBLIOTHÈQUE NATIONALE, PARIS

medicine can be traced as far as Sweden, where Nicolaus Lavreince (1737-1807) painted a gouache (Stockholm Museum) showing a sick person lying in a four-poster bed. Two women are paying him a visit. The poor man could not have been too ill: we can actually see him laughing at their jokes. One of them is holding her hips and roaring with laughter. Finally, there is an engraving, anonymous, dated 1774, a portrait of a famous doctor of the time, Michel Schuppach, known as Michel de la Montagne. He is shown in his consulting room. A fat, rather distinguished looking man, he is involved in the classic occupation of examining urine, watched over by an assistant standing behind him. A seated woman—perhaps the patient—and two richly dressed men accompanying her, are no less attentive. Though this picture does not tell us anything we did not already know about medical

practices in the eighteenth century, it is noteworthy both for the elegant realism of its execution and as the portrait of a quack about his business.

Epidemics

In the chapter on the seventeenth century, certain works of art inspired by the plague were presented, since in those days the disease still erupted periodically. In the eighteenth century, the frequency of these eruptions diminished, however, probably as a result of hygienic measures which, though on occasion somewhat ludicrous, had become law, notably in Lyons in 1628. And yet in 1720 there was an outbreak of the plague in Marseilles. The ravages

Tapestry based on a work by ANTOINE
WATTEAU (1684-1721)

Patient pursued by Apothecaries

Watteau, having his troubles with doctors, composed
a painting in which he depicted himself being chased
by apothecaries armed with clysters, while the doctor
himself was graced with a donkey's pack-saddle. This
painting inspired an engraving and a tapestry, of which
an important fragment is shown above.

of this epidemic were undoubtedly due to the irrational attempts on the part of the authorities and the local doctors to combat it. The University of Montpellier, in a typically medieval reaction, blamed the contagious nature of the disease on the people of Marseilles, and announced that it was a divine punishment for sins committed. The church was in wholehearted agreement with this diagnosis, and Monseigneur de Belzunce helped to make the ravages of the plague complete by exaggerating the religious implications. Many people from Marseilles fled to Lyons, and of course brought the plague with them. However, Doctor Goiffon, by enforcing severe regulations that had proved effective in 1628, succeeded in rapidly stamping out the epidemic. There is a very large painting in Marseilles by Jean François de Troy (1645-1730) showing a sinister and pitiful picture of this Phocaen plague with sick people lying on the ground and piles of contorted cadavers. In the foreground a man on horseback is giving orders for the hurried burial of the dead. The horseman is the Chevalier Rose, agent of the *Sûreté*. One notices that he has not taken any precautions against infection. The plague, as always, inspired several other painters of the eighteenth century, notably Gabriel François Boyen (1726-1806), who was David's teacher, and Tiepolo. In a sketch by Boyen (Musée Carnavalet, Paris) that depicts the *Plague of the Epileptics* we return to sick people abandoned on the ground, but we also have cherubim floating around in the sky while a woman appears to be begging them for a miracle. In a fresco in Este Cathedral, Tiepolo depicted Saint Thecla delivering the town from the plague. Once again, we have the sick and the dead, surrounded by mourning families. But Tiepolo would not be Tiepolo had he not arranged the whole canvas as if it were a ballet or a ceiling for an operahouse.

Apart from the plague, generally on the decline during the eighteenth century, there was another epidemic that came in to take its place, namely smallpox. This disease took so many victims that Charles Marie de La Condamine wrote: "It destroys, mutilates or disfigures more than a quarter of the population." The risk of infection was so high for young women that they became more marriageable, even if pock-marked. Yet even these, if they had had the disease before, were far from being immune. The discovery of vaccination by Edward Jenner in 1721 paved the way toward removing smallpox from the list of potential epidemic diseases. Although few artists were inspired by this subject, there are examples like the anonymous engraving at the Musée Carnavalet, Paris, entitled *Inoculation, or The Triumph of Vaccine*. But this engraving is dated 1800, indicating perhaps that the subject matter was of little interest to the eighteenth century.

Abnormality

If less occupied with this area—although more complacent about it—than their predecessors, the painters of the eighteenth century were on occasion interested in abnormality.

A painting by Norbert Sauvage dated 1703 depicts the cutting apart of Siamese twins joined together at the hip. The picture depicts them front and back before and after the operation. Above them, celebrities blow the trumpet, proclaiming the marvellous ways in which God works.

Jan Weenix (1640-1719), in a picture in the Louvre, painted a dwarf with a hunch-back. Wearing a tall hat, and with a monkey on his shoulder, the dwarf carries a trayful of trinkets which he is hawking to passers-by. This canvas is of interest because it simultaneously offers a street scene, a country scene, a port and a very carefully painted still life composed of game and fruit laid out on the ground.

The Italian painter Ceruti also used a dwarf in a very lively canvas preserved at Padernello. This fellow has particularly short legs, and his head and trunk are those of an adult. He is poorly dressed but looks congenial and rather intelligent.

Finally, there is the dwarf featured in many canvases by French artists. His name was Ferry, but he was better known as Baby, and was attached to Stanislas Leczinski, King of Poland and Duke of Lorraine. Judging by a painting in Versailles, Baby was a charming little man, with a child's face and a well—proportioned body. The anonymous painter of this portrait showed the little fellow to advantage, sumptuously dressed, with a greyhound standing beside him. Other engravings are less flattering.

Tiepolo did not flatter himself in his water color self-portrait where he is seen in a cloak, bespectacled, a heavy key in his hand and without minimizing his obesity which is obviously abnormal.

Miracles

The painters of the eighteenth century were as disinterested in miracles as they were in dwarfs. However, there are occasional examples like the one at the Wadsworth Atheneum in Hartford, Connecticut, which has a *Christ Curing the Blind* by Tiepolo, a very beautiful canvas, tinged with blue and gold. In the midst of a lush landscape with a medieval tower in the background stands Christ under a tree, in the process of curing a blind man. Many witnesses, old men for the most part, help to create a perfectly balanced canvas.

François Boucher
(1703-1770)

An Illustration for "The Imaginary Invalid" by Molière

PHILADELPHIA MUSEUM

Medical Satire

Medical satire, which had begun earlier, was at its most violent in England, with a ferociousness surpassing even that of the previous century. On the other hand, French medical satire of the eighteenth century was relatively kind. The enema syringe was still the main target for fun there.

Though Antoine Watteau (1684-1721) was primarily a painter of "fêtes galantes," on more than one occasion he also ridiculed doctors and apothecaries, who, as far as he was concerned, should all have been forbidden to practice, for they exhausted him with rectal syringes when

he was just quite simply consumptive. One of his best satires of doctors depicts the patient in a night-cap and dressing gown fleeing from the apothecary who is pursuing him with a syringe. Behind the latter is a doctor in a long robe, while other somewhat agitated apothecaries, all armed with syringes, surround him. In the background there rises an obelisk, and a sarcophagus upon which is drawn the head of a dead man. Variations of this famous picture are in existence, the original belonging to Doctor Debat in Paris. In this collection there is also an engraving by François Joullain, and a large Gobelin tapestry which places the scene indoors. Watteau also made several drawings of apothecaries. There is one of them in the Musée des Arts Decoratifs in Paris. Others, engraved by

DOMINIQUE LELEU
(1734-1805)
The Sick Child

PRIVATE COLLECTION

Benoît Audran the Younger (Bouvet Collection, Paris), may have been sketches for the picture just mentioned above. Finally, Watteau directed his skill and wit against Doctor Misaubin (Bibliothèque Nationale, Paris), whom he depicts holding an enormous syringe under his arm. Watteau made this drawing while seated in a café during a visit to London. François Boucher (1730-70), after having copied some hundred odd Watteaus for the engraver Laurent Card, went on to paint imaginary mythological scenes, and scenes of village life that were perhaps just a bit too sophisticated, and chinoiseries that were just a bit too Chinese. However, for the illustrations and scenic designs for Molière, he had to fall back on the neat, biting line of his master. An engraving of Monsieur

de Pourceaugnac being threatened by a group of apothecaries carrying their favorite instruments, among them the inevitable syringe, especially deserves to be mentioned, as do the engravings he made to illustrate *Le Malade Imaginaire*. Once again, we find the rectal syringe being the all-operative instrument; indeed it would seem that it was impossible to do without it. A urinal keeps the syringe company at the feet of the invalid. Women are bringing the latter some pillows (Philadelphia, Ars Medico Collection).

The third "great" of the eighteenth century was Jean Honoré Fragonard (1732-1806), Boucher's disciple. He painted children's games and happy mothers. However, we owe him a particular debt for *The Remedy*, engraved

RICHARD SAINT-NON (1727-1791)
The Sick Woman

by Martial (Bouvet Collection), a remedy that needless to say consists of the use of the rectal syringe. The scene, framed by the curtains of a four poster bed, is of a man lying on his stomach with a servant about to place we know what instrument up we know where, under the close observation of his wife, who, in bed herself, has moved over in order to give the servant and a valet more room.

The classical way of caricaturing men is to show them as animals. G. Huet did just this in a drawing engraved by Guelard (Bibliothèque Nationale) showing two monkeys using a rectal syringe on a third. A scene very much like this one was painted above a door at the Tohan Castle at Strasbourg. It was doubtless indecent, for it was later covered over by another scene of pink-cheeked children leaning over to perform the same operation on a sleeping Eros.

One could go on indefinitely listing the eighteenth-century works of art that showed the use of a rectal syringe. Why did they use this theme so much? Doubtless because

there were erotic intentions behind the satire which in many of the works borders on the licentious.

Up until this period, England had imported her painters. During this century, however, she was to give birth to a national art that was to become universally known with John Constable and J. M. W. Turner. In the particular field with which we are concerned, namely satirical-medical art, extremely virulent and talented draftsmen and engravers appeared on the scene, at the head of whom comes William Hogarth (1697-1764), who began his career by copying other people's etchings until he got the idea of doing his own work, as Blake was to do a little later. He began by doing a series of engravings entitled *A Rake's Progress* that appeared in 1733. They were followed by *Marriage-à-la-Mode* and the *Four Stages of Cruelty*. Medicine is often the target in these satires, and the engravings are of an exceedingly high technical quality, and in a style that was completely new and personal. One of the engravings that Hogarth treated in the French manner is called *The Visit to the Doctor*. In it we can see a smiling young aristocrat, cane in hand, about to offer the timid young girl to the tender ministrations of the rapacious midwife with her razor. Also in the picture is a fat man, apparently the quack himself, cleaning his spectacles. The atmosphere in the picture is very much that of a curiosity shop with skeletons, craniums and animal jaws. Medicine is also the target of satire in an engraving from the series entitled *A Harlot's Progress*, the inscription of which runs as follows:

"Once out of the hospital, Margot continues to ply her trade. Do you know one of these creatures that has not had the clap?
"Our Margot has had it. Elixirs, pills and emetics had so exhausted her, and she's tired of living.
"In short, she dies ... Her maid, upon seeing her dead, starts to yell and scream.
"The doctors blamed each other. Slim (one of the doctors) is furious, knocks over a table and treats his friend as a madman ...
"It was your pills that killed her," says Sqage (the other doctor) "and not my elixir.
"While they are blaming each other, a scrawny woman is filching from her chest."

Hogarth attacked alcoholism with the same virulence that he exercised with the harlot. An engraving dated 1751 (Bouvet Collection) and depicting *Gin Lane* exaggerates the iniquity of gin. In the foreground is a skeleton of a man still holding onto a bottle with one hand, and a glass in the other. Above him, a woman with her bodice undone is so drunk that she has failed to notice

WILLIAM HOGARTH (1697-1764)

The Reward of Cruelty, or an Anatomy Lesson in 1759 in the Hall of Barbers

"What a disgrace is his that death will not put an end to. Though refused Eternal peace, his fate will move no one. His tongue it torn out at the root, the eyes are scooped out of their sockets, and his poor heart is exposed for all to see. But from his bones, this terrible testimony of shame will arise."

WILLIAM HOGARTH (1697-1764)

"*Gin Lane*" or *the Evils of Drunkenness*

Nothing is omitted—neither the baby that a drunken mother drops on the ground, nor suicide, nor collapsing houses, nor the alchoholic being buried, nor a noisy squabble, nor degradation nor crime.

BIBLIOTHÈQUE NATIONALE, PARIS

WILLIAM HOGARTH (1697-1764)

Visit to a Charlatan

In this scene a young and lively aristocrat presents his frightened victim. Minute realism and ferocious satire blend beneath Hogarth's highly skilful brush.

NATIONAL GALLERY, LONDON

207

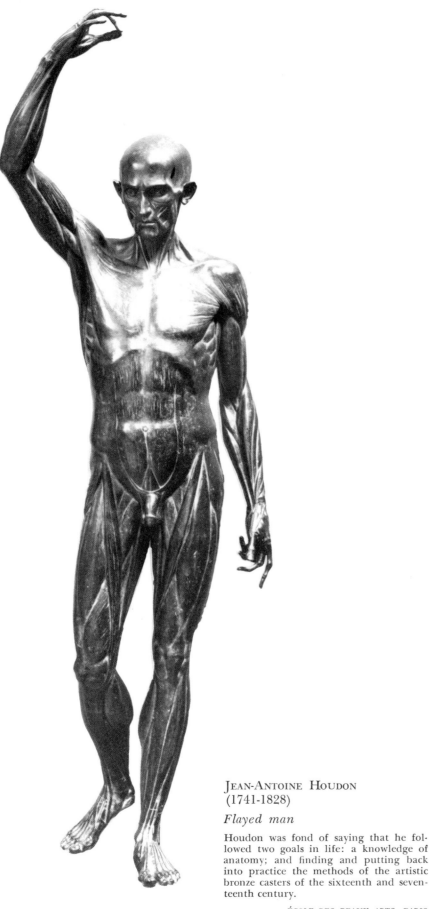

JEAN-ANTOINE HOUDON
(1741-1828)

Flayed man

Houdon was fond of saying that he followed two goals in life: a knowledge of
anatomy; and finding and putting back
into practice the methods of the artistic
bronze casters of the sixteenth and seventeenth century.

ÉCOLE DES BEAUX ARTS, PARIS

her child falling over the balustrade. In the background
a riot is going on in a tavern, a dead man being placed
in his coffin, a hanged man, a tumbled-down house—all
described with minute detail, with a neatness of line and
a sarcastic humor that sets this apart from other engravings of the time.

Alcohol leads to madness. Thus Hogarth, who knew
this well, takes us into an asylum. However, the people
depicted, rather than being medical studies, are more an
artist's impression of the inmates of a mad house. The
engraving entitled *The Mad of Bedlam,* 1768 (Bouvet
Collection), is in fact a gallery of disturbed people. Among
them are victims of alcohol, fewer in number than obsessed people, mythomaniacs and schizophrenics. One of
the inmates fancies himself a bishop; the other a king. A
third is perpetually playing the violin, a fourth interrogating the stars day and night.

After folly we have death. Hogarth unleashed his
black humor in an engraving entitled *The Reward
of Cruelty* (Bibliothèque Nationale), the last of the scenes
in the *Four Stages of Cruelty.* This is an extraordinary
and horrible work of art. At the foot of the chair occupied
by the professor are three surgeons working on a corpse
with almost ferocious speed. One of them is hacking off
a foot, while another is pulling out intestines. The third
is piercing the eye sockets. A fourth person, seated, is
emptying the intestines onto the floor, where a dog is eating them. In the foreground a boiling cauldron, containing heads and thighs, completes this lugubrious and
burlesque spectacle, which really has very little to do with
a genuine dissection class. In this series of prints Hogarth
is obviously satisfying the extremes of his macabre genius. And yet, perhaps he also has a few bones to pick
with surgeons and the teaching of anatomy.

As a kind of climax there were the fifteen famous quacks
he portrayed in 1736 in *The Company of Undertakers.*
Among them are Chevalier Taylor, who called himself
"Ophtalmiator Pontifical, Imperial and Royal," Mrs. Sally
Mapp, a masculine woman and Spot Ward, an Epsom
quack, who counted the King among his clients. These are
placed in the most prominent position at the head of the
engraving. Thomas Rowlandson (1756-1827), who was
born after Hogarth, was less ferocious in his caricatures.
He also did some medical satires, though only the symptoms of illness really interested him (rather than doctors)—in particular hallucinations and obsessions. For
these studies he deserves to be classed among the painters
of the fantastic. In *Ague and Fever,* the sick person, seated
by a fire, is enveloped by a curious bird with long talons.
The bird must surely symbolize the fever. In the center
of the picture is a nightmare character, half devil, half
monkey, with one arm in the air. On the right hand side

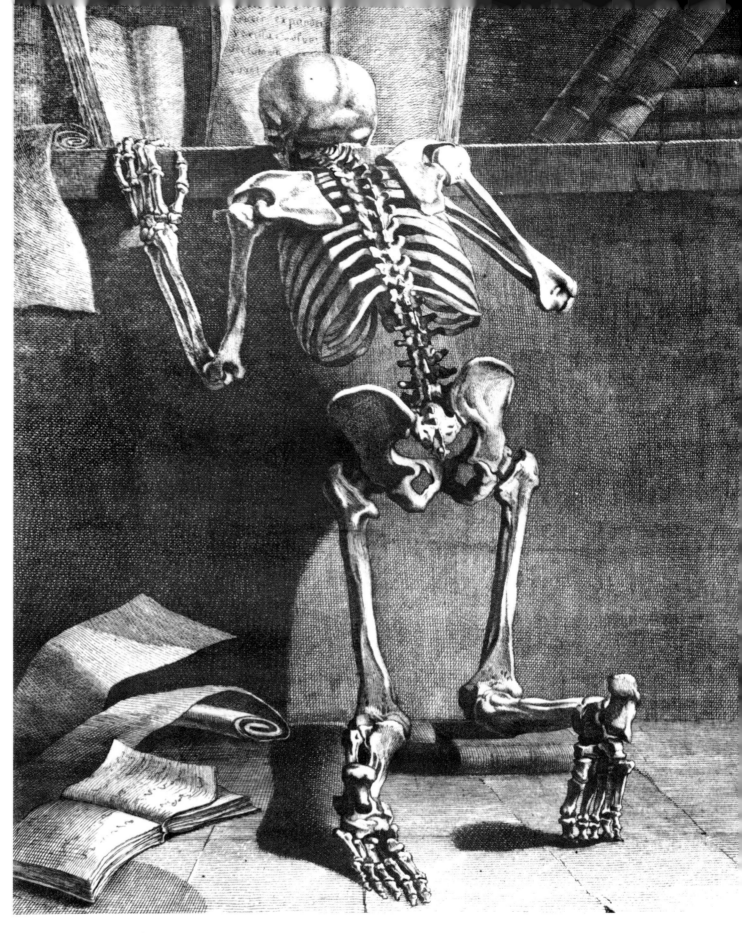

JACQUES GAMELIN (1738-1803)

"Pray not to be led into temptation"

One of the plates illustrating the "Nouveau Recueil
d'ostéologie et de myologie," Toulouse, 1779.

of the picture is the doctor, seen from the back. He is seated, holding a bowl of urine while making out a prescription. In the same series is the fascinating *Hypochondriac*. The invalid is lying on a sofa with a somber look on his face. He sees death walk past him, surrounded by people miming the various ways a man can kill himself—with alcohol, pistol, and sabre, etc ... An undertaker follows behind. The artist has placed himself in this sinister picture, which includes a doctor holding the pummel of his cane under his nose, probably impregnated with anti-infection salts, and the wife of the patient. The last two are talking to each other standing by a table laden with bottles.

Contemporary with these two English artists is the Spaniard Francisco Goya. However, Goya straddles two centuries. Born in 1746, a large part of his work is done before 1800, yet its entirety, ended by his death in 1828, seems to belong to the nineteenth century.

Illustrated Medical Books

The delights of the eighteenth century, where everything (at least for the rich and the aristocrat) consisted of pleasure and the indulging of the senses, were bound to be reflected in book illustrations of the period. Little vignettes replaced the austere frontispieces of the previous century. Though the medical books on the whole did not succumb to this frivolity, their illustrations did include some charming pieces which set out to be detailed rather than picturesque.

Obviously anatomy was to be the favorite subject for medical book illustrators. The work of Siegfried Albinus is perhaps the most representative: *Tabulae Sceleti et Musculorum Corporis* (Leiden, 1747) and *Supallix Anatomica* (Leiden, 1775), but from this period onwards, the English published remarkable books, particularly that of William Cowper entitled *Myotomia Reformata* (London, 1724), and that of William Cheselden entitled *The Anatomy of the Human Body* (London, 1741).

In the meantime, the anatomy lessons and plates illustrating flayed bodies were of less artistic interest than the engravings, frontispieces and vignettes of various medical and anatomical subjects. In particular, one thinks of the charming frontispiece by Charles Nicolas Cochin, the younger (1715-1790), engraved for *L'Etat de médecine ancienne et moderne*. It is entitled *A Medical Examination* and shows a sick woman seated by her bed surrounded by her visibly anxious husband and her children in tears.

A doctor is giving her a close examination. Henry Gravelot (1699-1773) drew a charming frontispiece for *De la conversation des enfants* by Joseph Raulin (Paris, 1768) that was engraved by Nicolas de Launay (1739-1792). It depicts a family scene that is mythological at the same time: a mother is seated in a park feeding a baby near a cot in which another child is asleep. Little boys and girls are playing with a kite under the watchful eye of Hippocrates. The latter is seated on a cloud and holds a book in one hand and the caduceus in the other.

The first medical and anatomical handbooks for artists appeared in the eighteenth century. The most remarkable among them were the *Anatomical Studies for the use of Painters* by Charles Monnet (b. 1730), himself a painter, and *The Elements of Anatomy for the use of Painters, Sculptors and Students of Art* (Paris, 1788). However, the most beautiful is that of Jacques Gamelin (Toulouse, 1779). When his father died, Gamelin inherited a large fortune. He had become the Director of the Academie des Beaux-Arts at Montpellier, and decided to use his fortune to publish a monumental illustrated volume devoted to myology and osteology. In a dissection studio that he had had specially built, he himself drew and engraved the most difficult of the compositions with the help of Guillaume Martin (1737-1801) and Etienne de Lavallée (1740-1793), his best students. It would be impossible to describe each one of these engravings—they are so many and varied. We can see many flayed men in all possible positions and skeletons that terrify the living, for they are depicted as appearing without warning. Gamelin did not have much of a success with his *Nouveau recueil d'osteologie et de myologie* (Toulouse, 1799). So little in fact that the publication of the book ruined him. The scientists of the time did not like these daring drawings which were nevertheless exact in detail.

The illustrations in surgical books that appeared in the eighteenth century were no different from those of the previous century. They depicted amputations, such as to be seen in a work by Croissant de Garangeot entitled *Treatise on Surgical Operations* (Paris, 1731), and that of Lorenz Heister, *Surgical Institutions* (Avignon, 1770). The former contains pictures of the "stone," as does a similar book by William Cheselden (London, 1723). However, the colored engraving was invented during the eighteenth century—not engravings colored by hand after they were printed—by Jacques Fabien Gautier d'Agoty (1717-1786). In his *Complete Myology in Colour and in Scale* he says: "We do not offer the public old fashioned illuminations today; instead we have original works showing nature itself, depicted by M. Gautier in his new form of colour printing, a technique he perfected."

THOMAS ROWLANDSON (1756-1827)

The Hypochondriac

Despite the summary and caricatural depiction, the obsessive swarming that twentieth-century art will try to capture and analyze is present here and there in this caricature by Rowlandson.

MOINEVILLE COLLECTION, PARIS

The Minor Arts

Medicine, and more particularly pharmacy, created the necessity of designing a number of utilitarian objects that at the same time are real works of art. The first were the pestles and mortars. They were made from the Middle Ages onwards. In the sixteenth century they began making them in bronze and giving them elegant shapes. The bowl was usually decorated with a frieze. The eighteenth century decorated them even more. The faïence medicine bottles and jars of various shapes were also decorated. Writing, large enough to be seen at a distance, was painted on the sides of the jars describing the contents. Some of these jars were decorated with medical subjects. One of these can be seen in Doctor Debat's collection. It depicts the old subject of administering the enema. A monkey is performing the operation on another monkey. Eigh-

211

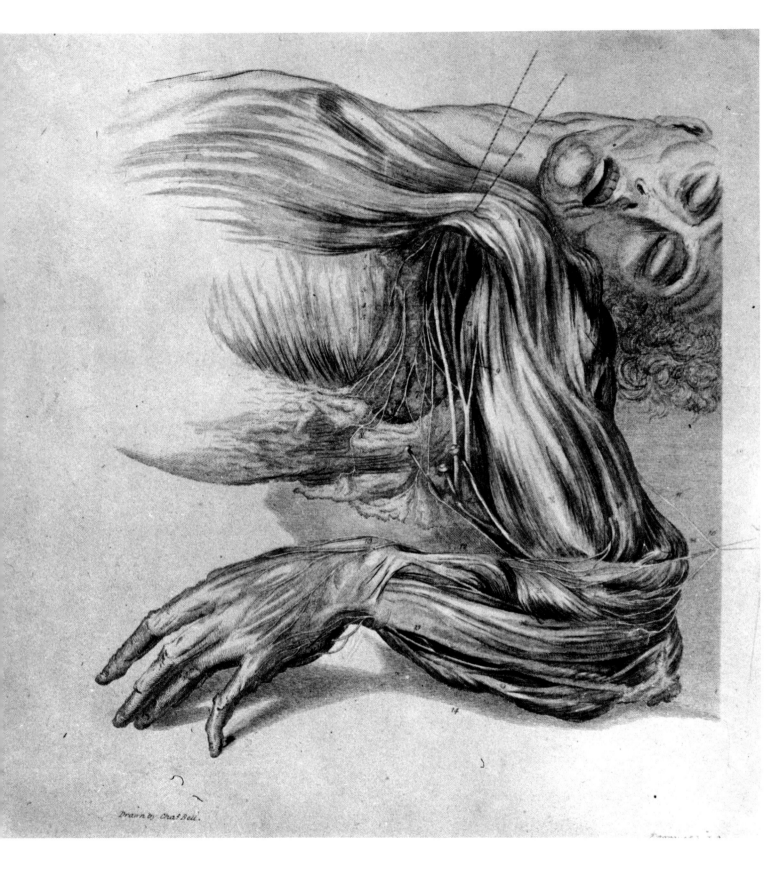

CHARLES BELL (1774-1842)
Anatomical Plate

teenth century pharmacies, and some that date back even further, have been preserved in several hospitals in France, for example at Beaune, Baugé, Besançon and Saint-Germain en Laye.

Apart from the medicine jars and bottles, one should also mention several other utensils that were on occasion artistically decorated. Examples would be the faïence bed-pans, which permitted travelers to relieve themselves without leaving their carriages, and the bidet with its decorated faïence bottom, sought after by collectors today. Also, there are the tin accessories: urinals, bed-warmers, tea kettles and last of all, the famous enema syringe, examples of which exist in carved ivory (Doctor Debat's collection, Paris).

THE NINETEENTH CENTURY

In the nineteenth century, both medicine and art underwent a somewhat similar development in that each progressed by leaps and bounds, or better, by revolutions. Before we investigate the relationship between the two, it might be useful to give a rough outline of their history.

First of all, we note that in the nineteenth century, medicine, advancing as far as Pasteur's discoveries and the stupendous consequences thereof, started off on what seemed to be a side street, namely biology.

Théodore Géricault

The Madwoman

A lover of antithesis, Géricault vigorously and lucidly painted beaten athletes and thunder-struck intelligence. The truly medical portrait he offers us here is simultaneously a highly dramatic work.

The century was nine years old when Lamarck published his *Philosophie Zoologique,* in which he elaborated his views on evolution. He claimed that the species instead of being biologically fixed, changed according to two laws: (1) that the development of organs is constantly in ratio to their employment, so that they develop if used and vanish if neglected; and (2) that all acquired characteristics are preserved and transmitted to offspring. Modern biology is based on these two laws, which are still under discussion today, particularly the latter, which is popular in the U.S.S.R.

Knowledge being what it was in 1809, Lamarck's notions could be taken at best as daring theories. It was only Darwin's (1809-1882) famous *Origin of the Species* that forcibly brought the idea of evolution to the attention of scientists, while Lamarck had suggested that "the function creates the organ," Darwin emphasized "the struggle for survival."

The ensuing phase was the work of François de Serre (1788-1866) and Fritz Müller, a German, (1821-1897), who

215

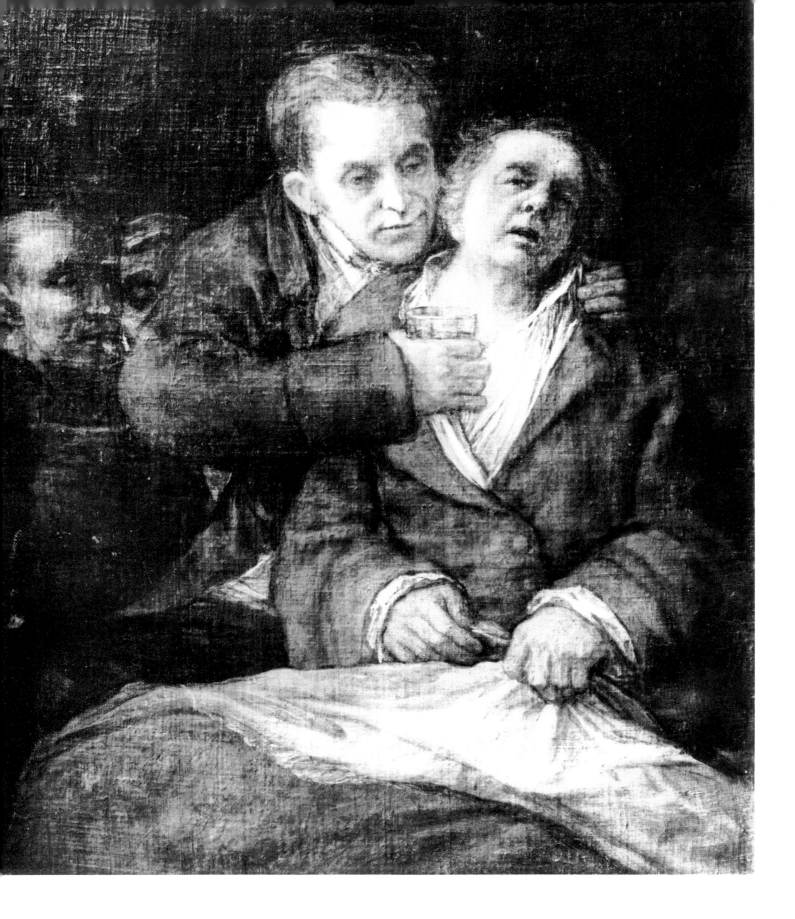

Francisco Goya (1746-1828)

Portrait of Goya sick

At the bottom of this portrait (1820), there are the
following words: "Goya, in gratitude to his friend Arrieta, who saved his life when he was dangerously ill
at the end of the year 1819, at the age of 73."

216

together established that the development of the individual is a recapitulation of the development of the species. Next came Pouchet's (1851-1938) treatise: *Hétérogénité ou Traité de la génération spontanée,* and not much later, Pasteur's *Mémoire sur les corpuscules qui existent dans l'atmosphère.* With the publication of these two contradictory works, a fierce struggle broke out between Pouchet and Pasteur, culminating in the latter's victory and leading to a whole series of discoveries that revolutionized medical science.

Meanwhile, Laennec (1781-1826), author of a two-volume work entitled *De l'ausculation ou Traité des maladies des poumons et du coeur,* turned clinics topsy-turvy with his inventions, especially the stethoscope; and Bouilland added his *Traité clinique des maladies du coeur* (1835) to these discoveries; finally, in 1838, Esquirol (who succeeded Pinel) published a *Traité des maladies mentales* which allows us to regard him as the founder of psychiatry.

This medical evolution is obviously connected to the social evolution. The bourgeois revolution of 1789 had paid scant heed to the proletariat, merely using him as infantry. Thus, provisional national depots were opened and bread was distributed among the people of Paris and several other big cities, and the wars of the Republic were fought by ragged soldiers on empty stomachs. In 1845, when Victor Hugo, who had been brought to power by conservative voters, delivered his famous address on the terrible poverty reigning in France, he barely could do justice to the indescribable lot of the workers. The Revolution of 1830 had wrought few changes in the frightful situation caused by the drain on French economy dur-

Francisco Goya (1746-1828)

The Insane Asylum

Though capturing the very climate of madness, the great painter depicts highly unconventional "types" of lunatics.

ACADEMIA SAN FERNANDO, MADRID

217

LOUIS DAVID (1748-1825)

Episode from an epidemic of the plague that ravaged Marseilles in 1720

LOUVRE, PARIS

ing the wars of the Empire, the inability and unwillingness of the middle class to create an equitable social structure, and the abuses of the dawning machine age. The riots in Lyons (1833) proved that this situation was not peculiar to the capital; the entire country was debilitated and chaotic. The revolution of 1848 was surely the purest one, because it was brought about in a spirit of egalitarianism, religion, nay, mysticism, by the people and their intellectuals. But in the end, the condition of the common man remained more or less the same, the Lamartine-style tribunes speedily transforming the revolution into one of shop-keepers. Then, the Second Empire,

another war, the Commune, the Third Republic, the "belle époque"—the rest is common knowledge; it was summed up in the cynical remark "make money" that Guizot snapped at the bankers and the industrialists who were putting nine-year-old children to work.

Such a situation itself was far from characteristic of France alone and could be found all over, notably in England, where Dickens produced descriptions of it that were as shocking as any by Hugo or Eugène Sue, and in Spain, where Napoleon's insane politics multiplied the ruins and the poverty. Doctors and surgeons had their share of work: tuberculosis raging through overcrowded slums and preying on constitutions weakened by hunger and exhaustion; epidemics carried by moving troops and abetted by the slaughters in civil and other wars (cholera struck several devastating blows at Paris); operations and amputations performed on battle-fields; starving stray dogs that spread rabies. The new vocational diseases which were as yet unidentified became an object of close study by doctors and biologists.

This medical action, which was growing more and more necessary—and multiplying *ipso facto* the scenes conducive to artistic inspiration—would most certainly have been carried out more easily and efficiently, had it been facilitated, organized, and financed by the public authorities. But unfortunately this was not to be; for a long time, medical and social aid remained a matter of private and religious charity. The nineteenth century bequeathed almost no new hospitals to the twentieth; and as for hygiene, the less said about that the better.

Yet, slowly but surely, and despite the opposition of the empiricists, there was a growing awareness of medicine. The doctor, though still jeered at à la Molière, had become an important and honored figure (note his significance in the works of Balzac). And for that matter, surgery—where are the blood-letters of yesteryear?—was now a discipline in its own right.

Thus, Berlioz' father, himself a doctor, wanted his son to follow in his footsteps, and during his first few years in Paris, the young student was an appalled spectator of numerous scientific autopsies and dissections. And it was in the nineteenth century that pharmacy finally went commercial and grew popular, largely with the help of advertising; a huge number of vignettes and posters embellished with the charming features of young girls vaunted sovereign remedies for "consumptive diseases." Since far too many consumptives could not afford these syrups, they went to the slaughter-houses for a glass of beef-blood or else drank water in which a handful of nails (preferably

Louis David (1748-1825)

Study of the head of a plague-stricken man

Even in his strictly historical studies, David never neglected realism or a technical diligence, the excess of which he condemned among his predecessors.

BIBLIOTHÈQUE NATIONALE, PARIS

Pierre-Jean David d'Anger (1788-1856)

Pain

Plaster bust, the only model in existence, finished in 1811. It won the *Prize for an expressive face* awarded by the Academy of Fine-Arts.

MUSEUM OF FINE ARTS, ANGERS

Antoine Gros (1771-1835)

The Plague victims of Jaffa

An initial sketch of this painting—one of the most famous nineteenth-century works inspired by the plague—showed Napoleon lifting with his own hands the body of a man who died of the plague. Here, the commander in chief of the Eastern Army is putting his bare hand on the bubo of a sick man just as kings touched scrofula. As early as 1799, the future emperor was already visible. The painting was exhibited in the Salon of 1804 and enjoyed an immense success.

MUSÉE CONDÉ, CHANTILLY, FRANCE

220

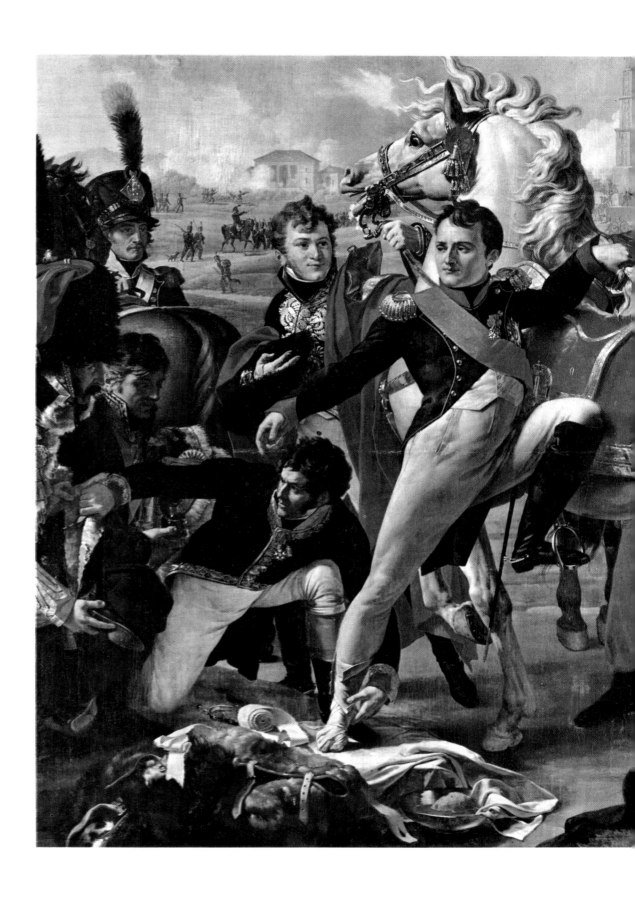

Claude Gautherot (1765-1825)
Napoleon wounded at Ratisbon

221

rusty ones) had been thrown: iron is good for the system.

And, while medicine emerged from its age-old empiricism, what was going on in the art world? We cannot answer this question without first examining the evolution of the artist's status. For a long time, painters, engravers, and sculptors had been considered artisans, dependent like any others on patrons and clients without whom they couldn't have survived. The obvious corollary of this subordination was an intellectual subordination involving the very choice of subject matter and even style. So many religious paintings were produced which except for a few masterpieces are often interchangeable, and so many portraits—the Dutch museums are chockfull of burghers and their wives "in the manner of" Franz Hals or Verspronck, and Watteau himself was commissioned to paint a shop sign for the picture dealer Gersaint. All this, because until the eighteenth century, most works of art were executed according to precise orders. The artist's submission to the demands of a clientele which in actual fact conditioned his output when it did not determine the canons he was to go by began to vanish, and in the twentieth century it was a thing of the past.

Why? Because the traditional patrons (princes, lords, popes, bishops, etc.) disappeared or lost their power and their fortune; because the social rise of the bourgeoisie increased manifold the number of clients and thereby spread a buying power that had previously belonged to a chosen few; and because like everyone else, the artist was taken with the idea of liberty even at the price of starving to death. In the eighteenth century, art exhibitions, "salons," became a new social factor. The artist no longer waited for an assignment; he worked at his own expense and at his own risk and went out to the public and sought buyers for his works. From now on, the competition of his colleagues and the judgment pronounced by his critics determined his fate and that of his art at least as much as did his creative will, the latter theoretically unshackled ever since the triumph of democratic ideas, whereas beforehand (as seen in the preceding chapter) the artist had to respect the esthetic ideas of an élite who were the sole purchasers of painting and sculpture.

The role of the critic cannot be exaggerated. He, too, had become a new social factor due to the extremely rapid growth and spread of the press, a growth corresponding in turn to a new social and mental law of human relations. Critics do not merely list the artistic qualities or shortcomings of the works they report on. They place these works quite properly in an aesthetic, ethical, philosophical, and social context which they cannot avoid having. Critics are simultaneously the guides, the commentators, and the judges of artists and have no small effect on the theories that the artists constructed all the more ardently now that they knew they were addressing an ever-increasing audience. Thus, Diderot's writings on contemporary painters—in particular Greuze but actually going beyond the personal cases of the individuals—are true meditations on art, on its function in the world of man, on its resonance and its moral aims.

The nineteenth century, which witnessed the huge increase in such mutual interactions of art and society, also witnessed a growing number of more or less peaceful feuds between artists (Ingres vs. Delacroix was not the least renowned of these battles) in the name of theories whose purpose is a more precise definition of art in regard to the laws and values of society. Individualism is the rule of the day, revolution is compulsory, movement is a

law of this nineteenth century, in which the first trains began belching smoke, God was declared to be dead, a painter (Courbet) was arrested and fined in 1871 for inciting the people of Paris to destroy a public monument, and a biologist effected the first cure of a child bitten by a rabid dog. We must add that this emancipation of the artist was inevitably accompanied by solitude and material hardship. Though free regarding his inspiration, he could not risk lack of direct appeal without jeopardizing his income. And though able, to a certain extent, to pride himself on being the new aristocrat in a society that had destroyed the aristocracy, he also ran the risk of becoming an outsider, a *maudit*. Before

EUGENE DELACROIX (1798-1863)

The Consultation

This both realistic and allegorical caricature by Delacroix was worthy of Daumier. It is one of the most ferocious caricatures ever inspired by medicine.

BIBLIOTHÈQUE NATIONALE, PARIS

223

studying the connection between art and medicine in this period, when from classicism to impressionism by way of romanticism, realism, and academic painting, the schools were legion, a few words should be devoted to the glory of a peerless artist, Francisco Goya.

As we have already stressed, Goya, though born in 1746, is vitally linked with the nineteenth century (in which he lived and labored for twenty-eight years) by the very nature of his genius, which eludes chronology and outdistances the crowds. Goya never paid attention to the artistic fads and laws of his times or classical doctrines despite recommendations to cast a respectful glance at them. "Nothing but lines and never a volume," he would say, "but where do you see any lines in nature? Personally, I see only volumes that are lit up and volumes that aren't, planes that jut out and planes that sink back, and reliefs and hollows. My eyes have never discovered lines or details. I don't count the hairs in a passer-by's beard, I don't rivet my eyes on the buttons of his suit, and my brush shouldn't see more than I do." This was in short the complete opposite of the theories of William Blake, who, referring to Michelangelo, considered the line the primary material and moral discipline of art ("leave out the line and you leave out life itself"). And, if we may add, Goya's words were a first draft for the credo of the Cézanne school.

Who were Goya's masters? Until he reached forty, one can easily discern nearby or distant echoes—Velásquez, Tiepolo, Watteau, Prud'hon—but mere echoes all the same. In point of fact, he had come into his own style, unpolished and yet subtle, cynical and affectionate. At most, one can say that like the Italians whom he watched at work in his youth, and like Greuze or Reynolds, he painted in light hues during the initial phase of his creativity. But, light or not, a continual drama is unrolling beneath Goya's brush, even when he produces genre paintings to make money. He was obsessed with ugliness, the grotesque, anything verging on pathology, with stupidity, injustice, poverty, and the horrors of war and peace. Beauty itself has to be slightly unwholesome to appeal to him, as we can see in the magnificent portrait of Isabella de Porcel de Cobos (National Gallery, London). Albeit a "court painter," he never lost his taste for the monstrous as evinced by the playful massacre in his highly official portrait of the family of Charles V (Prado). The king's obesity, his dim eyes, his stupid expression, the marred, evil features of the queen, find no mercy in the piercing eyes of Francisco Goya. He spares only the children and the ladies in waiting, and this painting, on which the golds and the glowing colors are applied with almost excessive complaisance, is the direct representation of imbecilic stylishness and degeneracy. His real master was Spain, its masochistic realism, so deeply ingrained in the national mentality that the members of the royal family

had no qualms about recognizing themselves in the ferocious caricature we have just described.

Goya was fascinated by the abnormal; his boundless imagination made him conceive monsters, and thus he couldn't avoid treating subject matter that was more or less plainly medical. In this respect, we must cite first of all his *Insane Asylum* (Academia de San Fernando, Madrid). In a vaulted cellar lit only by a high barred aperture, we see a gathering, or rather a conglomeration, of half-dressed madmen, whom Goya, just like Hogarth, represents in "typical" poses and situations which he actually gleaned from hearsay rather than first-hand information: one lunatic, wearing a crown, thinks himself a king; another, adorned with plumes, extends his hand to a woman who kisses it. Thus, this work should not be regarded as a document; yet, with these unhappy creatures wallowing about on the floor or kneeling in the heavy and probably foul air, the very climate of madness is recaptured, and so vividly that upon seeing *The Insane Asylum* we experience a nightmarish sensation.

The very same impression is conveyed by *The Old Woman* (Musée de Lille), also known as *Que Tal?* (How are you?). In a manner akin to that of Hieronymus Bosch in *The Carrying of the Cross* Goya depicts two old, horrible woman. One, a toothless skeleton with red eyes and chronically granular lids, is covered with jewels and ridiculously bedizened in a white muslin dress with blue ribbons and a plunging neckline. The other is holding a book with the words *Que tal?* which furnish a title for the painting; she is afflicted with very deep-set eyes and a deformation of the nose—a classical characteristic of hereditary syphilis. As our summary description indicates, this painting has an obvious documentary interest, even if the artist had no intention of presenting two medical portraits.

To this category of Goya's works that are more or less in rapport with the art of Aesculapius, we can add *The Pilgrimage to San Isidro* for the blind men appearing in it, and the entire series of the *Disasters of War,* (which was only published in 1863) for the enormous number of "anatomical abominations" in these engravings, in which the artist returned to Rembrandt's black and white: bodies—tortured, amputated, twisted, stretched out by hanging, etc. And finally, in the series of *Caprices,* Goya

MARGUERITE GERARD (1761-1837)

Bad News

Smelling salts! Smelling salts. It is mostly in high society that smelling salts are used. Actually only someone in high society can take time to faint at bad news.

LOUVRE, PARIS

gave free rein to his frenetic and halucinatory imagination as well as to his caricaturing realism for which he found ample subject matter in the spectacle of everyday misery: e.g. *The Hunt for Teeth,* in which we see a woman, her face covered with a handkerchief, pulling out the teeth of a hanged man, and *The Clubfoot* (Louvre), in which a cripple, stared at by three woman, is afflicted not, properly speaking, with a clubfoot but with a dreadful malformation analogous to modern ones such as are caused by thalidomide and which produce humans whose feet and the hands are directly attached to the body, the legs and arms having been forgotten by nature.

When depicting physicians, Francisco Goya never spared them. The sixteenth century liked to make monkeys of them; Goya preferred to make asses of them with or without spectacles. Yet there is one exception, a painting he did in 1820 in honor of a doctor who had treated him and to whom he wrote the following dedication at the bottom of the canvas: "Goya, in gratitude to his friend Arrieta, who saved his life when he was dangerously ill at the end of the year 1819, at the age of 73." There is furthermore a self-portrait. Sitting up in bed, Goya, supported by Dr. Ar-

rieta, is taking the medicine that the physician gives him. Goya's times were no different from ours; the healthy man pokes fun at doctors, yet the moment he grows sick, he can't wait to call them in.

Classicism

The revolution had brought an end to " fêtes galantes " in art as in life. Virtue and austerity were the watchwords. People talked about nothing but good citizenship and cited the Romans on every occasion. When the Republic collapsed and Napoleon came to power, the words Triumvirate and Consulate flourished anew in the Gallic and Capetian vocabulary of France. The people dreamt of seeing their new masters in togas. Shop-assistants got Titus haircuts. In short, France went "Antique." The artists had no choice but to follow suit. They turned as once before to Italy, to rediscover a cold and grandiloquent Antiquity, in which the Horatii swore an oath while brandishing their swords with noble, draped movements,

226

and with elegant and quite mysterious vestiges of pre-Roman, i.e. Etruscan, times—of which Percier's and Fontaine's drawings had fixed a few images—or else clear and sober motifs such as adorn the apartments of Pompeii, which inspired the imperial furniture designers.

The wars, especially the Egyptian campaign, enriched and perceptibly modified the artistic mentality. Obelisks, pyramids, mummies, scimitars, pschents (Egyptian crowns), mamelukes! And then—which brings us back to our theme—wounded soldiers, dying men, surgeons rolling up their sleeves on the battlefield, epidemics ravaging conquerors and conquered alike.

The most famous painting inspired by the plague in the nineteenth century was Baron Gros' "The Plague-stricken of Jaffa" (Louvre), the final version of which was preceded by various preliminary studies. An initial sketch shows Bonaparte lifting with his own hands the body of a man who died of the pestilence. The final canvas shows him nobly raising his arm to touch the sore of a suppliant plague sufferer.

LOUIS BOILLY (1761-1845)

The Vaccination

There is an obvious documentary interest in this infinitely graceful painting. Even the extremely attentive expression of the onlookers informs us of the current newness of this preventive therapy and the importance attached to it.

COLLECTION OF COUNT DU BOURG DE BOZAS

Baron Gérard recalled the Marseilles plague of 1720. An excellent excuse for a painting in Antique style: Monsignor de Belzuno, previously mentioned as having played a somber part during that epidemic by ordering public religious demonstrations which merely helped to spread the disease, is shown distributing food and comforting words among the sick. Others also went back to the same plague of 1720. Guérin (1774-1839) in a painting (now at the Museum of Marseilles), in which Chevalier Rose, the Chief of Police, is directing the interment of the dead; and David in his study (dated the seventh of Germinal of the year VIII) of the head of a plague-stricken man, which he did for the Saint Roch hospital of Marseilles.

Baron Gros and Baron Gérard represent "official painting"; this genre, so encouraged by Napoleon, who was always on the alert about his glory, cannot help but abound in military scenes with medical incidents. Thus, in Gros' *Napoleon on the Battlefield of Eylau,* a surgeon is bandaging a Lithuanian (1808, Louvre); in a painting by Meynier (1809, Versailles) the surgeon is tending the wounded soldiers of the battle of Wagram; and Dalecluze did a watercolor (less grandiloquent than the above-mentioned canvases) showing "the wounded of the Imperial Guard returning to Paris on the 17th of August, 1814, after the battle of Montmirail,"—a procession of cripples either limping along or riding in a wagon (Versailles).

ALFRED JOHANNOT (1800-1837)
The Duke of Orleans visiting the cholera victims at the Hôtel-Dieu in 1832

MUSÉE CARNAVALET, PARIS

PAUL GAVARNI (1804-1866)

"Don't you recognize her? It's Eugénie. The beautiful
blond at Badinguet? The one who doted on custard
and gave herself such airs...? Badinguet had her
mounted for thirty-six francs..."
"Really?"
"Don't be silly! This was a drummer in the National
Guard... Can't you tell it's a man?"

BIBLIOTHÈQUE NATIONALE, PARIS

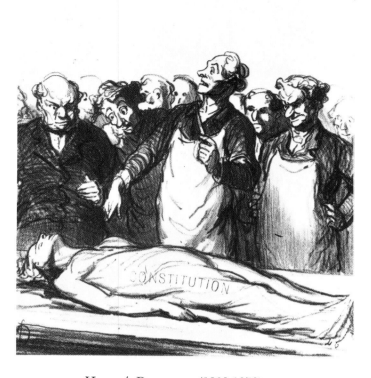

HONORÉ DAUMIER (1808-1879)
The Anatomy Lesson
The political and the medical caricaturist join hands.

BIBLIOTHÈQUE NATIONALE, PARIS

Let us pause at Véron Bellecourt's painting (also at
Versailles), which depicts Napoleon's visit to the infirm-
ary of the Invalides on February 11, 1808, for this work,
albeit extremely official, has a documentary side as well.
Beyond the glowing colors and tawdry ornamentation of
the imperial retinue, we notice that the hospital ward is
as different from a medieval one as from a modern one in
that every bed has a canopy and curtains, thus assuring a
relative isolation for the patient. We know that this im-
provement, which was introduced in the sixteenth century
and documented in the works seen in the preceding chapters (notably those of Bosse) survived as late as the nineteenth century, when, with rare exceptions, hospitals returned to the system of a common, unpartitioned ward,
the possibility of isolation being reserved for the dying
who *in extremis* are surrounded by a screen. Another
painting (anonymous), at the Carnavelet Museum, has
similar documentary value, in that is shows the layout of
hospital wards in that period. We see Dupuytren at the
Hôtel-Dieu, in the presence of Charles X, about to oper-

ate on a cataract. It may be noted in passing, that though
the regime may have changed since Véron Bellecourt did
the preceding painting, the official atmosphere and the
uniforms remained the same. And so did the style. Antiquity was still the ideal.

This fondness for draped grandiloquence and Roman
subject matter persisted for a long time. As for works
which had some connection with medicine, we might
mention David's (1748-1825) *Blind Belisarius Recognized
by a Soldier* (Lille). The Latin inscription on a stone
cube, "Give alms to Belisarius," avoids any risk of the
soldier's not recognizing his former general; and then there
is the *Stratonice, or the Illness of Antiochus* (Montpellier),
which Ingres painted while still under David's influence.
It may have seemed normal for the costumes and the
settings of these paintings to be antique (Ingres depicted
an imaginary Syrian palace); but it appears less natural
in Gibelin's (1839-1813) painting of a blood-letting (Eco-
le de Médicine) for all the actors to be draped in Roman
garments, if one recalls that Broussais had just restored

229

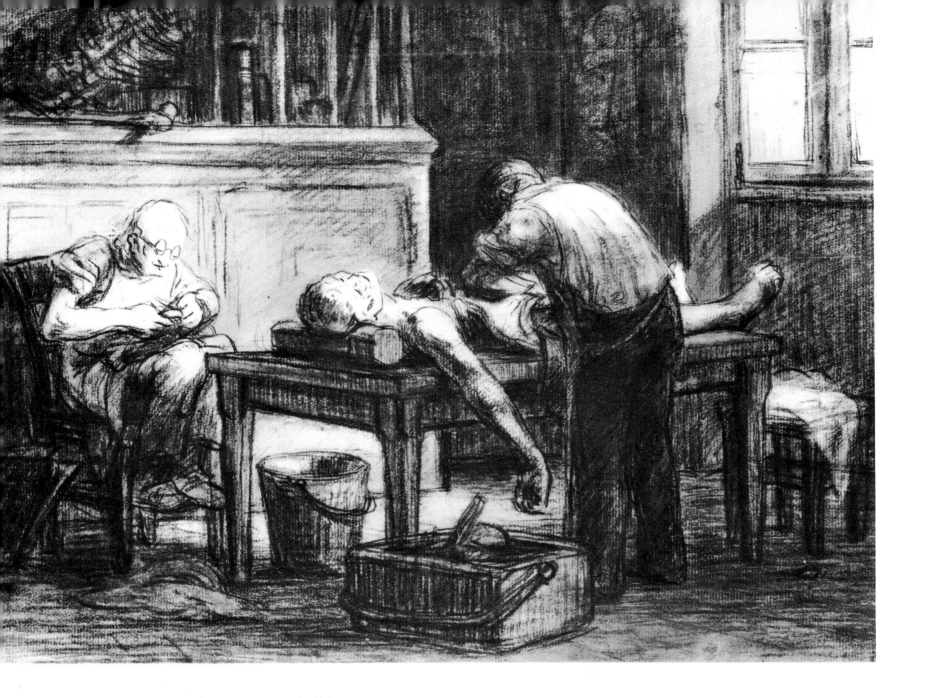

HONORÉ DAUMIER (1808-1879)

The Autopsy

Daumier put his entire sarcastic and emotional verve
into this scene of the "handicraft" of dismemberment.

blood-letting to honor at the very moment the picture
was being painted. The medical world was returning to
the system of Fagon and other "sawbones," even perfect-
ing it, if one may say so, with the application of leeches.
Thus, at Broussais' instigation, millions of those repug-
nant annelids were imported into France during the
early part of the nineteenth century. The Republican
and Imperial wars had mutilated France, and now Brous-
sai was bleeding it dry. The cholera epidemic of 1832
might not have claimed so many victims if the generations
it struck had not been rendered anemic by such methods.

Among the "classic" works more or less inspired by medicine, we can include Baron Gérard's portrait of *La
Pasta* (private collection). The painter didn't neglect the
tiny goiter and the slight exophthalmos afflicting this
bewitching young lady and indicative of Basedovs' Disease.

And last but not least, David d'Angers (1783-1856)
has left us a poignant cast of the death mask of the poet
Hégésippe Moreau showing the stigmata of galloping
consumption and even of starvation. In addition, we
have the plaster cast of his study of pain, the original
bust having unfortunately vanished.

To round out our discussion, we must speak of a certain number of foreign works executed in the same spirit as the French works we have rapidly taken stock of. Throughout the nineteenth century, all European artists took their cue from Paris. Just to mention one of the most important artists, who, like Goya, belonged to two different centuries, we recall William Blake's (1757-1827) watercolor (Museum of Fine Arts, Boston) depicting the Seven Plagues of Egypt. In his poems, Blake frequently evoked the bubonic plague and other calamities, such as venereal disease, especially the syphilis epidemic that afflicted France:

> " 'Let the brothels of Paris be opened
> With many an alluring dance,
> To awake the physicians thro' the city!'
> Said the beautiful Queen of France...."

And in his engravings, he could not neglect depicting these very same scourges. The engraving in question shows the plague: in the background, a brazero has been ignited to purify the air, and in the foreground, a patient on a stretcher is being carried to the temple. Among the innumerable works of Blake, we find many more details pertaining to our subject, including bodies drawn with scrupulous accuracy and then again others that are monstrous, ambiguous, deformed by torture, etc.

Romanticism

The break between Classicism and Romanticism appears less clean if we scan these two periods of sensibility from a comparative distance. In point of fact, there was a gradual transition from one movement to the other, and even after the vociferous literary battle of *Hernani,* painters often claimed to be what they were not or denied being what they were. Baudelaire, for example, was quite piqued when someone told him that his finest poetry had a Racine-like essence; and Xavier Forneret, whom we consider today the most frenzied of romantics, never could understand why Louis Philippe, to whom he regularly dedicated his books, didn't even deign to open them. Delacroix claimed to be classical; and as for Ingres, it was a peculiar error on the part of his contemporary critics to regard him as a romantic and praise him for it. It would be easy to demonstrate that there was a frequent overlapping and even intertwining of styles: a classical subject would be treated in a romantic manner, and an eminently classical technique would be used for some new subject matter. Gradually however, these tendencies came to a halt, because society itself made new choices. People grew more interested in the psyche than ever before, at any rate more than in the Revlutionary period, when human life had become worthless, or during the

Empire, when every new day meant the celebration of some new national victory. After ostentatiousness, parades, and great civic celebrations, the time was ripe for grand love and wild romanticism. The *Sufferings of young Werther* and the flourishes of Rossini brought tears to many lovely eyes. Even shop-keepers sighed while polishing their National Guard equipment. Young men aspired to being honorable bandits, "giaours," and "romeos." Being pale and slender was a must, and it was quite the thing to spit blood into a cambric handkerchief.

Exoticism is a natural inclination of the mind when social circumstances allow for leisurely reflection. Romanticism was favored in this respect in the sense that the Napoleonic wars brought a whole collection of exciting images: on the one hand Spanish; on the other, German and Russian. And then, the world was in motion, borders were no longer fixed, barriers and foreign languages no longer impenetrable. France discovered hitherto unknown literatures and cultures. Philarète Charles translated the German Jean-Paul, and Ossian (who possibly never existed) described Scotland, its spunkies and demons, its nocturnal sabbaths in the ruins of cathedrals. When Byron left Ravenna for Missolonghi, the news spread like wildfire. Berlioz' wild and unhappy passion for Harriet Smithson, the blonde Irish girl, became the personal business of all young France. In the arts, the reaction against Classicism—nourished in turn on Antiquity—took singular and highly contrasting forms. On the one hand, it revived the somber and leafy Gothic; on the other hand, with the help of Delacroix's brush, it endowed the women of Algiers with brilliant colors and languid poses. Anyone seeking an example of the extreme confusion to which the union of these two exoticisms can lead, need only visit Mazagran, near Mostaganem. There, one of the most troubled Romanticists, Pétrus Borel, built the home of his dreams, a Rhenish castle! A castle amid palm trees beneath a metallic-blue sky. Even Victor Hugo was not exempt from such vagaries. Just take a look at his Parisian home at the Place des Vosges, and see how far his eclectic exoticism went.

And to be sure, there were large doses of fiction, quaintness, and fraudulence in Romanticism. But this didn't prevent the movement from coming closest to life both in art and literature and being passionately and violently human. Its strength was in its colors, cries, provocations, its unwillingness to yield to violence. It was the future itself.

Medicine could not fail to interest the Romantic painters. Searching for unusual subject matter that would allow for a melodramatic and tormented style, they turned to hospitals, asylums, and epidemics, too, since cholera struck several times in the course of the nineteenth century, decimating Paris, France, and Europe.

Using the theme of Queen Marie-Amélie's visit to the out-patient department of the Bourse, on August 23, 1830, Gosse (1787-1878) was able to paint a "beautiful disarray" of human bodies. In this respect, the primary sketch (Carnavalet), which doesn't show the queen, is more significant than the final version (Versailles), which, due to Marie-Amélie's presence has a more official character. Tony Johannot (1800-1837) showed *The Duke of Orleans visiting the cholera victims* on a canvas now hanging in the Carnavalet. (The cholera epidemic of 1832 claimed the lives of 18,400 Parisians between March and October.)

Though we may not find any connection between Géricault's (1791-1824) *Raft of the Medusa* and the science of medicine, despite the presence of dying men and corpses among the survivors of the wreck, this painter who only looked for subject matter in real life, did leave us true clinical portraits such as *The Mad Child-Snatcher* (Springfield Museum of Fine Arts) and *The Madwoman* (Louvre), the models for which he found in hospitals, and which appealed to both his sense of pity and of the unusual.

Delacroix, greatly influenced by his senior Géricault, was also interested in madness. His *Tasso in the Madhouse* (private collection) may not aim at direct observation or at Géricault's modernism, but nevertheless, in the features of the two madmen peering aggressively at the poet, we can see the exact stigmas of their obsessional derangement. And finally, Delacroix has left us a drawing *The Consultation* (Bibliothèque Nationale, Cabinet des Estampes) that is very nearly a caricature, while their patient is breathing his last, four doctors sitting in a circle are talking endlessly, unaware that Death has joined them.

The themes that artists owe to medicine are not numberless. We should therefore not be astonished that the Romantic painters always dealt with the same ones, returning, albeit with their own techniques, to the more or less conventional subject matter that had inspired their forerunners in the eighteenth century. In a painting by Constant Desbordes exhibited at the Salon in 1822, Doctor Alibert is vaccinating a child whom the artist's niece, Marcelline Desbordes-Valmore, holds in her arms (Museum of Douai). Boilly (1761-1845) did a less sentimental treatment of the same subject. We see the same figures as on Greuze's canvas: the nice old doctor, the well-behaved child on its mother's lap, the numerous spectators touched by the sight. Géricault used the theme of a fainting-spell

in a work exhibited at the Musée Bonnat (Bayonne), and Deveria (1800-1857) went back to the "beautiful patient" in an engraving entitled *Anemia,* a charming family picture. And finally, Hersant, in his lithograph *The Remedy* (1819), brought back the enema, on which the painters of the seventeenth and eighteenth century had harped, and so we come to the Romantic caricatures inspired by medicine.

Epilly did many caricatures of doctors and patients. In *The Sick Woman* (Cabinet des Estampes), the comic effect is in the physician's goggles and the cotton nightcap of the patient who is sticking out her tongue. In *Magnetism,* the magnetisor's efforts and the obstinate way his client, an old lady, shuts her eyes and turns her head make for comic relief. In drawings engraved by Constans, Boilly laughingly showed us the "first tooth"—that of a small child on his mother's lap—and the "last tooth"—which an old woman is showing to her daughter and her grandchildren.

Realism

At the beginning of this chapter we sketched the rapid development of medicine in the nineteenth century. This rise was particularly swift as of the middle of the century, and it might be useful to recall some of the stages. After 1846, the American chemist Jackson discovered the anesthetic properties of sulphuric ether, and Simpson discovered those of chloroform. Later on, the Hungarian Semmelweiss hit upon the idea of antisepsis, and the Englishman Joseph Lister thought up the antiseptic surgical method which led quite naturally to aseptic surgery. Pasteur's work was followed by that of Claude Bernard who published his *Introduction à l'étude de la médicine expérimentale* in 1865. Marey perfected recording devices for laboratory studies and conceived the idea of the cinematograph; the German Roentgen, utilizing the cathodic rays of Crooke's tube proved that x-rays can pass through opaque bodies; this led to the birth of radioscopy. In short, by the end of the nineteenth century, medicine and surgery had made such great progress that we may speak of a new age.

What course did art follow during this time? In 1855, Courbet (1819-1877), who was refused admission to the Salon, set up a booth to exhibit his works and hung out a sign in front: "Realism." But in point of fact, realism began before 1855. In almost every part of Europe, a realistic current, originating in earlier centuries, continued through the Classical and Romantic period. In the final phase of Romanticism, this current revived simultaneously with a classical strain of which Corot's work was not the least convincing example. Courbet systematically painted

233

CONSTANTIN GUYS (1803-1892)
The Hospital of Pera

"stone-breakers," thus putting an end to the exoticism of his predecessors, but this representative of "socialist realism" before the fact was not the only artist interested in social themes. Almost everywhere, and long before Millet painted his gleaners and his *Man with the Hoe* (a work in grand style prefiguring Van Gogh), artists had been drawing and engraving countless rural scenes, half realistic and half sentimental, which were a great success with the middle class who found other people's misery poignant.

Realism, of which Courbet and Millet were certainly the greatest masters, was not as triumphant as Romanticism. Delacroix had been awarded the Legion of Honor. But Courbet had to pay for his insolence and his political opinions as well. The official salons were swamped with virtuous works that were pompous, enormous, and favored by the establishment. A new Academic style was emerging. Bonnat, Bouguereau, Carolus-Duran, etc., were the artists who found buyers, until new painters named Manet, Cézanne, Renoir, Degas, Monet, at first considered madmen or practical jokers, succeeded by the end of the nineteenth century in compelling recognition. Derisively labelled "impressionists," they accepted the challenge. After Classicism, Romanticism, Realism, and Naturalism, a new "ism" was born.

The paintings honored by admission to the Salon quite frequently depicted medical scenes. Some are "anatomy lessons," related to those of the seventeenth century, and they were intended as decorations for amphitheaters and other medical rooms—e.g. Feyen Perrin's (1826-1888) painting (Tours) which shows Professor Velpeau surrounded by his students and about to demonstrate his lesson on a corpse. Among those huge works, which are both documents and portraits, we must mention Lhermitte's painting which adorns the Sorbonne (Claude Bernard carrying out a physiological experiment before other scientists) and Gervex's canvases (Musée de Versailles) entitled *Doctor Pean demonstrating the pinching of blood-vessels.* The surgeon, dressed in street-clothes, and clutching his tweezers is about to do a demonstration on the dead body of a young woman, who is bare from the waist up. In the same spirit is Chartran's late Sorbonne fresco, Edelfelf's portrait of Pasteur, showing the scientist in his laboratory, and Robert Fleury's (1719-1890) composition, in which Pinel, head physician of the La Salpétrière asylum, is seen among the inmates. This work is interesting in that it brings to mind how, with Pinel, the attitude toward mental disease had changed. There was actually more than symbolic intent behind the depiction of Pinel unchaining the insane (one of whom kisses his hand).

With the works we have just enumerated, we have not as yet left "official" painting, a genre to which foreign schools did not fail to bring their offerings, especially the Americans, their most illustrious representative being John Singer Sargent. Thus, in one of his canvases, we can see portraits of four members of the first medical faculty of Johns Hopkins: Howard Attwood Kelly, William Henry Welch, William Osler, who lent his name to a disease, and William Steward Halsted, who lent his to a surgical technique. And it was in the United States that Thomas Eakins produced *The Gross Clinic,* a painting renowned in the medical world.

Both in France and abroad, many works in the second half of the nineteenth century were inspired in a less solemn way by medicine, sometimes in an intimist fashion, sometimes with more or less emphatically realistic intentions. Constantin Guys did an appealing drawing of the Sisters of Charity. Thomas Roberts (1820-1901) showed a sick adolescent lying in his bed before an open window, while his mother looks at him tenderly. And it was quite natural for the state to buy Jean Geoffry's work *Visiting*

ALBERT EDELFELT (1854-1905)

Pasteur in his laboratory in 1885

MUSEUM OF VERSAILLES

JEAN GEOFFROY (1853-1924)

Visiting Day in the Hospital

There is a social background to this almost photographically realistic painting. "Sickness is the luxury of the poor," said Stefan Zweig.

TOWN HALL OF VICHY

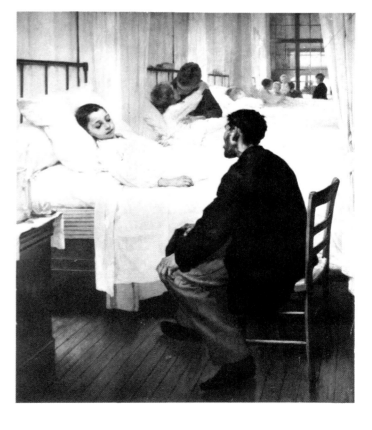

235

THOMAS EAKINS (1844-1916)

The Gross Clinic

It was Dr. Samuel D. Gross, professor of surgery at Jefferson Medical College, Philadelphia, who gave Thomas Eakins the idea of painting the Gross Clinic. This work dates from the time the young artist was actually studying anatomy at that very college and under the immortal professor.

"The Gross Clinic" was bought by the Alumni Association of Jefferson Medical College and presented as a gift to the faculty. Today, this painting is the most precious emblem of that institution. It cost 200 dollars around 1880, and today, although the faculty has been offered as much as 200,000 dollars, it refuses to sell the work.

COLLECTION OF THE JEFFERSON MEDICAL COLLEGE,
PHILADELPHIA, U.S.A.

Hours in the Hospital, which was really an excellent advertisement for the public authorities: impeccable beds, brightly glistening floors, and so forth.

A special chapter would be needed for popular engravings, which became more and more numerous as the techniques of reproduction improved and which were also inspired by medical subjects. We have *The Empress Eugénie's Visit to the cholera patients* (Bouvet collection); *Françoise the Canteen-Keeper of the 88th* (Bibliothèque Nationale), whom we see dressing a soldier's wounds in the heart of battle; and *Cornil's Experiments on the Consumptives in the Laënnec Hospital,* an engraving as demonstrative as one could wish, although we do wonder what sort of experiments these are.

Caricature

The number of medical caricatures increased greatly in the second half of the nineteenth century, the French and English competing with one another, and the latter coming out on top. Yet the ferocity of British humor had diminished after Hogarth, for medicine had made enormous progress, and physicians were no longer the arrogant and ignorant beings of earlier times. Aware of this, the artists drew in their claws slightly, though occasionally sharpening them on the patients. But enemas remained a source of inspiration for the humorists until the end of the nineteenth century, and Honoré Daumier (1808-1879) brandished Molière's rod again to castigate doctors, who however had no connection with the oldtime "sawbones."

Daumier was assuredly the greatest caricaturist of the second half of the century, and, in addition, a very great painter (this cannot be overemphasized) who might be likened to Goya not only for the enthusiasm of his satirical force, but also for his lyric touch and his dramatic use of light. The captions of his drawings (Bibliothèque Nationale) are all worth quoting, for instance the dialogue accompanying his *Doctor and Nurse*:

"How's the patient?"—"Unfortunately he died at six a.m."—"Aha! So he didn't take my potion?"—"Oh, but he did, Doctor."—"He must have taken too much."—"Oh no, Doctor."—"Well, then he didn't take enough."

And this simple phrase taken from life: "Doctor, I think I've got T.B.," is the caption for the picture of a monstrously obese man having his pulse taken by a worried-looking physician. But at times no caption is necessary, and Daumier is content with a simple title: e.g. *Paris has a cold,* which shows that medicine has no better remedy for a common cold than a handkerchief; or *The Autopsy* (private collection), in which we see the operation being performed on some sort of table in a darkened room with the instruments strewn about; or *The Anatomy Lesson,* in which the professor is endowed with laughable pomposity. Daumier even zestfully takes up the "purge, bleed, and give him an enema," convincing us that all these good old systems had not yet been abandoned.

Gavarni (1804-1866) is fond of captions, too, such as the one on a drawing from *Charivari* which applies to our theme. We see a pregnant girl and her mother sitting beneath the portrait of the child's father.

"Really, my child, it's unwise of you in your condition to let an ugly face like that hang under your very eyes all day long."—"What can happen?"—"My Caroline's latest baby will simply resemble that Monsieur Coquardeau, that's all! Not a very pleasant prospect for a mother!"

The English school deserves a longer study. It was

JOHN S. SARGENT (1856-1925)

The members of the first medical faculty of Johns Hopkins, Baltimore, Maryland, founded some sixty years ago.
(From left to right: Sir William Osler, Howard Attwood Kelly, William Stewart Halsted, and William Henry Welch.)

JOHNS HOPKINS UNIVERSITY, BALTIMORE, MARYLAND

VINCENT VAN GOGH (1853-1890)
The Vestibule of the Hospital of Saint-Rémy

patient who is visibly on the verge of death: "Dear sir, this morning you seem to me the very image of good health. I do not doubt that at my next visit, I shall find you relieved of all earthly ailments." (Bibliothèque Nationale). Was England afflicted with overweight or was Rowlandson merely possessed by it? In an engraving now at the Bibliothèque Nationale, another obese man is testing the virtues of oil of Macassar. Will this oil, supposedly capable of restoring hair, help his bald pate? It has certainly had a peculiar effect on the young woman before a mirror, staring in horror at her own shaggy hair. And equally corpulent is the customer whom a tailor is unsuccessfully trying to help into breeches that are too tight for him. Gillray, too, dreaded fat people. He ridiculed them in two engravings entitled *The Emetic* and *The Purge,* giving free rein to his ferocious irony. And then again there is the engraving entitled *Consumption, Gout, and Colic cured by Punch,* which condemns those who are underweight and is probably the source of the legend abroad today that whiskey is excellent for heart patients.

Illustrated Medical Books

In the nineteenth century, the illustration of medical books evolved along the same lines as art in general—twenty years of grandiloquent and sculptural compositions in the style of David, twenty years of Romantic sighing and weeping, and thirty years of Realism—until the invention of photography put an end to artistic illustrations as such.

Anatomy was the subject of plates engraved by Antommarchi after drawings by Mascagni (Paris, 1823-1826) and there are also anatomical plates in the works of Jules Cloquet (Paris, 1821-1831) and Jean-Baptiste Marc Bourgery (Paris, 1831-1854), the last edition of which was done with the help of Claude Bernard. The books on surgery were also illustrated with engravings, some of them rather noteworthy. The most interesting works are those by Assalini (Naples, 1819), Larrey (Paris, 1812-1817), Charles Bell (London, 1821), Dupuytren (Paris, 1836), and Malgaigne (Paris, 1847).

dominated by three great men: George Cruikshank (1792-1878); Rowlandson (1756-1827), whom we discussed in the preceding chapter, because like Goya he lived and worked in two centuries; and finally, Gillray (1757-1815), who similarly belonged to both epochs. Cruikshank produced countless satirical drawings on medical or para-medical subjects. A beef carcass suggests to a man peering at it a comparison with his own anatomy; a skinny giant is accompanied by an obese lady dwarf; under the title of *Indigestion,* an unhappy fat man is reaching into his clothes to clutch at his stomach while a circle of gnomes is torturing him (Yale Medical Library, Collection of Doctor Fry). Rowlandson, in a color engraving entitled *The Doctor's Visit,* shows an obese physician and a

VINCENT VAN GOGH (1853-1890)

Self-portrait with one ear cut off

The "lightning-rod" (against insanity) that Van Gogh claimed to see in his art was out of commission, and the painter mutilated himself during a fit of madness. This portrait remained as a depiction of an obsession: "There's something inside of me; what is it?"

COURTAULD INSTITUTE, LONDON

238

In the new field of psychology, we must make special mention of Esquirol's book *Des maladies mentales considérées sous les rapports médical, hygiénique et médico-legal* (Paris, 1838), which Ambroise Tardieu illustrated with twenty-seven excellent copper engravings. One of them depicts Théroigne de Méricourt, the infamous bloody amazon of the Revolution, whom Baudelaire portrayed in *Sisma*:

"Have you see Théroigne, the lover of carnage,
Urging an unshod people to the onslaught,
With cheeks and eyes aflame, playing her role
And clutching her saber as she climbs the royal
stairways?"

In the engraving, Théroigne, who died in 1817 in La Salpetrière insane asylum, is shown as a hapless lunatic. Another engraving recalls the atrocious custom that obtained before Pinet and especially in England, of keeping the mentally ill in chains. Shackled at the neck, the waist, and the feet, the poor unfortunate couldn't even lie down at full length. Physicians cite the case of a former naval officer who spent nine years in this fashion.

VINCENT VAN GOGH (1853-1890)
Portrait of Doctor Gachet, 1890
The swirls and spirals of Van Gogh—whether in a portrait or a landscape—are an expression of his torment.

JEU DE PAUME, PARIS

Charcoal portrait of Vincent Van Gogh on his death bed, July 29, 1890, in Auvers-sur-Oise. Drawn by Doctor Gachet.

COLLECTION OF PAUL GACHET

Daumier—whose work in caricature we have reviewed briefly—did the illustrations for Dr. François Fabre's *Nemesis médicale* (Paris, 1840), a collection of satirical writings about medical and para-medical topics. One of the most striking pictures—showing cholera—is at the same time the most sinister one. We see a man stricken suddenly with the disease and dropping to the ground, a woman fleeing, a raven winging by, and a dog with a desolate expression.

Medicine and the new schools

Impressionism, Neo-impressionism, Divisionism. The end of the nineteenth century teemed with new doctrines. Some were mutually antagonistic, but all of them had nevertheless one point in common: the refusal to submit to the subject. Thus Manet reconstructed what he saw, what "impressed" him, not by modeling light and shadow, but by juxtaposing planes which do not necessarily owe their plasticity to Euclidian perspective; Toulouse-Lautrec exaggerated the features of *La Goulue,* the posture of *Double-Jointed Valentin,* the bodies of the inhabitants of brothels, for the sake of significance and truth; Odilon Redon painted chariots in a dreamlike sky; for all these artists, the real subject of painting is painting itself, and the pretext for a picture hardly counts, or at any rate counts less than the artist's conception of the reality he is treating. At times, it is difficult to establish a valid connection between reality and the representation thereof. Monet's famous *Nympheas* are not more significant in this respect than Cézanne's many variations on *Mont Sainte-Victoire* or the admirable Renoirs which, starting with plump, heavily bedecked women become lyric apologies for the flesh.

It would not be surprising for such an art to have relatively few points of contact with medicine. Yet they do exist and on occasion in highly important works. One of the foremost examples is Degas' (1834-1917) *Absinthe* (Jeu de Paume), which depicts an alcoholic couple sitting in a tavern before two glasses of their favorite poison. Though the man, smoking a pipe, may seem alert, the woman's face has all the symptoms of her alcoholic decay. We could almost think it a documentary done from life if we didn't known that two actors, Ellen Andrée and Marcellin Desboutin, "composed," and posed for, the two characters in Degas' painting.

Cézanne (1839-1906), of whom we know that at first he had no other aim than to imitate the academic work of the established painters, actually went so far as to paint an *Autopsy.* Yet in spite of himself, he produced a genuine "Cézanne" and not a mere "remake" of a Feyen Perrin. In this composition, the corpse is half sitting

HENRI DE TOULOUSE-LAUTREC (1864-1901)
Tracheotomy operation by Dr. Péan in 1891
STERLING AND FRANCINE CLARK INSTITUTE OF ART,
WILLIAMSTOWN, MASSACHUSETTS

against a block of wood; on his left thigh, a practitioner is leaning with his shirt-sleeves rolled up, but we see neither an incision nor an instrument; an assistant, in profile, is watching the scene.

Van Gogh (1853-1890), whose genius now and again verges on neuropathy, touched upon medicine in a number of works, notably those he painted in the asylum and in his self-portrait with one ear cut off. Furthermore, the symptoms of monomania appear in all the portraits he did of himself.

Toulouse-Lautrec (1864-1901) had a personal connection with medicine, since he himself was a typical case of dwarfism, although his family claimed that the stunted growth of his body and his limbs was due to a childhood accident. Thus his by no means flattering self-portrait is a medical document. The dreadful skinniness of *Double-Jointed Valentin* and of the dancing-girls and prostitutes

901

HENRI DE TOULOUSE-LAUTREC (1864-1901)

An examination at the Medical Faculty of the University of Paris

Gabriel Tapié, who was Toulouse-Lautrec's first cousin, dedicated his dissertation (which he defended in 1899) to the memory of Péan. The head of the examining commitee was Professor Tillaux; the others, Professors Landouzy, Wurtz, and Legueu.

MUSEUM OF ALBI

Toulouse-Lautrec liked to depict also have documentary value, though this may not have been the artist's intention. It may have been however in *The Tracheotomy* (1819), which shows Doctor Pean, with a towel around his neck apparently inserting an instrument into the mouth of a patient—which leads us to believe that the painter didn't know the true place of incision. Another painting which depicts Dr. Pean operating, but shows him from the back and before an audience, should be cited as a further example of Toulouse-Lautrec's contribution to medical iconography. And we shouldn't forget the lithograph he composed to illustrate a satirical monologue in the *Chat*

Noir: "Carnot taken ill"—sick of the government—is depicted wearing a cotton nightcap and lying down, between a doctor feeling his pulse and a nun bringing him a bowl of food.

Did the nineteenth century, so important in the field of medicine and so exceptionally rich in the field of art, toll the knell for any connection between the two? The artist did shrink from being the faithful chronicler of society (doesn't the Realism of those times seem classical today, i.e. in a certain measure unrealistic?) and of the medical and surgical exploits that became more and more a part of daily life. Still, the positive answers to these questions would be as arbitrary as a negative one based on the relatively large number of works inspired by the field of medicine.

The truth of the matter is that the relationship did not come to an end—how could it?—but it was going to change, and indeed had already changed its character. We will deal with the problem at greater length in our chapter on the twentieth century. The symbolic modes of expression toward which the European arts are tending more and more, may, in the final analysis, be closer to medicine than the strictly figurative expression of past ages. This is particularly true since modern times have furnished us with a myriad of unconscious psychopathological documents which would not have been expressed so clearly had not the artistic psyche (always ahead of the general psyche) come into contact with new ontological notions and concepts stemming from the works of biologists, physicists, and doctors of the mind and body.

THE TWENTIETH CENTURY

If the depth and significance of the relationship between art and medicine were to be judged merely on the basis of the number of works reproducing, more or less directly, such medical "facts" as consultations, operations, anatomy lessons, etc., we could say that in the twentieth century, where such works are quite rare, the connection is almost non-existent.

This is quite astonishing when we stop to consider that in our century medicine has made immense progress in all areas, and due to the democratizing of its application

as well as the rise in cultural level has become one of the determining factors in general awareness and in everyday life.

It is even more astonishing when we recall that both the public's growing curiosity for everything concerning medicine and the spectacular side of the new techniques have been greatly exploited by new media. Thus a film about a cardiac operation nowadays is watched by millions of absorbed TV viewers who, incidentally, are moved as much by an avid curiosity for unusual things as by a desire for knowledge.

If what so many people repeatedly claim is true, to wit that ours is a civilization of the image, why is it that contemporary artists hardly ever give us *those* images.

We could ask the same question about the dearth of landscapes and of busts of great men, of street scenes and of battle scenes in today's art, and we could give the obvious and apparently logical answer that ever since the invention of photography and moving pictures the artist

CHAÏM SOUTINE (1894-1943)

The Village Idiot

The spontaneity of the great hallucinated painter Soutine is in perfect accord with the subject matter. This lyric caricature, with its twistings, its hastiness, its awkwardness, expresses the mixture of bestiality, candor, and cunning making up this country lunatic, who was probably drawn from life.

CALVET COLLECTION, FRANCE

245

can no longer claim to depict reality and may even consider himself absolved from doing so. Yet this would be actually an unfair reply, since the artistic process has never consisted in depicting reality, but rather in identifying with it, transfiguring it, mastering or subjugating it, and finally, during the present phase, passing beyond the mirror of reality to discover another, a different reality, to which the atomic scientist Oppenheimer claims only mystics and scientists can have access, the former " by the suppression of the senses and introspection," the latter "with mathematics and inductive reasoning."

The study of the relationship between art and medicine in the twentieth century reveals a separate evolution in each of these fields; and we would like to show that both evolutions are moving in the same direction, that in the last analysis, the connections between art and medicine are closer, more complex, and more decisive than ever before.

We have called the progress of surgery spectacular; and no one could deny it. But the progress of psychoanalysis the younger science is far less spectacular although the most artistic of them all, if we remember that it makes use of "psycho-drama," pencils, and tubes of paint. But can we say that our knowledge of man has grown at a dizzying speed? No operation of the heart or the brain will ever permit us to wander through the labyrinth of dark emotions, secret thoughts, subconscious desires, and murky anxieties, though these may be the "true truth" of man. Psychoanalysis can. Can art? Yes, if art penetrates into the depths of those "masses of the subconscious," (about which a poet, Pierre Jean Jouve, using Freudian terminology, has said that they are only "dimly lit on the surface by sunshine,") and if art takes as much care to describe them as Greuze did twisting a corkscrew-like stocking on an ankle or Troyen curling a fleece.

But how can an artist paint something that has no substance? How—to quote Ibsen's formula with some slight modification—can he "liberate the demons dwelling in the secret cells of the mind?" First of all, he must discard the age-old notion of his dependence on a reality that must be reduced to palpable forms. A musical inflection can be inscribed in wax, yet it is neither form nor matter. But the artist must go even further: he must make himself a medium in order to see himself from the inside. When Van Gogh desperately strove to scrutinize his own gaze in his many self-portraits, wasn't he merely trying to pass into his own self? "There's something inside me, what is it?" he sighed in one of his letters. Several years later, Freud answered that this was "the arena of the struggle between eros and the death instinct." A pity that Van Gogh didn't live long enough to hear this. But

the twentieth century artist *has* heard and understood it. And has realized at the same time that Van Gogh was a sacrificial offering rather than a suicide. This merely strengthens the modern artist's desire to peer into, reveal, make concrete, a subconscious which is not strictly his alone, because at a given point in history the entire species is obviously affected by mythologies, aspirations, and threats which are shared by him, too, but a part of which is personal to him and enables him to practice in and on himself, in full knowledge of the cause, an exorcism whose success will be valuable as an exemplary demonstration.

For after all that is what it amounts to: an exorcism. André Malraux was perfectly right when he said that "the artistic creation is not the result of a yielding to the subconscious, but of a natural disposition to overcome it." An enterprise such as *L'Immaculée Conception,* led by André Breton and Paul Eluard in the name of pictorial and literary surrealism did not contradict this; it proposed to demonstrate "that the mind is capable of reproducing in bold outlines the most paradoxical and eccentric verbal manifestations, that the mind is able to master at will the main delirious ideas without any lasting disturbance and without compromising its balance in any way." We must remember, however, that the risks incurred are greater than this quotation admits (the madness and suicide that wreaked such havoc among the surrealists would be sufficient proof); and with the second reservation that the ability of the human subconscious to see ahead, with the help of art as well as medicine, approaches very closely to what Eluard and Breton call "the concept of simulation in mental medicine," the subconscious and madness not being meant to be confused.

It would never occur to anyone to claim that prior to our century art was uninterested in what goes on in the murky depths of man. From Greek tragedy, which Nietzsche examined so brilliantly from this point of view in his *Birth of Tragedy* (the least decisive passages are not those envisaging the "curative power" of art) to Racine's *Phèdre*—a Medusa in full sexual convulsion; from Shakespeare's *Tempest* ("we are such stuff as dreams are made on") to Nerval's *Chimères* (supposedly written "in a state of supernatural reverie" by Dr. Blanche's patient), literature has often cast its nets into these depths. And so have painting and sculpture. The very wings of the Niké, the *Victory of Samothrace,* owe something (according to Malraux) to the sphinxes and harpies born of obsessions as old as mankind; the swarming hells sketched or painted by Bosch and Brueghel were expressions of fears hovering on the surface of the collective psyche; the *Mona Lisa* with her ambiguous smile and sex hints volumes about Da Vinci's psychopathology. But these attempts at fathoming

the unfathomable were for the most part accidental and dangerous, and never moved by the systematic will that animates present-day art to delve into Hadean and marvelous gulfs across which human reason, unaware of their contents, thought it could navigate blindly.

"The Ancient world," writes Marcel Réja in *The Art of the Insane,* "never even suspected the existence of mental diseases and attributed psychological disorders, like genius, to divine intervention." And André Malraux writes: "...these arts of madmen, children, primitives are barbarous and savage, the works seem uncontrolled and subject to individual instinct, yet we know that they give expression to the most profound and mysterious regions of man." Rounding off these two quotations with the following phrase from a letter of Van Gogh's: "...in my work, I risk my life, and my reason is half disintegrated," we can see how closely linked the most ambitious new medicine is to a whole area of contemporary art, which, in Jean

EDOUARD VUILLARD (1868-1940)

Professor Gosset Operating

The painter proves his ability to observe details. His painting faithfully reproduces an operating room at the turn of the century. The anesthetist holds the ether-mask on the patient's face; the patient is covered up by the "operating fields." Even if we didn't know what progress has been made since then, this work of Vuillard's would suffice to show that at the time it was painted, surgery had already reached the age of reason. Hence, the documentary value of this art is great.

PROPERTY OF THE GOSSET FAMILY

RAOUL DUFY (1877-1953)

The Operation

The five hooded figures show life only in their eyes.
This is symbolic of the idea that art, like medicine,
pierces beyond appearances.

MUSÉE MUNICIPAL D'ART MODERNE, PARIS

248

Cocteau's very wide use of the term, liberates the "schizo-phrenic" who has always lurked in the darkness of the best-balanced artist, and who now closely copies the infinitely reasonable New Guinea native, whose reasons, aren't ours, or the child, who carries on a lyric and magical monologue, or the lunatic, who creates a dialogue for which he supplies both questions and answers. Or else the artist bombards the canvas with globs of paint, with or without the gesticulation that strives to be aggressiveness, separation, and release.

EDVARD MUNCH (1863-1944)

Next to his powers of observation, the Norwegian Edvard Munch shows here, as in all his works, a tormented lyricism and a love of the fantastic.

We have spoken of a struggle against appearances. And now we must broach the topic again. This process may have been precipitated in the twentieth century—more precisely from the moment these appearances proved to be particularly pernicious and threatening on an economic, social, political, and philosophical level, so that Vlaminck's challenge "Cubism is war!" makes more sense. But the process itself began long ago. Diderot wrote: "I once knew a young man of excellent taste, who before starting a new painting, knelt down and said: 'O God, deliver me from the model.'" Was this young man Greuze, in whom Diderot saw the great painter of his time? Perhaps. One need merely take a look at his sketch for *Aegina and Zeus,* the true "model" of which is the terrifying tentacled blaze surrounding the models, who are mythological at this juncture and not models per se. And then, is the suppression of the model necessary and sufficient? Is it possible, with or without the model, to go beyond appearances? "Modern art," writes André Malraux, "is the combining of forms by means of an interior scheme which may or may not represent figures or objects, but of which figures or objects are merely an expression." Thus, Van Gogh, with a simple *Chair* (Tate Gallery) was able to express all the anguish of a man to the point of his absence from the world. And like Van Gogh, Soutine worked on the motif, and on the model; when he wanted to paint trees he went off to the country, and when he wanted to paint a *Flayed Ox* (private collection), he had one hung from his studio ceiling; it soon gave off an abominable stench, but didn't prevent this ailing, anxious, maniacal Jew from almost turning his trees into instruments of torture and his beef into a kind of tragedy in which we can recognize both his obsessions and personal suffering, the torments of his people, and the prophecy of the new collective martyrdom awaiting them.

The penetration of appearances, or rather their submission to an internal vision whose envelope or attitude they form, stems from a desire to annex the world, a desire which is part of the story of human history. Man, delivered from his gods, or at least imagining it, wants to test to the very limit, the powers he has discovered for himself and the rights he has arrogated. Deciphering his own appearances and knowing his hidden motives and incentives are not the least urgent of his tasks. And so, for the artist and the scientist and the poet and the physician, the actions taken are approximately the same and

249

JULES (1884-1944)

The Business Agent

A manual laborer with no educational background,
Jules began drawing at the age of forty-three. "His
works burst forth like a volcanic eruption and died out
for no apparent reason."
An extract from "Little Masters of Madness" by Jean
Cocteau, G. Schmidt, H. Steck, and A. Bader.

CLAIREFONTAINE, LAUSANNE, 1961

occur almost simultaneously. It was in 1900 that Freud
published *The Science of Dreams,* in which he showed
that our world of dreams is at once the storehouse of our
frustrations and suppressions and the titanic force behind
our future actions. (American neurophysiologists have
since taught us that one can cause a person to die by
merely preventing him from dreaming). Five years earlier,
the Poet Alfred Jarry had remarked in his review *L'Yma-
gier* that if you stared at Dürer's *Martyrdom of Saint Cath-*

erine in a certain way, the entire image, i.e. the apparent
subject of the engraving, revealed the face of a decapitated
woman, which simultaneously contained the kneeling
saint, the headsman, and a part of the landscape. As far
as we know, this observation was a cornerstone of the
"paranoically critical" method perfected and employed by
Max Ernst and Salvador Dali, two painters who were extremely well-versed in psychoanalysis. Freud himself made
a magnificent contribution: in Leonardo Da Vinci's *Saint
Anne,* he discovered a vulture, discernable only if one
looks at the painting from a certain angle, or rather in a
certain way so as to adjust the field of vision if not the
view itself. The painter seems to have unconsciously
enclosed the vulture in external saintliness as a Prome-
thean childhood memory. Marcel Réja's *The Art of the
Insane,* which I have quoted above, came out in 1905. In
1908, Picasso painted *Les Demoiselles d'Avignon,* distorting in all sense and with a provocative cruelty, the "appearance" of a female body. In 1910, one could read, on the
walls of Montmartre, the scrawlings of conservative painters: "Matisse will drive you insane... Matisse is more
dangerous than absinth." And in the same year, in
Munich, Kandinsky, who had previously done figurative
work, noticed that one of his paintings, when viewed in
moonlight showed something completely different, and so
he made up his mind to become an abstract artist ("objects harm my painting"). And finally, Einstein formulated his famous law of relativity, which was not the lightest
blow dealt at the "appearances" that Western civilization
had been accustomed to for such a long time, whereas in
the Far East they had always been accustomed to "evil"
(metaphysically speaking).

Such relationships have but one end: to show that at
the beginning of our century, art, medicine, and science in
general deliberately cooperated on nothing less than a new
questioning of man, or rather his position in a mental
and physical universe no longer corresponding to the con-
venient "working hypothesis" to which it had been reduced up till then. This questioning, as we have said, had
already begun, notably in art, but in the manner of an
immature insurrection not quite certain of its aims.

CHARLES DUFRESNE (1876-1938)

Medicine

The "humanized" cubism of Dufresne makes a classical
projection of the pharmacopoeia of medicine and
surgery.

MUSÉE DE L'ANNONCIADE, SAINT-TROPEZ

At the end of the nineteenth century, the Impressionists
may have ridden rough-shod over Euclidian perspective—
for Manet, Sisley, Pissarro, a flat surface was truer than
relief, a luminous spot more suggestive than a contour;
for Monet, the canvas was a blurry mosaic of all the elements of which deserve the same color treatment—yet they
never dreamt of discarding appearances; subjecting them
to the civilization of their eyes sufficed. Cézanne, in his
old age, went further. He abstracted from these appearances primal geometric forms—cones, cubes, cylinders—
which are pure human conventions. At approximately the
same time, Van Gogh—whose painting seemed "insane"
to Cézanne—used appearances as ideograms and, expressing himself only in swirls and vortices, had achieved, as
Pierre Cabanne wrote in *La Nuit est un soleil,* a prodigious burst of colors in which he suggested "the age-old
smashing of elements, the dreadful elemental pressure."
And another contemporary, Gauguin, the eternal child
crushed by our Western appearances, went off to Tahiti,
hunting for different appearances which he conceived of
as magic, miraculous, simple, and in which he thought he
might materialize his dreams.

Thus, in the late nineteenth century, appearances may
have been viewed and employed differently, attacked with
more or less daring or naiveté, but they were not discarded
until the twentieth century. A passage by Guillaume
Apollinaire, discovered in 1959 by Pierre Francastel, sheds
light on this transcendence:

"Cubism... was above all a kind of Impressionism of
forms such as Cézanne had discerned toward the close of
his life. By the end of 1907, Cubism was no longer an
exaggeration of Fauvism, whose violent coloring was an
exasperated impressionism. The new meditations of Picasso, Derain, and another young painter, Braque, culmi-
nated in downright Cubism, which was above all the art
of painting new cohesive wholes with elements drawn not
so much from visual as from conceptual reality."

Conceptual reality. Throughout our investigations, we
must bear this formula in mind, in terms of the relationship between art and medicine, and of the artistic production of our time. We have already spoken of the
general meaning of the development of this production.
We must add that this development did not progress without jolts and throwbacks. Thus, at about the same time
that Degas, already halfblind, was doing pastel drawings
of luminous but hazy landscapes which could pass for
clouds, moirés, or the materialization of inner phantasms,
Braque and Picasso were replacing our three-dimensional
universe with a two-dimensional "plastic" one; Léger
twisted men and women into right angles with tube-like
limbs; Duchamp, protesting against the cult of the machine, invented functionless machines, Mondrian and
Malevitch did purely geometric paintings and even mono-
chromic squares which we must regard as the incunabula
of abstract art—the offical salons were still brimming with
classical nudes and gigantic color prints, and the coils and
soft curves of "modern style" or art nouveau, which was
inspired by the figures of women of fashion, plantlife
forms, and Japanese art, were still in vogue in both
architecture and furniture. Thus, after World War II,

there was a co-existence of such resolute realism as Bernard Buffet's, such total abstraction as Soulages' or Hartung's, such almost medieval naiveté as Aristide Caillard, and finally, Jean Dubuffet's famous "art brut," which had some of the characteristics of primitivism, children's art, and the very unusual calligraphy of the insane.

We will mention simply as a reminder works deliberately dealing with classic medical subjects, and going against the stream of contemporary art development: *The Doctor's Visit* by Louis de Joncières, *The Hospital Ward* by Lucien Simon, and *The Annunciation* by the American Negro, Henry O. Tanner (1851-1937). In this painting (it might be interesting to compare it with Van Eyck's) Eakins' pupil has treated the idea of motherhood and infancy with eloquent and profoundly religious feelings, that by no means exclude the truth.

Louis Lacombe's (1868-1916) bas-relief *The Dream* (private collection) would be more in keeping with our

253

ROGER DE LA FRESNAYE (1885-1925)

The Sick Man

By straining the colors and playing paradoxically with lines, La Fresnaye, a fauve and a cubist, achieves a perfect depiction of the feverish state of his model.

MUSÉE MUNICIPAL D'ART MODERNE, PARIS

254

purpose. The realism of what is in point of fact a meticulously reproduced birth scene is transformed by the symbolic value accorded to the veiled woman praying in the background. She is the image of the Nativity—and to the physician, who with his beard and his thick hair recalls the traditional image of God, the Supreme Parent.

And the Intimists? Vuillard's (1868-1940) *Interior,* showing a sick woman huddling beneath her blankets and tended by a large woman sitting next to her, may fall under the heading of medical painting; and the same artist's *Professor Gosset's Operation* may have supplied us with an irrefutable document on the progress of surgery. But this area of painting does not reveal any really new, one could say, existential relationship between art and medicine. At most, we see a beginning in Vuillard's and Bonnard's impressionistic way of viewing appearances (medical or not) and eventually turning reality into a spiritual or mental state rather than letting it remain a model per se.

And the Fauves? We must first of all find out what became of Marquet, Derain, Vlaminck, and Dufy, to name but a few, since their common Fauvism was merely a brief fad, though a very intense one in 1905, and their gushes of pure colors, which shocked the clientèle of the official Salon, prefigured the liberation of instinct that is of eminent interest to pathology and more generally to medicine. One of these painters, Raoul Dufy, even returned to the reproduction of medical scenes in a very fine sketch *The Operation* (Louvre), in which five figures are shown in cowls, and only their eyes are alive. This is quite a remarkable symbol, and comes singularly close to our purpose.

It is no digression to mention the healing power that Matisse, accused of causing insanity, attributed to his painting (thus, twice he thought he had cured his friends Carco and Marquet by leaving them in a room filled with works of his); and it is very much to our purpose to cite Georges Rouault, a visionary, who from the very first saw in modern man—as Louis Vauxcelles wrote in 1911—"a swarm of larvae, epileptic fits, and souls in torment." Was Rouault a pathological case? His ordered life and his asceticism seem to indicate the contrary. In reality, his art is an outlet. "It may be so frightening only because the painter ejects from his consciousness all the feelings and desires which in other people would find expression in grave disorders; we seem to be witnessing the prodigious drama of a man struggling among phantoms and holding them fast on his canvas in an (perhaps unknowing) attempt to blot them out, to be rid of them."

This quotation from Georges Charensol could actually serve as a preface to everything that came later. Are the storms that shake most of Vlaminck's paintings something other than the tempests which this more than healthy Fleming sublimated by flinging them on his canvases? One could similarly trace the weird disturbing, and occasionally terrifying works of the Anglo-Flemish painter James Ensor (1860-1949) to the more or less conscious intention of exorcising persistent childhood impressions whose horror and strangeness his imagination could still exaggerate (a murky store-house of terror, full of frightful spiders and animals from faraway oceans, fine porcelain, cast-off clothing the color of rust and blood, red and white corals, stuffed monkeys, turtles, sirens and Chinamen); thus, the countless macabre, sarcastic, hallucinatory paintings produced by Ensor in the course of his highly eccentric lifetime have something blatantly obsessive about them: cf. *Melancholy Fishwives, Skeletons Arguing over a Hanged Man, Skeleton Examining Chinese Paintings.* But, with James Ensor, we come to a category of painters—the Expressionists—who quench their thirst at the fountain of violent emotions and deep complexes and, simultaneously, at the fountains of the collective subconscious as well as the darkest aspects of reality, which these painters reveal more or less consciously.

Expressionism was a Nordic vocation and burst forth, in 1905, in the Dresden-based group *Die Bruecke* (The Bridge), with Nolde, Kirchner, Heckel, Pechstein, Mueller, and several others. There was a germ of expressionism in Van Gogh, in Rouault, and in Soutine. Next to Permeke, Ensor is the most important Belgian expressionist. Kokoschka in Austria and Munch in Norway are closely linked with this rich and durable movement, which suffered so greatly at the hands of the Nazis when they persecuted so-called "degenerate art." We will not deal with all these painters in detail, but only with those whose works bordered on the domain of psychopathology. Like Soutine, whose strange personality we have already evoked, the Norwegian Edvard Munch (1863-1844) bore throughout his life the weight of memories of an unhappy childhood. His mother and his sister died of tuberculosis; he had to accompany his father, the neighborhood doctor, through the workers' slums, the poverty of which was as extreme as that which so shocked Van Gogh during his youth in Flanders. After reaching adulthood, Munch was shot in the hand by a jealous woman, and from that moment on, he could no longer endure the sight of human hands, including his own. "There is nothing more naked or more disgusting than fingers," he said, and he wore gloves until the day he died. When he did his *Portrait of the Painter with Cigarettes,* he had a friend pose for the hands. No wonder his paintings, whether or not they deal with medical topics—*The Sick Girl, The Sick Child*—treat

GEORGE GROSZ (1893-1959)

The draft board

According to Henry Miller, Grosz is superior to "all
the satirical slush and the lies of our time by virtue
of his deliberate ferociousness."

MUSEUM OF MODERN ART, NEW YORK

his own case more than anything else, exorcising it so to speak. Munch suffered from a morbid hypersensitivity, exasperated by the misery of the lowly around him as well as by a dark inner flame. This explains the strange, sinister, and disquieting pathos of his works even when the motif happens to be *The Next Morning* or *The Frieze of Life.*

Emil Nolde (1867-1956), known as the "painter of Christs"—primitive Christs of an oriental sumptuousness—was also a painter of masks before World War I, grinning demoniacal masks, whose grimaces, as Henri Certigny so fittingly said "seem to announce the death-grins of Verdun."

Ernst Ludwig Kirchner (1880-1938) was so terrified by the war that he fell ill in 1917 and had to be confined; and he was so frightened at the rise of fascism that he committed suicide in 1938, although, living in Switzerland, he had nothing to fear personally. He, too, is one of the "revealing" artists whom I have just spoken of.

We will dwell for a while on Oskar Kokoschka (b. 1880), who can match Kirchner in that respect. During his youth, Kokoschka was struck by the sculpture of African and Oceanic primitives; he realized that this was an expression of depths rather than savage handicraft. Becoming both a playwright and a painter, he never stopped probing these depths and did so in the manner of an ingenious mime capable of identifying himself with the object he is depicting; and in his painting, he described characters if not souls. "It is a curious coincidence," notes Rüdlinger, "that the scientific psychologist Freud and the artistic psychologist Kokoschka produced their essential works in the same period and in the same city. Between 1908 and 1914, Kokoschka painted a series of portraits whose psychological accuracy and human quality make them extraordinarily interesting documents." Kokoschka's subsequent work was greatly conditioned by the war, in which he was badly wounded. Not only did he evoke its horrors in *The Knight-Errant,* but he went even further. He showed something of those horrors and of his desire to negate them by a redistribution of appearances, in the very way he painted: jumbling, piling up forms, shifting them beyond the globe in a lyric and demiurgic earthquake. Fleeing to England during World War II, he devoted his visionary art to the cause of liberty by increasing the anguished allegories of violence, tyranny, and human downfall, e.g. *Why We Are Fighting.*

Modigliani and Utrillo are also in keeping with the purpose we have defined earlier—to show that the relationship between art and medicine in the twentieth century, though different from earlier times, is just as close if not closer. Both these painters were terrible alcoholics,

PAUL KLEE (1879-1940)
The Buffon

"Klee lived entirely in the unique world he created daily, a world of childhood and dreams." (Michel Ragon).

WALLRAF-RICHARTZ MUSEUM, COLOGNE

and it was precisely this drinking problem which determined the connection between art and medicine. "He painted in order to drink better, and he drank in order to paint better," Francis Jourdain writes about Maurice Utrillo (1883-1955). He could have said the same about Amedeo Modigliani (1884-1920). But there the comparison ends Drunkenness didn't give rise to same artistic orientation in these two friends (who often tried

257

drinking one another under the table) because after all, Utrillo, a tender, melancholy picture-maker, and Modigliani, who combined Botticelli with Cubism, were in no way alike. A further observation is necessary. Their works, though done under the influence of liquor, do not have the character of delirium. They show order and intention in every respect. "I need fire to paint and to burn... what does it matter if I amputate a few moments from my life," said the Italian. But this combustion liberated the painter in him, the great painter. The same goes for Utrillo who, toward the end of his life, on a steady diet of water with a few drops of red wine, did poor paintings. This brings us to the topic of drugs and stimulants. The artists using them to find some entrance into their inner selves ("Inner Space," says the poet and painter Henri Michaux, a large consumer of peyote and other mescalines) will not necessarily find what they are looking for, and even if they do, they will not always bring back a medically or artistically worthwhile painting. The tentacled vibrios and tormented figures Michaux comes back with from his pictorial excursions into the fake domain of his subconscious, do not seem to equal the extraordinary descriptions in his poems of non-stimulated visions or even secondary states.

We must dwell on Picasso (b. 1881) for a while. This devil of a man has done everything, including works that might figure in a catalogue of strictly figurative painting and sculpture of medical subject matter. Thus, when he was about fifteen, he painted a consultation scene, complete with everything, even a chronometer for the doctor taking the patient's pulse (let it be said in passing that the latter's hand resembles an empty glove). This was followed by *The Sick Child* (Barcelona), one of the masterpieces of Picasso's "classical" period. We see a pale, rickety little boy, with a thin, almost skeletal face and a deep dispairing look in his eyes; the grief-stricken child is huddling with all his dwindling strength on the breast of the sad-eyed woman. In his Cubist phase, Picasso produced *The Glass of Absinth,* a piece of sculpture that is both a demonstration of Cubism and a deep, probing portrait of the besotted and emaciated alcoholic in the last stages of his illness. The relationship of Picasso's art to medicine seems even more obvious in numerous phases of his work not dealing with medical topics. This "great wild beast that escaped from Altamira"—as Jean Cassou calls him—never really stopped probing the subconscious, that prehistory of reason, and simultaneously pushing to their extremes the subtleties of Western intelligence and mirroring its anxieties and fears. The horrors of war, a traditional subject, which was treated by Brueghel, Callot, Goya, etc., and whose connections with medicine are evident,

was a source of inspiration for several Picasso paintings such as the renowned *Guernica*. Here the style—its twistings, deformation, laceration—rather than the theme communicates the feeling the artist wishes to express, especially his sense of universal laceration and torture. One of the chief figures in *Guernica* is a bull, symbolizing—according to Picasso—not strictly fascism, but brutality and darkness. Throughout his works, he often made use of this symbol or else one closely connected to it—the minotaur. "Isn't this monster," writes Yvonne Deslandres, "half-man, half-beast, an image particularly suggestive of all that is unknown and disquieting in a human being?" Even Picasso's unusual power over the artistic sensibilities of our age makes him an interesting subject for the psychoanalyst—not to mention the cruel and tireless liberty with which he destroys, crushes, and arbitrarily re-invents appearance. A devil of a man!

Ronald Penrose writes: "Since Picasso's works are a field day for psychoanalytic research, the painter ought to make some comments concerning this domain. A Swiss physician once showed him some drawings by patients and asked him what connection he felt existed between them and modern painting. The painter turned around wordlessly and with gripping realism, mimed the gestures of a long-armed, monkey, then he did a pencil sketch devoid of any sense and handed it to the professor with blatant satisfaction." We will come back to this relationship between art and insanity. But first, let us continue with the history of the relationship between art and medicine.

This relationship asserts itself with the Dadaist painters, particularly Arp, Picabia, Duchamp, whom I have already named, and Schwitters. What was "Dada"? A gathering of poets and painters who, rebelling against "appearances" and more precisely their cruel and bloody form in World War I, founded in Basel, in 1916, a movement which they very symbolically decided to name at random. Opening the dictionary they chanced upon "dada" (hobby horse), a childish, cretinous, negating word. They couldn't have made a better choice, since they proposed to attack logic, reason, and the systematic order of objects and minds. How did they go about it? Each in his own way. Thus, some of them, such as Schwitters, invented their own Dadaism, unaware of what was going on in Zurich around the poet Tristan Tzara.

Hans Arp, an Alsatian (b. 1887) expressed himself with scraps of paper, ovoid or spherical sculpture, which recall such elementary and natural forms as an egg, a cloud, a pebble, primal forms in the sense that we say psychoanalysis is a descent to the primal forms, the *Urformen* that Goethe spoke of so eloquently. Picabia, a Spaniard (1879-

1953), dubbed himself "a painter in all genres." He put his mind to work practicing all genres—and he excelled in all of them—in order to negate successively Impressionism, Dadaism, Surrealism, the most conventional figurative art, and abstract painting, in which he placed his grain of salt in 1912. This derisive attitude of his—which Picabia illustrated with practical jokes in real life such as buying Fords by the dozen "because they're so practical," converting the land on his Provençal estate into fake cemeteries, adding a mustache to the Mona Lisa—harked back to a self-destructiveness, which Van Gogh succumbed to after burning his hand in a lamp flame during his youth and cutting off an ear toward the end of his short life. Van Gogh was convinced that he hadn't really been born and that he was taking another person's place (his parents' first-born, christened Vincent, had died young, and so the future painter received the same first name, and thought of himself as a "surrogate"); thus his own personality was of interest. But in the case of Picabia and the other Dadaists, interest revolved around the image of man in a generation refusing a harsh and unjust civilization.

Marcel Duchamp's attitude illustrates this refusal. He grew famous overnight in 1913 for his *Nude Descending a Staircase* (and this descent is in itself a symbol), which was exhibited at the Armory Show in New York. Ten years later, Duchamp stopped painting to devote himself to chess, while America, where he still lives, devoted several rooms in the Philadelphia Museum of Fine Arts to his works, in which the *ready-mades,* objects of everyday life presented as works of art, occupy a large space. The same could be said of Kurt Schwitters (1879-1948) who spent his life, first in Germany, then in England, accumulating rubbish, odds and ends picked up in the street, any waste products of civilization, and offering the following explanation: "After all, I couldn't see why a painter couldn't use materials other than commercially manufactured paints, for example, old streetcar or métro tickets, pieces of discolored wood, wardrobe tickets, bits of string, the spokes of a bicycle wheel, in short, all the old bric-a-brac lying around in attics or garbage-cans. This was, in a way, a social point of view, and artistically a personal pleasure. I named my new style, which was based on the

Hyman Bloom

Autopsy

In this painting, the very movement of the artistic act suggests the swarming of the viscera and of the conscience as well.

WHITNEY MUSEUM OF AMERICAN ART, NEW YORK

259

PABLO PICASSO (b. 1881)

The Sick Child

One of the masterpieces of Picasso's classical period.
Worried and protective motherhood is in a sense the
true subject of the painting.

MUSEUM OF BARCELONA

260

employment of such material 'Merz', the second syllable of the word 'Kommerz.'"

The distance between Dadaism and Surrealism is but a step, yet an important one, since the second movement, born of the first, supplants destructiveness with reconstruction. We have already mentioned that the scientific character of the Surrealist experiment owes a great deal to Freud's influence. The primary aim was the investigation of the subconscious; thus, sometimes scorning plastic quality, Surrealist works accumulated a dreamlike, obsessional, paranoid material, the very same on which psychoanalysts and therapists "work," with the reservation that, at the beginning at least, the procedure of Surrealism was that, of the hyperconscious simulation of nightmares and disturbances of the conscious. The most remarkable of these painters were assuredly Giorgio de Chirico (b. 1888), Yves Tanguy (b. 1900), Joan Miró (b. 1895), Max Ernst (b. 1891), and Salvador Dali (b. 1904).

Chirico, born in Thessaly, Sicily, actually preceded Surrealism, for in 1910, he began painting a Greco-Roman world filled with strange shadows. And he could never put up with the discipline of the movement which claimed him for its own. He made modern skyscrapers an integral part of his mythological universe, and in 1930 he returned to a desolating academic art. The obsessiveness of his Surrealist works is manifest: dummies and plaster statues replace man in monumental and patently useless perspectives, and before any of these canvases we feel an anxiety-ridden impression of cold, of premonitory silences, as in nightmares most deserving of Freud's attention. Chirico even had premonitions. Starting in 1914, he depicted Apollinaire with a hole in his forehead, and in 1918 his friend died of a bullet wound in the forehead; and Mussolini's fascism erected in the suburbs of Rome a mass of grandiose palaces, which were destined to remain deserted after the fall of his regime.

The same silence and cold reign in the works of Yves Tanguy, a Breton, who paints strange rocks, and submarine or extraterrestial deserts; and in the works of Joan Miró from Catalonia, we have a whole world of simultaneously childish and erudite signs (which actually owe a great deal to Klee, whom we shall discuss later on). Their Surrealism consists more in the audacity of the relationships they establish rather than in the conception itself which stems from a sort of cosmic identification with a pebble, the whorled flight of a bird, the sickle of a moon.

Max Ernst, from the Rhineland, planned to become a psychiatrist. He joined the Dadaist adventure, then the Surrealist one. World War II was a terrible experience for him, but he was finally able to come to the United States and settle down in Arizona as a farmer in order to paint

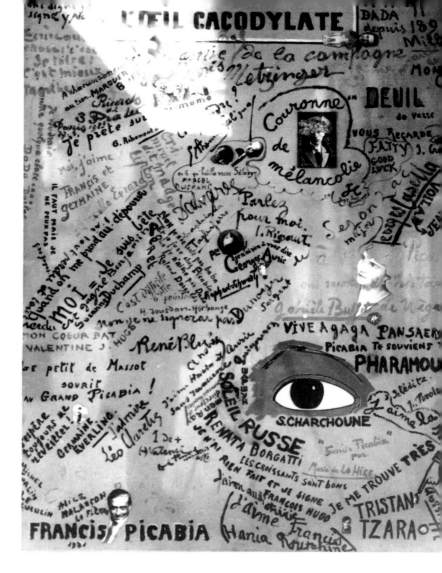

FRANCIS PICABIA (1879-1953)

The Ill-smelling Eye

The entire dadaist family collaborated with its adversaries (notice Roland Dorgelès' declaration in the center) on this document.

PRIVATE COLLECTION

and sculpt, in free solitude, fantastic landscapes and gigantic figures. His favorite subjects are the lop bird "Loplop," blazing tigers, and the "nocturnal lemurs" that old Horace had already situated in these depths of our consciousness. In 1930, by cutting up old magazines, he put together an album entitled *A Week of Goodness* (recently reproduced in the review "Planète"), which we can regard as one of the best contributions of Surrealist art to psychoanalysis and which Patrick Walberg defined with the following words: "The old-fashioned character of the costumes, the sonambulistic character of the gestures, the astonishing juxtaposition of unused machines, terrifying animals, poisonous plants, accentuate to the point of paroxysm the dreamlike qualities of this spellbinding fiction."

In the case of Salvador Dali, a Catalonian, we are dealing with a man who is a Surrealist in real life without our

261

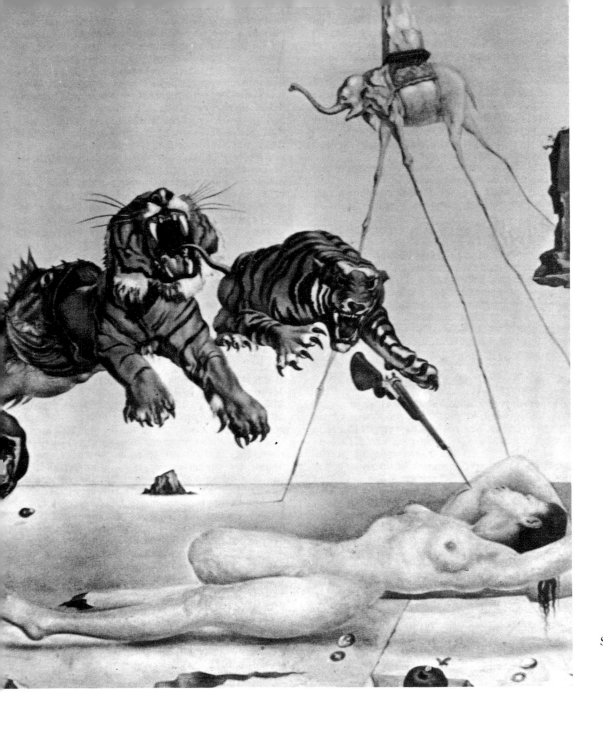

being able to distinguish simulation or provocation from genuine schizophrenia and paranoia. We won't say it doesn't matter, but on the basis of his work rather than his life we can claim that this genius of a painter has brought us face to face with the most complete pandemonium of our obsessions and implacably expressed the anxieties of mankind, even when he draws his references from classical or baroque architecture, traditional painting, the dusty lithographs of diocesian museums, as well as his dreams, his unbridled phantasies or his consumption of serious books, beginning with the works of Sigmund Freud. *The Three Sphinxes of Bikini,* expressing atomic terror, *The Christ of Saint John of the Cross,* (Glasgow, poorly repaired after being slashed by a lunatic), and *The Last Supper* (National Gallery, Washington D.C.), which gave his Christianity cosmic proportions, are "the dream created by the flight of a bee around a pomengranate," as well as irreplaceable documents for the study of what Jung called "the general activity of the mind and the productivity of the psyche."

The South American Matta, the last of the important Surrealists, broke with a certain academic execution gravely encumbering numerous Surrealist works. He is less intent on "figuring" the mental world than capturing its violence and rhythm, its concatenation and speed. If frankly medical obsessions exist in him, they are suggested rather than described. Thus, in several paintings, filled with a clear, implacable "surgical" light, we can see the flying and whirling of sharp, brilliant forms, which are simply scalpels or forceps.

With the Russian Marc Chagall (b. 1897), we enter a realm of modern art in which Primitivism, Expressionism, and Surrealism merge. The relationship of Chagall's Russo-Judaic-Christian imagery to medicine is defined by his melancholy—the heavy legacy of a poor and nervous ghetto child—by his wild imagination, which blends the rational and the irrational with the logic of a dream and, concerning the works done on the eve of World War II, by the premonitory horrors—progroms, exoduses, and tortures—invading the imagery as if the painter were such a marvelous sensitive-plate that even the future could leave an impression on him.

We have referred to the Russian Wassily Kandinsky (1886-1944) and the circumstances of his break with objects and appearances in favor of the schema of the creative act.

Another great figure in modern art, Paul Klee (1879-1940), had a German father and a Swiss mother. His "plastic" universe was not, properly speaking, abstract. Michel Ragon very intelligently said that "Klee lived entirely in the unique world he created every day, a world originating in childhood and in dreams." And Klee himself told us that if he did "do abstract painting," it was "with memories"—of the earth, herbs, animals, lunatics slipping into his canvases like mischievous sprites. Thus, in *Blue Night,* in which the eye cannot identify a single "object," we can discern something like a portrait of the night, painted by a man who was sufficiently sensitive and openminded to identify himself with his model—a cosmic and ontological night, material and mental, visible and secret, surrounding him, surrounded by him, and recalled by him. Among the memories that inhabit Klee's art, cats are quite important: large-eyed cats opposing "the crumbling world" (the painter's own definition) with the interrogation or rather the permanent enigma which they symbolize. It is interesting to note, in this connection, that Klee had several cats which he loved and spoke to in a language that was unintelligible but that they seemed to understand and in which he even composed a poem in their honor. Sometimes, when his watercolors were still moist he liked to put his favorite cat on them. In a number of paintings, Klee dealt with medical subjects: *A Consumptive, The Dwarf, The Ghost of Hunger, Doctor.* And he did a colored lithograph, *The Loved One,* a perfect image of erotic obsession, with eyes turning into breasts and breasts into eyes.

I have already mentioned the Russian Kasimir Malevitch (1878-1935) and the Dutchman Piet Mondrian (1878-1944), as further promotors of abstract art. The former, who authored a book entitled *Le Monde de la non-représentation* (The World of Non-representation),

did a painting in 1913 which showed merely a blank square on a white background. This constituted the ultimate rejection of appearances. Malevitch offered the following explanation: "This square... was not an empty square but the palpable sense of the absence of the object."

Starting in 1910, Mondrian devoted himself to the experiment of a progressive abstracting (of a tree), which enabled the observer to follow the ideal process of the deciphering of appearances. Phase by phase, the tree was finally reduced to a cross. This religious symbol was obviously personal to Mondrian, a Huguenot, for with any other painter, the tree, reduced to the essence of its structure, would have become a circle, a spiral, or a triangle. And if we compare this crucifix to Malevitch's last wishes, namely: to be buried in bare soil with his arms crossed, we are forced to admit that the artistic temperament of our age is in close rapport not only with psychoanalysis but also with mysticism and eschatology as well. "It would be fascinating," writes Mircea Eliade in *Aspects du Mythe,* "to do a thorough study of the process of the reevaluation of the myth of the end of the world in contemporary art. We would conclude that artists, far from being the neurotics they are often called, are on the contrary mentally healthier than many modern men. They have realized that a true beginning can take place only after a real end."

We cannot study all the twentieth-century artists who, deliberately or not, have made their contribution to a psychopathological study of man and to a mythic depiction of the collective psyche of our time. But several major artists deserve special attention. Wolfgang Wols, a German (1913-1951), lived intentionally with closed eyes, opening them only to register the unusual images that flitted through his mind.

At the threshold of our century, the members of the Group of *Eight,* who were pioneers in American painting, produced few works of interest to medicine—the one exception being *The Anatomy Lesson* by John Sloan (1871-1945). John Marin, one of the most important American innovators of the years 1910-1920 (along with Dove, Hartley, and Stella) fostered the ambition of depicting "what goes on in the world," and thus he painted, using both hands at once, shimmering water colors that were closer to the inner world than the visible one. But other Americans produced a great deal of material relating to our study. Robert Riggs (b. 1896) produced violently beautiful lithographs of psychiatric interest, such as *Psychiatric Ward;* Hyman Bloom painted *The Autopsy;* Joseph Hirsh (b. 1910) drew up a sort of accusal against illness in several canvases, notably in *Children Care,* a pediatric document of the first order; finally, Jackson Pollock (1912-1956), strongly influenced by Jung and Freud, placed his

263

immense canvases flat on the floor and, walking over them as in an enchanted forest, covered them with random splashes of paint.

Elsewhere Bernard Buffet (b. 1928) is so obsessed with his own face that he lends it to all his male and female figures and always creates the same cold, miserable, almost concentration-camp-like universe, peopled by angular skeletal beings, who are often hermaphroditic, and whose bellies, unhealthily swollen, will never bear children. Atlan, a Judaized Berber (1913-1960), is a simultaneously "savage" and refined painter who has put into his works an enigmatic and sumptuous genesis shaken by the great elemental rhythms of ritual dances and childbirth. The walled-in labyrinthal paintings of Vieira da Silva, reminiscent of Klee and of Surrealism, convey an impression of nightmarishness in which one is constantly opening doors only to find further doors beyond them, and so on until infinity. The non-figurative work of Sutherland, an Englishman, (b. 1903), and that of Sugai, a Japanese, is full of volutes, claws, and points. While Sutherland makes us think of bombings and the mass of metallic skeletons they leave behind, the Japanese evokes monsters, and it is interesting to note that whereas Soutine was deeply impressed in his youth by the slaughter of a goose, Sutherland was lastingly impressed by the London blitz and Sugai by childhood stories of a dreadful red dragon with hooks and horns. The baroque and dreamlike painting of Apell and others belonging to the Danish "Cobra" group, the work of Tobey and other Americans belonging to the "Pacific school," whose investigations remind one of the ink-blot tests in which the oracles look for diagnoses or prognoses. Georges Matthieu, who literally throws himself on his canvas and in matter of hours, sometimes less, paints gigantic historic frescos, capturing not so much the event itself as the movement; Fautrier, whose crushing plasters and paintings give unbearable expression to the horror of death camps; and finally Dubucet, an exasperated Daumier, with an apparently infantile, primitive, or delirious style. All these painters offer us an abundance of illustrations for our theme.

However, with these last-named artists, we can discern two particularly significant phases in the evolution of today's artistic mentality and its relationship to medicine. We must talk first of all about "l'art brut" and its relationship to the art of the mentally ill; and second, about the birth of a "new figuration."

It is quite remarkable that the great post-war exhibition of drawings and paintings by the insane, in the Asile Sainte Anne, in 1946, coincided with the first manifestation of Art Brut which, originated by Jean Dubuffet (Mirobolus et Macadam) and practiced by such artists as Scottie Wilson, a Scotsman, Miguel Hernandez, a Spaniard, and Gaston Chayssac, a Frenchman, comprise the works of modern European primitives, i.e., the self-taught painters. With little education, these men took up art out of a necessity to rid themselves of nightmares, haunting memories, mystic obsessions, etc., without having the technical means of doing it and thus being obliged to invent such means gathering the very first root to make a Christ of it. We will not dwell on particulars in works (some of which are of an astonishing "convulsive beauty" as André Breton put it) done by the insane or by modern primitives. But we ought to say that the curiosity our age feels for each of these two groups proves that our civilization, and not only our art, has a keen desire to break with intellectual disciplines that have brought us nothing but ruin and sorrow and now threaten to blow up our planet, for want of taking into account an organic overlapping of man's intelligence and instinct, his psyche and the cosmos, the world of dreams and tangible reality. We have already touched on the "healing" character of artistic expression. A longer study would be necessary. We note, for example, that though it may be a regrettable confusion to assimilate the artistic process of the mentally ill to the deliberately extra-rational one of well-balanced painters or to the naively and awkwardly realistic one of children and primitives, the fact remains that art constitutes for all of them release and alleviation. Modern psychiatry uses art therapeutically and as research material—a fact which only confirms what the artist has always known instinctively and what he gives expression to when he speaks of his work as "childbirth," or an "ejaculation," or even a "defection." I would like to support this with three quotations. The first is by the great American writer Henry Miller, who, without having learned to paint, tried his hand at it, because "painting is loving all over again." The second, by Georg Schmidt, and the third by Alfred Bader, are taken from *Insania Pingens* (Ciba, Basel).

"Painting refreshes and regenerates me," wrote Miller. "Water colors have become a refuge for me... I didn't realize I'd become a painter... I was simply struggling to get out of a strait-jacket..."

"It is illness," wrote Georg Schmidt, "which generally constitutes losing one's rational inhibitions and provides effective stimulation for artistic activity. Only rarely does a sick man draw or paint before being struck by insanity... Claustrophobia, which is particularly frequent, can give rise to grandiose spatial composition. But next to visions produced by anxiety, we also encounter paintings expressing indifference, or calm and serenity."

"Aloyse," writes Alfredo Bader, "draws very rapidly without interrupting an incoherent and almost continuous

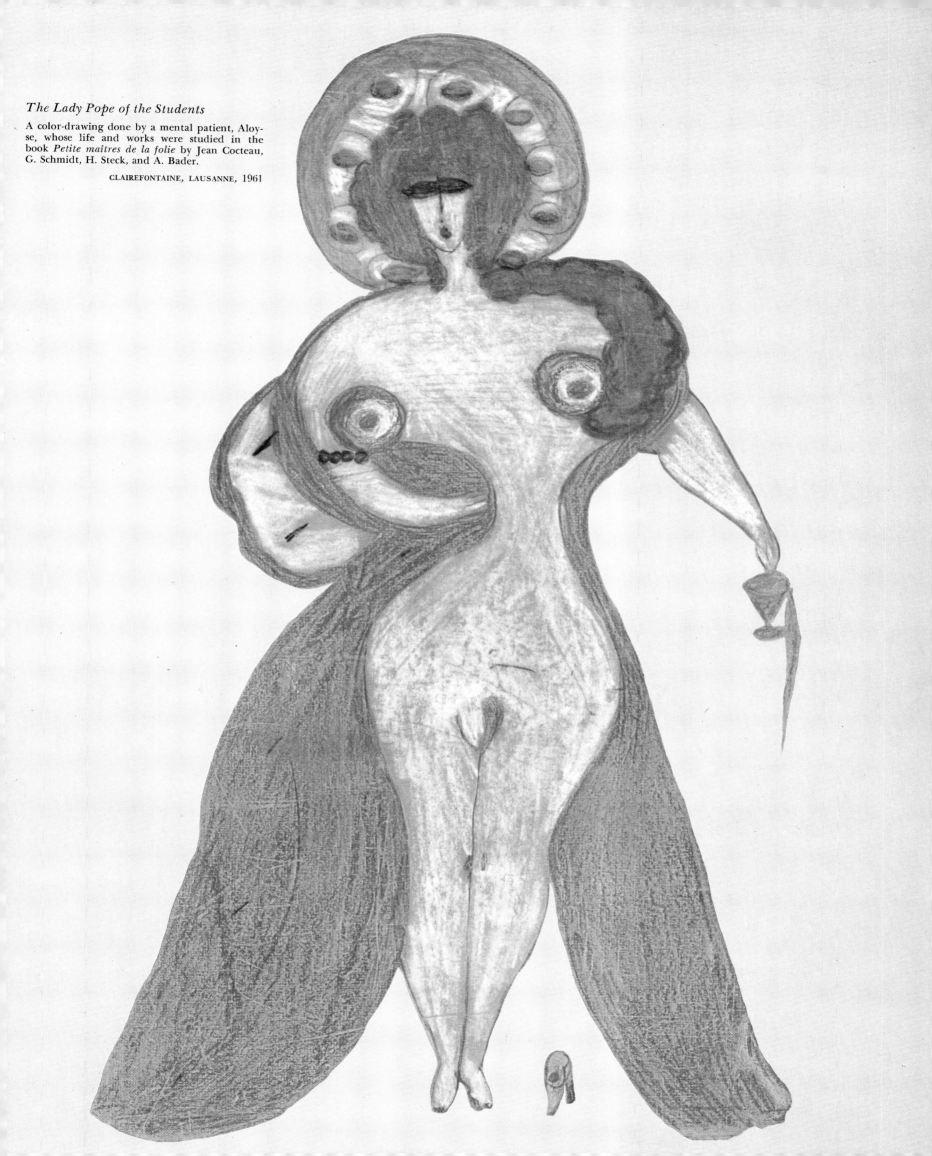

The Lady Pope of the Students

A color-drawing done by a mental patient, Aloyse, whose life and works were studied in the book *Petite maitres de la folie* by Jean Cocteau, G. Schmidt, H. Steck, and A. Bader.

CLAIREFONTAINE, LAUSANNE, 1961

speech. She works with unbelievable fervor, sweating heavily and wiping herself at every moment with her cloth or with her paintstained fingers so that her face winds up almost as colorful as her drawing. As soon as she finishes her work, she seems relaxed, almost liberated, and the first thing she does is to wash herself thoroughly."

Thus, art relaxes, liberates, purges. We suspected as much after Van Gogh's letters, which are as lucid as his paintings, for nothing is less mad, less delirious, less insane than the works of this madman, who penned the following pathetic phrase: "I struggle with all my strength to master my work, telling myself that if I win, it will be the best lightning-rod for my illness." Art permits man to conquer himself and to conquer evil and death!

If we go on to "new figuration," which for several years now has been gradually supplanting abstraction, we find as in all other areas of twentieth century art, many excellent examples of a new and deeper relationship with medicine. By "new figuration," nothing less is meant than a resurrection of traditional figuration—"both reasonable and rational," as Michel Ragon put it. Or else, these painters are learning from the Expressionists to the point of completely distorting and smashing appearances. Or else, like Schwitters, they are using the debris and refuse of civilization. Francis Bacon, a Scot (b. 1909), paints "massacre games," whose most constant figures are "sacrilegious popes"; Antonio Berni, an Argentine (b. 1905), uses pieces of rusty sheet metal, broken bottle ends rags he finds in vacant lots, and defaced posters; César, the Italian sculptor, works on old crushed automobiles destined for the flatting mill; Lebenstein, a Pole, is obsessed, according to Michel Ragon "with a monstrous form, half louse, half man, crushed in mud. This is the world, the aftermath of nuclear war, with its abominable mutations. One is reminded of Kafka (*Metamorphosis*), and of the Warsaw Ghetto, of man tortured, pulverized, flattened—a bat nailed to a barn door..."

Caricature is extremely close to art. In modern caricature (whether or not the subject matter is medical), we could find numerous illustrations of new relationships between art and medicine. Naturally, traditional medical caricature per se, at the turn of the century, added several more successes to those of the preceding century. We are thinking of minor masters such as Jean-Louis Forain (1852-1951) and Adolphe Willette (1857-1926), of Félicien

266

Rops's admirable *Mort danseuse,* and humorous works of Abel Faivre or Hermann Paul. But how much more revealing are those caricatures which by their very style condemn the mental order of our times as well as the present-day order of things! Such works actually combine art and straight caricature; why shouldn't we include along with the eminently caricatural works of Rouault, Soutine, Dubuffet, and the "new figuratives," the frightening social caricatures of George Grosz, notable for his album "Ecce Homo," of which Miller so fittingly said that "it is far superior to the satirical slush and the lies of our age by virtue of its deliberate ferociousness." Wherever we look, whatever the theme of recent caricatures such as Torpor's may be, we notice that their deliberately primitive or aberrant scrawl is a considerable contribution to that "new inquiry into man and rational appearances" that mental medicine and modern art are both undertaking.

We must mention, though in passing, the multiplicity of drawings with medical themes done to advertise pharmaceutical products or to serve as illustrations in some public health and hygiene campaign. We are thinking of Ogé's astounding poster of the year 1900, which, though an advertisement for *Doctor Trabant's supreme pills,* is also a vehement caricature of Queen Victoria, who was sick... of the Boer war.

The list of these commercial works, which at times are truly artistic, would be too long for this context.

We will not, however, leave out one last picture far removed from advertising: Harry Sternberg's water color entitled *The Secrets of Life* showing a foetus in utero position hovering in a setting of stars and comets between a biologist and an astronomer. Why have we chosen it? Perhaps, because it seems to symbolize the destiny of art and of man. Both are always being born and yet have existed from the very beginning. We know that neither is anything without the other. But would the medical and cosmic signs surrounding the image of a being torn from the primal womb have any sense for us if twentieth century biology were not accompanied by another "biology" which probes the cells of the mind and is practiced by artists as well as physicians.

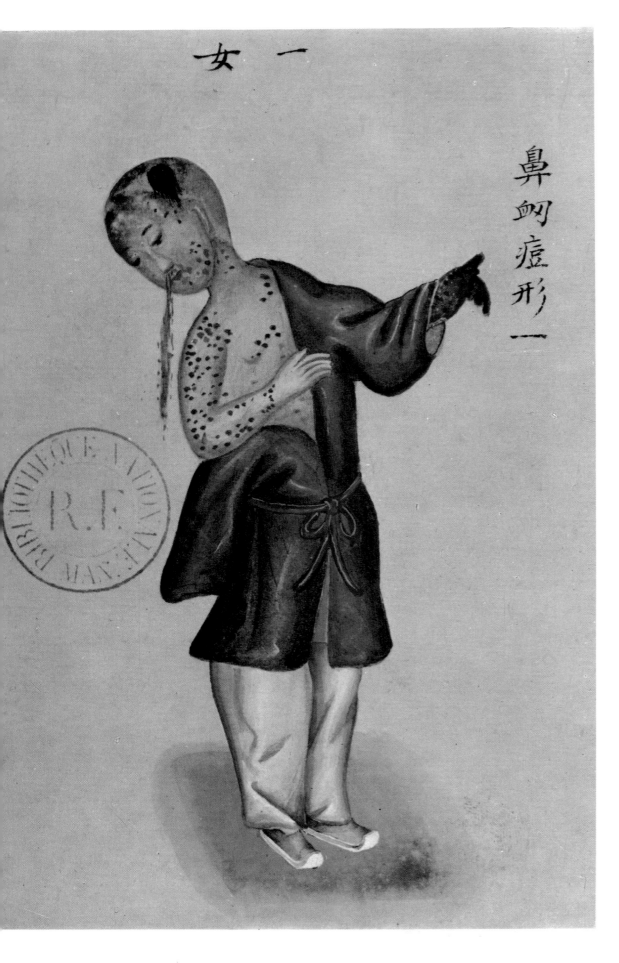

鼻衄痘形一

女一

Infantile eruption. Chinese silk—painting of the
eighteenth century.

ILZA VEITH

THE FAR EAST AND THE MIDDLE EAST

China

Confucius is often quoted as having said that one picture is worth more than a thousand words. If applied to Far Eastern medical concepts and practices, this statement is extraordinarily apt since the ancient oriental medical theories and practices are so far removed from anything known to the Western world that they can scarcely be visualized on the basis of words alone. Although the medical concepts of the Far East lend themselves so well to pictorial representation, far from all of the medical works were illustrated, but the custom of illustrating them evolved gradually with the eventual systematization of the medical theories. But it is not only the purely medical illustrations that elucidate the intricacies of Far Eastern medicine; further insight can be gained from the works of artists who were concerned with all aspects of life of their day and who thus included scenes depicting health and disease and the current medical practices.

The origins of Chinese medicine are veiled in legend, and are popularly attributed to three mythological emper-

ors who were thought to be divine. Shen-Nung, whose name has been translated as the "Divine Husband-man" and who developed agriculture, was also thought to be responsible for the enormously rich and variegated Chinese pharmacopeia. Indeed in order to test the benefit of the remedies, he was said to have cut open his abdomen and to have inserted a window into the abdominal wall so as to be able to observe the action of the drugs by means of a mirror, which he held in front of his abdominal window. To Shen-Nung also is attributed the authorship of the *Pen Tsao,* the magnificent "Great Herbal" which contains all pharmacological substances of the animal, vegetable and mineral kingdoms. Fu-Hsi, the second of the legendary emperors, gave the world the basis for the philosophy of life and medicine. Huang Ti, the "Yellow Emperor," was venerated as the supposed author of the *Huang Ti Nei Ching Su Wen,* "The Yellow Emperor's Classic of Internal Medicine," and hence this emperor was considered to be the founder of internal medicine.

高大如天地
光明如日月
千億萬年後
其德永不鴉

寛政十年吉月冬至之日
大日本太墅令從五位下
朝散大夫大和守和氣成
美君人題書

The three gods of Chinese medicine: Fu Hi, Shen-Nung
and Huang Ti.
Anonymous silk painting (eighteenth century), exalting
the merits of the deities.
"Great and strong as heaven and earth,
Brilliant as the sun and the moon,
A hundred million years from now
Their perfection will still be intact."

SAN FRANCISCO MEDICAL CENTER,
UNIVERSITY OF CALIFORNIA

270

While it is not possible to state with any certainty when this great work was actually written down, a number of textual references point to the fourth or third century B.C. The form in which *The Yellow Emperor's Classic* has come down to us was given to it in A.D. 762 by Wang Ping of the Tang dynasty, the ablest and most vigorous of the many scholars who interpreted, commented upon, and elaborated this fundamental book, which is even now the basis of Chinese medicine.

It is significant in many ways that the work should have been attributed to an emperor traditionally accorded such an early rule. Even at the time when it was first conceived, the *Classic* was obviously destined to be of lasting value, and its actual author, or authors, sacrificed the desire for personal glory to the supreme task of creating a work for eternity. This could best be done by ascribing the authorship to an exalted and ancient being, for China's reverence of antiquity dates back to its earliest days.

The naming of one of the ancients as an author was not without some justification, since the wording of the work makes it evident that its contents had been the intellectual property of the Chinese for a very long time before they were formulated and put down. The traditional dates of the Yellow Emperor make him a perfect choice for a hypothetical author of a work that stresses health and long life. He himself is supposed to have lived for one entire century, and this, according to the precepts of Chinese medicine, is the ideal span of life. But there is another, and perhaps more interesting purpose, which can be inferred from the text of this earliest medical work: the work is written in the form of a dialogue between the Yellow Emperor and his prime minister, in which the emperor—often in the humblest way—seeks instruction in all questions pertaining to health and the art of healing. Although the conversation can hardly be considered a historical fact, the involvement of the names of these two personages is strongly indicative of the exalted place accorded to medicine in ancient China. It seems certain that the authors of the *Classic* considered knowledge of the forces that cause life and death worthy of an emperor, and the art of healing to be the predominant responsibility of the elect. The grave obligation imposed by the mastery of the healing art finds expression in the emperor's solemn vow: "I shall smear my mouth with blood and take an oath that I will not venture to receive this information were I to use it recklessly or neglect it." (p. 186)

Beyond doubt, the practice of medicine has often been connected with an awareness of the moral responsibilities of the practitioner, and the wording of the Yellow Emperor's vow brings to mind the Hippocratic Oath. But the Chinese text differs from the Hippocratic writings which form the basis of Western medicine. The latter were written to give practical advice to the practicing physician; the former goes far beyond the scope of a medical textbook, being a treatise on life itself.

In the modern mind medicine is regarded as perhaps the most highly developed of all natural sciences. Religion, philosophy, thoughts on the creation of the world and the course of the universe hardly influence the actions of the present-day physician; ethics is a professional guide that helps the doctor guard himself from professional mistakes, but the patient's ethics, except in so far as it may influence his psychological well-being, is of no concern to the doctor. The traditional Chinese physician, on the other hand, is eminently concerned with his patients' ethics.

Here we see the immense difference in the Chinese concept of the art of healing. A medical science does not exist by itself; the art of healing is part of philosophy and religion, both of which propound oneness with nature and the universe. In this connection mention must be made of three essential features which form the basis of all reasoning underlying Chinese medical theory and practice.

These three features are the *Tao*, the *Yin* and the *Yang*, and the five elements, all of which have their place and function in the Chinese concept of the creation of the world. Since Chinese traditional thought conceives of man as composed of the same elements as the universe, and as functioning along the same principles as the macrocosm, it is necessary here to summarize briefly the Chinese concept of cosmogony.

That this concept of creation was the result of philosophical rather than religious thinking becomes immediately evident when one realizes that creation was never attributed to a superior or superhuman being. It was thought that the world had created itself, driven by *Tao,* the Way, an abstract motivator, which remained active and turned into a moral guide, once creation was accomplished. It was Tao, the Way, that caused the original state of chaos to divide into two forces, known as the Yin and the Yang,

OKUBO TODATAKA

Shen Nong, Chinese god of medicine.
Painting done c. 1600.

SAN FRANCISCO MEDICAL CENTER,
UNIVERSITY OF CALIFORNIA

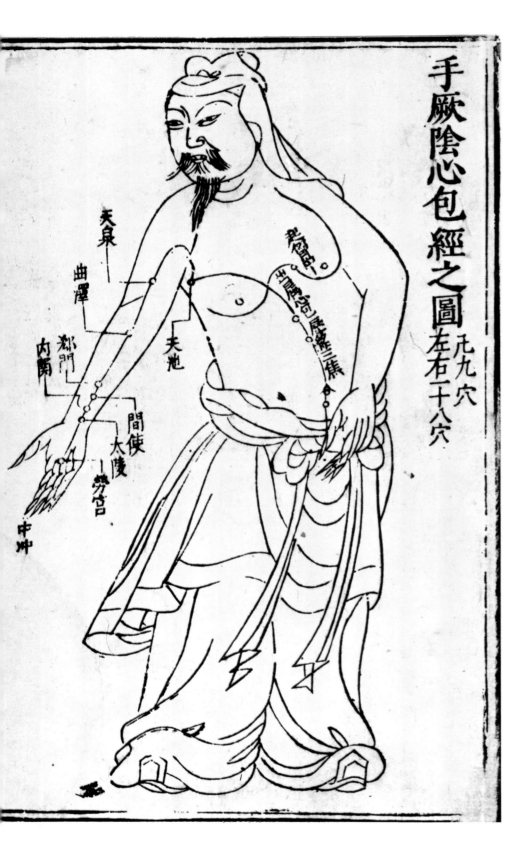

手厥陰心包經之圖　元九穴　左右二十八穴

Needle-pricking plate and anatomical scheme, from "T'ong-jen chen Kieu King" by Wang Wei-tö, 1031 A.D.

272

the female and the male, the negative and the positive elements. Even after creation was completed, *Tao* remained effective in guiding the functions of everything within the universe, while Yin and Yang in their ebb and flow of opposition and attraction to each other maintained all things and beings of the newly created world in their proper balance and harmony.

During creation, the Yin and the Yang brought forth the five elements: water, fire, wood, metal and earth. These elements formed the material substance for everything in this world. The correct proportion of these elements was preserved by the workings of the Tao and the interaction of the Yin and the Yang.

In the macrocosm the visible result of perfect balance was the change from day to night, the rising and the setting of the sun, the waxing and the waning of the moon, the unchangeable sequence of the seasons, the planting and the growing of the crops. Droughts and floods, failure of the crops and other natural phenomena were indications of a disturbance in the balance of nature.

Man, who was created with the universe and in its image, owed his health and hence his life to the harmony of natural forces; if this harmony was upset, the result was disease and death. But while the macrocosm of the universe was left to the course of Tao and the natural forces, it was up to man to shape his fate by compliance with Tao, the Way, and thus to keep the proper balance of Yin and Yang, the two opposing forces.

The Yellow Emperor's Classic is the first book that explains to man what he can expect by living according to the Tao and thus to nature, and how he can learn to adapt his life to this system: "Just as the breath of the blue sky is calm, so the will and the heart of those who are pure shall be in peace, and the breath of Yang will be stable in those who keep themselves in harmony with nature. Even if there are noxious spirits they cannot cause injury to those who follow the laws of the seasons." But the book also stresses the effects of disobedience to the Tao, the resulting disease and premature deterioration: " Those who fail to preserve this will have their nine orifices closed from the inside, and the development of their muscles and flesh will be obstructed from the outside, and the breath of protection will be lost to them. This then is called: 'to injure one's own body and to destroy one's own force of life.' " (p. 106)

The preceding quotations show that the medical text was directed to the educated layman as well as to the physician, but for the physician there is much specific ad-

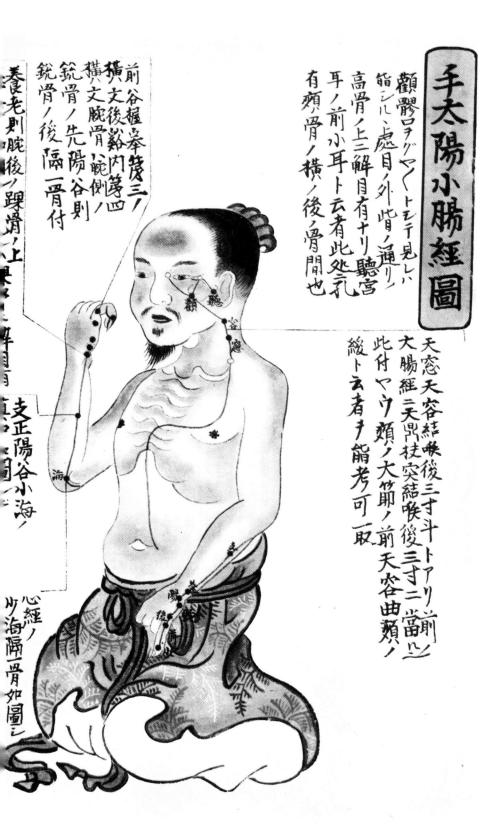

手太陽小腸經圖

vice which reaches its highest wisdom in the following exhortation (p. 105):

"... the sages did not treat those who were already ill; they instructed those who were not yet ill. They did not want to rule those who were already rebellious; they guided those who were not yet rebellious. To administer medicines to diseases which have already developed and to suppress revolts which have already developed is comparable to the behavior of those persons who begin to dig a well after they have become thirsty, and of those who begin to cast weapons after they have engaged in battle. Would these actions not be too late?"

It is easy to see why the Chinese conceived a naturalistic philosophy and clung to it for thousands of years. They have been and still are to a large extent an agricultural people, totally dependent upon nature's immutable course. Thus it was natural for them to think of themselves as one with the universe which provided them so directly with their livelihood. Because of this it was possible for the theories of cosmogony to become the basis of all subsequent medical writings and to survive up to the present day.

One may wonder how this transferral of the concepts of the macrocosm to the body of the human being was brought about. First of all, it must be said that this could have taken place only in a society that venerated the ancestor—and hence the dead—that considered the study of anatomy a desecration of the dead, and performance of surgery a permanent disfigurement and an infringement upon the sacredness of the body. In such an atmosphere of thought, human structure and physiological processes could not be investigated; they had to be taken for granted. It will be realized that under these conditions it was possible to explain human anatomy and physiology by an analogy to the universe and in terms of the theories of Tao, Yin and Yang and the five elements. The following discussion will reveal that such analogies were not carried out altogether arbitrarily, and that occasional flashes of insight and wisdom went into their making.

In accord with the prevailing taboos concerning the sacredness of the body, most succeeding Chinese medical works restricted their investigation to a vague study of

273

樟一種

女眞
眞

本邦表柏屋部仲
原村志賀宮伸木

樟
女眞 連理

本両
大国
平両
極

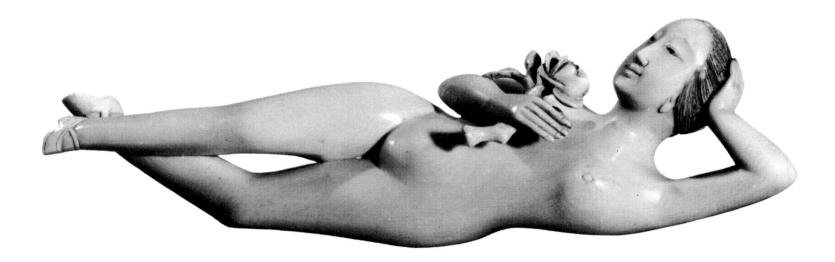

Beyond their decorative function, these ivory or alabaster figurines, which were found in the homes of Chinese high society, were used medically: if the mistress of the house was ill, instead of disrobing in the physician's presence, she simply showed him on the statuette the exact part of the body that was causing her trouble.

ROUGÉ COLLECTION, PARIS

surface anatomy. The description of internal structure and organs was as follows: man was composed of the "intestines," the five *Tsang,* of storing organs, and the six *Fu,* or eliminating organs. The five *Tsang* which were held to be more important than the eliminating organs were the liver, the heart, the spleen, the lungs, the kidneys. The six *Fu* were the stomach, the large intestine, the small intestine, the urinary bladder, the gall bladder, and the "three burning spaces"—an imaginary organ, whose three components were held to be distributed over the upper, middle and lower parts of the body. The storing and eliminating organs were connected by a system of vessels of which there were two kinds: those which carried blood and those which carried air or a vital pneuma.

This is a bare outline of the existing anatomical descriptions, but it may be sufficient to establish a parallel with the components of the universe and to form a basis for theories on the functions of the organs. In the *Classic* the Yellow Emperor is quoted, saying: "Covered by Heaven and supported by Earth, all creation together in its most complete perfection is planned for the greatest achievement: Man. Man lives on the breath of Heaven and Earth and he achieves perfection through the laws of the seasons." (p. 213). The analogy between the human being and the seasons was fortified by a preconceived numerical concept of the components of man: thus the body was believed to consist of 365 individual parts obviously corresponding with the 365 days of the year; the number of main vessels carrying blood and air was twelve and thus conformed with the twelve months; and lastly there were the *Tsang,* the five main organs representing the five elements.

Physiology, like anatomy, was based on the theories governing the creation of the world. The function of the body depended upon the two forces that created the world and man, the Yin and the Yang. While *Yang,* the male or positive principle, predominated in man, and *Yin,* the female or negative principle, predominated in woman, neither of these forces ever existed alone, but a certain proportion of both had to be present in every well-functioning human being. These two ever-active forces, alternately opposing and supplementing each other, were held to exist within all parts of the body and to circulate through the vessels that carried blood and pneuma. Pathological conditions arose out of over-abundance of either the Yin or the Yang, and out of obstruction of the flow of

Japanese engraving by Sadahide, done c. 1860, showing smallpox patients.

SAN FRANCISCO MEDICAL CENTER,
UNIVERSITY OF CALIFORNIA

276

The charlatan oculist

Japanese painting on paper, attributed to Mitsunaga or Yoshimitsu. Beginning of the Kamakura period. Thirteenth century. The patient was foolish to entrust himself to the charlatan's care; according to the text, after this barbarous treatment, he will lose his eyesight completely.

Childbirth

Japanese painting (ink and gold on canvas). Yamato-e
school. Fourteenth century.

INSTITUTE OF CHINESE ART, WASHINGTON, D.C.

blood. All these deficiencies and obstructions disturbed the balance of the organism as a whole, but usually affected one particular organ.

The concept of a disease entity as it is known to modern medicine did not exist in traditional Chinese thought. Some specific fevers were known and even distinguished according to a vague groping toward a knowledge of etiology, but even the possible causes of disease were subordinated to the general scheme of the universe. Thus, the five atmospheric conditions—wind, heat, humidity, dryness and cold—closely related to the five elements could bring about such diseases as "injuries of the heat," "the wind within," "humid warmth," etc. Smallpox, leprosy and various forms of intermittent fevers were also believed to arise out of atmospheric conditions. But it was generally believed that whatever immediate cause was held to be responsible for a particular disease, the patient had laid himself open to such an attack by a major infringement of Tao, the Way, and the invariable result was a disturbance of the balance of Yin and Yang.

It is noteworthy that the Chinese medical texts do not present these doctrines in flat statements, but that they are clothed in symbolic imagery which compares the functioning of the body to that of a state. The relations of the various organs to each other are likened to those of the high officials, and all are dependent upon the heart, which is described as "the minister of the monarch who excels through insight and understanding."

By means of these seemingly abstract theories, the ancient Chinese arrived at two extremely important conclusions: firstly, that disease is rarely localized, but generally affects the entire human being; and secondly, that disease is often associated with behavior and with a feeling of guilt, derived from the infringement on a moral law. The medical texts abound in statements concerning the effect of emotional states on health which can truly be termed precursors of psychosomatic medicine. It might be well here to quote some of the most pertinent ones:

"Man's place of residence, his motion and rest (his circumstances of life), his courage and cowardice—they also cause change within the vascular system (pulse)."

" In order to examine the course of a disease one must investigate whether man is courageous or nervous and cowardly, and one must study his bones, flesh and skin; only then can one know the facts which are necessary for the methods of treatment." (p. 195).

From the preceding discussion it is not to be wondered at that even the infringements of the laws of behavior were systematized to the point of absurdity, as may be seen in the following sentences:

" Those whose demeanor is dissolute and licentious get a disease of the lungs. Those who are lazy and full of apprehension and fear have difficulties in breathing, emanating from the lungs. Those whose demeanor is immoral and dissolute will injure their hearts." "Thus in Spring and in Fall, in Winter and in Summer, during the four seasons and during the periods of Yin and Yang, diseases are created, that are caused by faulty practices and transgressions which have become habit."

But even these schematizations do not detract from the basic wisdom which realized the existence of such a strong bond between the human body and the mind. With such principles in mind the ancient Chinese physician functioned not only as a healer of disease but even more as a moral guide who helped his patients to acknowledge and rectify their infringements of moral and natural laws. Being a judge of man's behavior as well as of his health presupposed a high moral and ethical attitude on the part of the early Chinese physician and a fairly well-organized state of the medical profession. And indeed, in the annals of the Chou Dynasty, which flourished between 1122 and 221 B.C., we find the outlines of a medical organization with a well-defined hierarchy graded according to achievement.

It is clear that neither the knowledge of disease as affecting the entire human being, nor the realization of a psychic factor as a cause, absolved the Chinese doctor from making a diagnosis in which we find the least trace of realism and the greatest amount of schematization.

The main diagnostic method employed by the Chinese physician of antiquity, and still that of the traditional Chinese and Japanese physician of today, is the taking of the pulse. This means of diagnosis is so intricate that it required several separate treatises of many volumes, entirely given over to the study of the pulse. The importance attributed throughout the centuries to pulse diagnosis can be gauged by the fact that from the third century A.D. until today, at least 156 books have appeared on the subject. The instructions concerning the pulse are briefly summarized here.

The pulse, it was said, consisted of six pulses on each wrist, each connected with a particular organ of the body, and each able to record even the minutest pathological changes taking place within the body. The procedure of palpation differed according to the sex of the patient; the physician first examined the pulses on the right wrist of female patients and those on the left wrist of male

KUNIYOSHI (1797-1861)

Hua T'o operating on General Kuan Kong

The general, though wounded in the arm by a poisoned arrow, nevertheless played chess until Hua T'o arrived; he refused anesthesia and continued the game unflinchingly while the highly skilful surgeon pulled out the arrow, scraped and cleaned the wound, and then sewed up the incision.

SAN FRANCISCO MEDICAL CENTER,
UNIVERSITY OF CALIFORNIA

patients. By means of the pulse the physician was supposed to be able to judge the site, and the state of the disease, its cause and duration, whether it was chronic or acute, and whether it would result in recovery or death. When we realize that the seasons, the time of day, weather conditions, and the age of the patient were held to cause differences in the sounds of the pulse beats, we become aware of the immense difficulties confronting the Chinese physician. And yet, their diagnoses were surprisingly accurate. Western physicians who were present at a number of such examinations tell that " many visits to patients in company with proficient Chinese physicians of the old school have shown how almost uncanny is their power of recognition of organic conditions through pulse observation alone."

Diagnosis of the pulse was supplemented by a study of the patient's complexion, the changes of which were held to indicate the future development of the disease. The ancient Chinese physician also interrogated the patient and his family and—interestingly enough—interpreted the patient's dreams in relation to his illness.

A study of therapy as advocated in the medical works indicates the everpresent preoccupation with the laws of the universe: "In order to effect a cure and relief, one must not err towards the laws of Heaven, nor towards those of the Earth, for they form a unit." (p. 166) Accordingly the physician was told that the five elements were paralleled by five methods of treatment. Since, however, disease was not a natural phenomenon—the earliest and wisest inhabitants of the earth were reputed to have been entirely free from it because of their virtuous mode of life—these five methods of treatment were not developed simultaneously; they evolved successively with the increasing lawlessness of succeeding generations.

It is reported that the first method of treatment evolved by the Chinese was the cure of the spirit. This method, strangely reminiscent of the most modern medical theories, consisted in helping the patient find the right way of life, that is, in finding contentment, repose, and in avoiding excesses and driving ambition: It was said that "those who are satisfied with their station in life will rise above it." (p. 203)

The second method of treatment was the nourishment of the body. To do this correctly, the physician had to consult the five elements and the various factors related to them. The Chinese physician believed that each of the diseases of the four seasons and the five main organs reacted to one of the five specified flavors. These five flavors—sour, bitter, sweet, pungent and salty—were held to be related in this order to the liver, the heart, the spleen, the lungs and the kidneys, and were supposed to have in this connection a binding, strengthening, retarding, dispersing and softening effect upon the intestines. This rather rigid scheme of concordances of the five flavors was softened by the statement that in general the produce of each season and each particular region constituted the ideal nourishment.

The next method of treatment concerns the true effects of medicines. Here again we are referred to the five predominant qualities contained in each of them. Most works dealing with internal medicine do not contain much pharmacological information; this is reserved for the numerous treatises specifically devoted to the description of China's famous materia medica.

The fourth method instructs the physician on how to combat disorder of the bowels and the viscera; this was

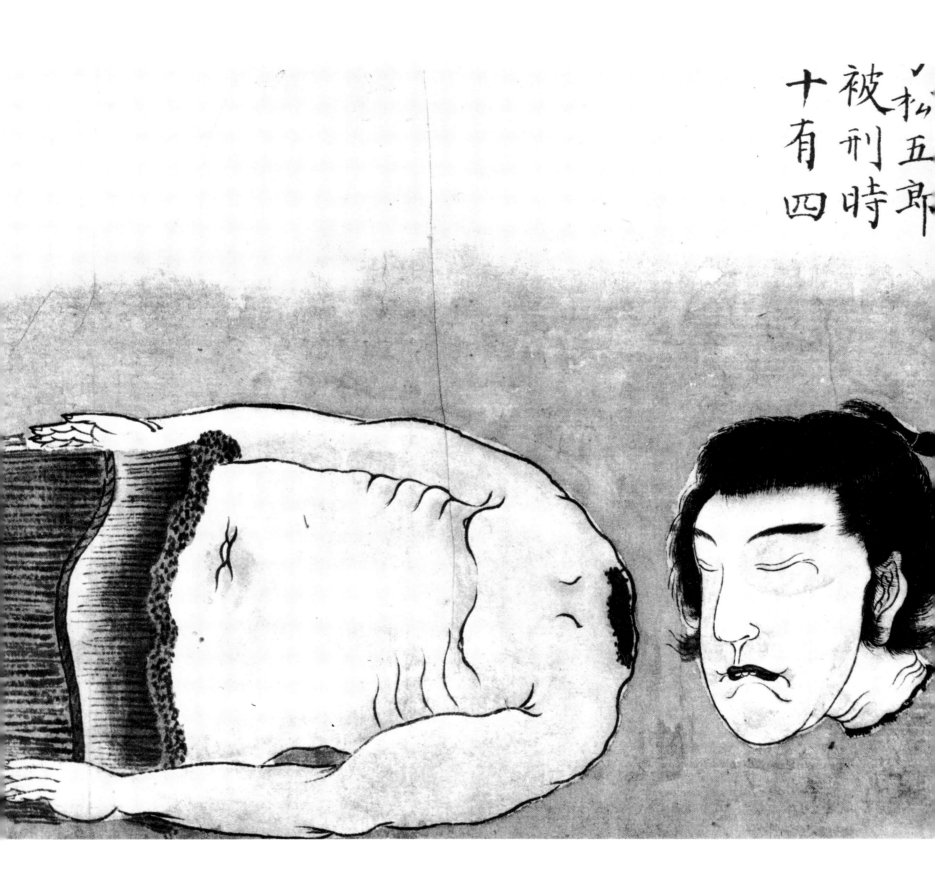

松五郎
被刑時
十有四

Toguda

Dissection of the body of Matsugoro, a twenty-four-year-old criminal.

Japan. Beginning of the nineteenth century.

281

Painting on paper.
Japanese painting attributed to Mitsunaga or Yoshimitsu.
Beginning of the Kamakura period. Thirteenth century. The man and his children were born with the tips of their noses black.

done mainly by massage and by insistence upon evacuation of the bowels and elimination of the waters.

The methods of treatment so far discussed presuppose an attitude of watchful waiting on the part of the physician. The guidance towards proper conduct, the establishment of a correct diet, that designation of a few medicines and the insistence upon daily evacuation appear to us as an encouragement of the healing power of nature rather than as active means of curing disease. It is the fifth method of treatment, however, that enables the physician to take an active part in combating illness; and since this method represents the most important expression of universalistic philosophy as applied to actual medical practice, I should like here to devote some time to its description. This method is the application of acupuncture and moxibustion.

Acupuncture, also known as "needling," consists in the insertion of needles of various shapes, sizes and materials into specific points of the body, the extremities and even the head. These needles may be withdrawn immediately, left *in situ* for some time, or rotated a number of times, depending on the nature of the ailment. Moxibustion, or moxa treatment, is practiced by applying to the skin combustible cones of the dried and powdered leaves of *artemisia vulgaris* or Wormwood; these cones are then ignited and allowed to burn down to the skin until a small blister forms. Both remedies are of great antiquity and must have been well known at the time of the composition of the earliest medical work, for the books deal with refinements of procedure, rather than with basic instructions concerning their use. The cosmological significance of both these methods of treatment lies in the location and number of acupuncture and moxibustion spots, and in the motivation given to their use.

In order to understand the theories behind acupuncture and moxibustion we must bring to mind again the basic concepts of pathology and physiology as discussed above. Disease was believed to arise out of an imbalance of the

282

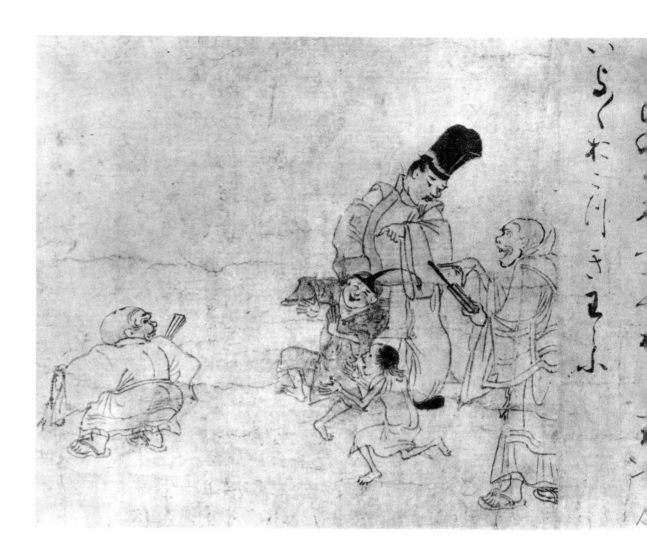

TOSA MITSUNAGA
The Hunchback

dual force of Yin and Yang, leading to an obstruction or insufficiency of either element within the twelve main vessels which were held to be connected with the various parts or organs of the body. Significantly, there are 365 points where these vessels rise to the surface of the body and thus present the spots for acupuncture and moxibustion. The effect of the insertion of the needle and the blistering of the moxa cone is to create openings for the relief of congestion caused by a plethora of Yin and Yang. According to the Chinese medical literature, acupuncture and moxibustion were applied for a vast variety of complaints, and especially for acute pains produced by rheumatism and neuralgic conditions, cramps and colics; both were recommended in cases of mental disturbance.

The description of these various methods of therapy concludes the discussion of the fundamentals of Chinese medicine. But these fundamentals conceived in the dawn of China's existence and recorded centuries before our era have not been relegated to the realm of history. In spite of the advent of Western practices, the Chinese have never completely ceased to employ their own art of healing, mainly because it continued to fit into their specific philosophy of life, but also because it appears that in frequent cases it was good medicine. Even though many Chinese doctors and patients of more recent centuries may no longer have been consciously aware of the cosmological basis of their treatments, the ancient medical works provided such detailed methods of procedure that individual reasoning was unnecessary.

However, the thought of man's origin and composition as part of the universe never quite left the Chinese mind and was the only existing theory until the introduction of the study of anatomy and the practice of surgery by Western scientists.

If the ancient theoretical foundations were kept alive, it is even less surprising that the methods of treatment have continued to be practiced in China and Japan. The examination of the pulse has remained the main diagnostic

Hokusai (1760-1849)

Blind men fording a river

This famous engraving evokes Brueghel's painting "The
Parable of the Blind."

Musée Guimet, Paris

method of the traditional Chinese and Japanese practitioner. And while the materia medica has become richer and more varied than had been described in the earliest works, the drugs are still applied according to the same principles Acupuncture and moxibustion too have remained in uninterrupted use.

At present the preoccupation with ancient Chinese medical methods is no longer the exclusive domain of the indigenous practitioner. Articles, books, and numerous personal communications bring to light that Western-trained Chinese and Japanese physicians have begun scientific investigations into the actual value of these methods in practice for more than 2500 years.

Acupuncture is by no means the only aspect of Chinese medicine that is shared by Japan. Therefore, even if it may appear strange if we here refer to Far Eastern medicine as comprising that of both China and Japan, the two countries do indeed share an almost identical medical history, owing to the fact that the Japanese adopted the medical system of China *in toto* in the seventh century.

Japan and Korea

Although Japanese intercourse with China dates back to the period of the former Han dynasty (about 200 B.C.), the formal introduction of Chinese learning is of a much later date. Japanese chronicles contain a number of legendary reports which attempt to account for the occasional fragments of Chinese medical knowledge that found their way into Japan during the centuries between 200 B.C. and 500 A.D. But these legends seem to be an artificial explanation for a natural phenomenon, for it is self-evident that the Chinese of the Han dynasty left notions of their intellectual achievements, like those of medicine and philosophy, as well as their crafts, such as the making of mirrors and bronzes. At the time when Chinese medicine was formally introduced into Japan, Japanese medicine had for centuries already been tinged with Chinese medical concepts. And while these Chinese medical concepts were scattered and had become part of Japanese practices, they nevertheless helped in the understanding and integration of Chinese medicine when it was introduced during the sixth and seventh centuries.

Chinese learning found its way to Japan not from China directly but by way of Korea. Nor were Chinese script, literature and philosophy introduced independently, but as by-products of Buddhism. Since on the one hand Korean Buddhism decisively influenced Japanese medical history, and since on the other hand the adoption of Buddhism was influenced by medical considerations, it is necessary to devote some space to the political circumstances that led to the importation of this new religion.

Contrary to the later practice of seclusion, the Japanese in their earlier history strove to establish concrete links with the Asiatic mainland. For this purpose they brought under their sway the smallest and southernmost of the four kingdoms into which ancient Korea was divided. From this colony, Mimana, the Japanese were able to use their influence to maintain a balance of power among the other three independent kingdoms, Paikché (also known as Kurada), Silla (also known as Shiragi), and Kokuli. This balance was, however, precarious, because the war-like attitude of the men of Silla tended to threaten Paikché, which had become more peace-loving with the adoption of Chinese culture and civilization. To insure military protection, Paikché submitted to a voluntary dependency upon Japan, which was expressed by means of regular embassies bearing gifts and tribute. Paikché had adopted Buddhism at the end of the fourth century A.D., and several embassies of the fifth and sixth centuries were composed of Buddhist scholars carrying volumes of the sutras and even an image of the Buddha.

This image was accompanied by a recommendation of the King of Paikché that the Emperor of Japan accept the new god. The Emperor, a great admirer of Chinese civilization but indifferent in the matter of religion, left the decision as to the acceptance of Buddhism to his ministers; only the chancellor of the empire, Soga Iname, adopted it. He thereupon received the statue of the Buddha and propagated the new religion; but two severe epidemics (accompanied by skin eruptions that are now generally believed to have been measles) (page 268) followed each other at short intervals and proved to be a retarding factor in the general acceptance of Buddhism. Clans opposed to Soga, the hereditary custodians of the ancient Japanese religion, advised the Emperor and the people that the importation of the foreign deity had incurred the wrath of the ancient native gods, who had therefore sent the pestilence as an expression of their displeasure. The Emperor, unwilling to share the responsibility for the plague, ordered the destruction of the image of the Buddha and the new temples, and the proscription of the new religion. Yet his successor, the Emperor Yomei, when taken seriously ill, sought healing by joining the Buddhist faith. He thus permanently bestowed upon

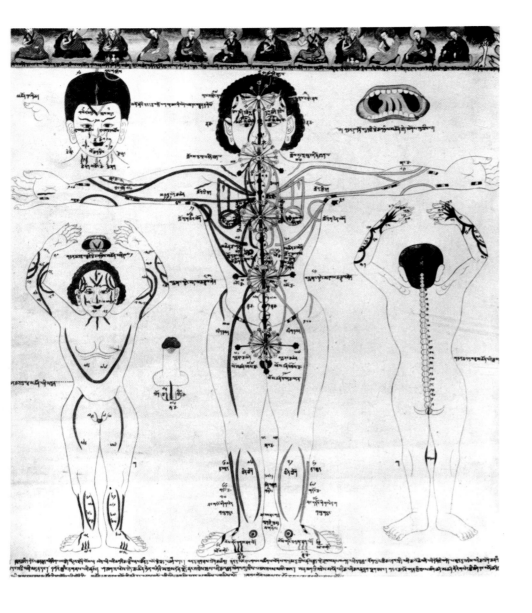

Tibetan painting
Anatomical plate.

them, nor were many Japanese at the beginning of the sixth century ready to search for philosophical meanings in Chinese religious texts which they were barely able to read. However, the emphasis on the healing powers of the sutras could be appreciated by all. After the Emperor Yomei had been converted to Buddhism, elaborate rites were held whenever an emperor was sick, and soon temples, devoted to the worship of Yakushi, the King of Medicine, were erected in many places.

While Shintoism prescribed that its priests must keep themselves rigidly aloof from the sick and the dying, Buddhist priests, almost from their start in Japan, performed the double function of priest and physician. They paved the way for the Buddhist scholars who in the latter part of the sixth century introduced and explained Chinese medical tests to the Japanese. These Buddhist priests had succeeded in stimulating interest in foreign medical knowledge to such an extent that the Japanese were no longer content to depend upon the mere chance that an embassy from Paikché might bring them scholars learned in the art of medicine. Instead, when their country was threatened in 553 A.D. by a recurrence of the earlier epidemic, the Emperor Kimmei requested the King of Paikché to send a physician and several kinds of medicine to Japan to help avert the dread disease. In compliance with the request the King dispatched one of his best physicians and teachers of medicine, Nasotsu Nurioda (Oyu-Ryoda), and two herbalists who were to search for medical plants in Japan. These men were later followed by other Korean physicians who taught their art to the Japanese.

As Buddhism spread in Japan, inability to read the Buddhist scriptures became intolerable to Japanese scholars, who wished to obtain a deeper insight than the Korean priests were able to provide. The necessity for Chinese studies was further emphasized when Chinese medical books were brought to Japan. Thus, in 607 A.D., Japan sent an envoy to China, her first official ambassador to that country. Having established official relations between the two countries, he returned to Japan the following year accompanied by two Chinese envoys. In 608 he traveled once again to China, this time followed by a group of young scholars and physicians who had been selected by the government to study Chinese methods in their respective fields of interest. After spending many years in China, the Japanese physicians returned fully equipped to teach the Chinese system of medicine.

Since there were now in Japan a number of Japanese who had received their training in China directly, it was

Buddhism the imperial favor, without, however, giving up Shintoism; and his example of adhering to both religions became a lasting practice throughout the nation.

The sudden change from the belief that Buddhism was the cause of disease to the assumption that it healed disease was the result of the efforts of the first Buddhist priests who came to Japan from Korea. Many of them did not actually practice medicine, but, knowing the value attached to health, they also knew how to convince the Japanese that the Buddhist Scriptures were effective in warding off and combating illness. It is clear that the scriptures were not read for their philosophical content; the early Korean priests were not trained to interpret

no longer necessary to depend upon Korean scholars for the interpretation of Chinese medicine. To make this new learning effective in Japan, it was imperative to make medical studies possible for a wider circle of Japanese than could be sent to China. For this purpose medical schools were opened which implemented definite courses of study as they had been laid down in the Taiho-Ryo, or the "Code of Laws of the Taiho Era" (702 A.D.).

It is interesting to note that admission to one of these medical schools was based not only upon a knowledge of the Chinese language, a *sine qua non* for the study of all the texts to be used, but also on certain rigid social prerequisites. Medicine was taught in two types of institutions, the Diagaku, or university, and the Kokugaku, or provincial schools. The university was located in that city which at the time housed the Imperial Court, and an average of about forty students was recruited from the leading noble families not below a certain social grade. (According to various authorities the grade varied between the fifth and the eighth). The pupils of the provincial schools, of which there was one in each province, were selected from among the sons of the governors and other high officials of the provinces. The enrollment varied with the size of the province and ranged from twenty to fifty students. In each province there was also one physician selected to instruct a small number of young men who were interested in medicine but did not have the social qualifications for admission into one of the medical schools.

The training of a medical student in the university and the provincial schools was long and arduous. The average time spent at the university was seven years, after which the graduates were taken into the imperial service. The rigor was relieved only once every ten days; twice a year the students were allowed fifteen days for recreation. Numerous routine examinations were held by the instructors of the schools; the important annual examinations, however, were held under the supervision of high government officials and provincial governors. The latter examinations served as a check upon the teachers as well as the students, for the professors whose disciples had done

Statue from the Khajuraho

Contrasting with the usual Khajuraho temple sculpture in which sex dominates, this figure has always intrigued archeologists. Medically, it seems to depict an extremely rickety child, with its bloated stomach and emaciated face.

MUSÉE DE L'HOMME, PARIS

287

SHAH NAMEH

The Birth of Rustam

Having undergone a Caesarian operation, the mother has a hemorrhage, whose intensity doesn't faze the surgeon in the least, although the patient will probably die of it. The Book of Kings, by Firdusi, Indo-Persian. Sixteenth century.

MUSÉE CONDE, CHANTILLY

brilliantly were promoted above those teachers whose students had shown mediocre results.

The curriculum was based entirely upon Chinese precepts, even as to the study of such works on general conduct as the *Book on Filial Piety,* the Confucian *Analects,* and the *Classic of Thousand Characters.* The medical texts included the *Tai-so-kiyo,* which was composed during the Sui dynasty (596-618 A.D.); the *Mei-do-kiyo,* a treatise on acupuncture of uncertain date and authorship; the *Miya-ku-kiyo* or "Classic of the Pulse," compiled towards the end of the third century A.D. by Wang Shu-ho; the *Ko-otsu-kiyo,* compiled by Huang-fu Mi of the Chin dynasty; the *So-mon* and the *Rei-su,* which were parts of China's most ancient medical work; the *Nan-kiyo,* a small treatise written in the third century B.C. with the purpose of elucidating the difficulties presented by the two last named works; and the *Sho-hin-kiyo,* a collection of miscellaneous prescriptions. The list of required reading increased rapidly and soon included nearly all Chinese medical literature.

Since Court and provincial physicians were recruited from the ranks of the young men who had received their training at the university or at one of the provincial schools, it is surprising that Buddhist priests were still called on for medical assistance. This was due to their clever adjustment to changing times. While many of the early Korean Buddhist priests were actual practitioners of medicine, dispensers of medicaments and scholars in medical science, their successors were no longer learned in the art of medicine. Their methods of combating and preventing disease were based upon their alleged possession of magic powers. With their practices of incantation and exorcism—familiar to the Japanese from their ancient Shinto rites—the priests appealed to a great part of the population. Even a number of emperors fell under their sway and participated in Buddhist ceremonies performed to avert pestilences.

Buddhism and the practice of Chinese medicine suffered a temporary setback during the first decade of the ninth century A.D. when Japan was struck by several waves of the plague. Chinese medicine was unable to cope with the disease, and the Emperor Heijo decided that only the return to the old Japanese ways could save the youth of the country from the dreaded return of the disease. He therefore commissioned two physicians, Abe no Masanawo and Idzumo no Hirosada, to gather material on the methods of pure Japanese medicine, so that it might again be practiced. The resulting book, the *Collection of Methods of the Daido Era,* contained prescriptions and

treatments supposedly discovered during the "Divine Age" by the founders of the Japanese art of medicine, Onamuchi and Sukonahikona. In addition to medical formulae, the book contained new and strict laws for the conduct of physicians and furnished a list of punishments and fines for possible infractions. Among other restrictions the laws forbade any contact between physicians and Buddhist priests; even an accidental meeting on the street necessitated a day's absence from Court. These reforms were enforced for a short time only; with the passing of the plague they fell into disregard without having caused any serious disruption of medical education.

At the beginning of the eleventh century, imperial grants were made for the enlargement of the university in general and the department of medicine in particular. Moreover, all medical schools profited by a custom followed by the majority of their graduates, who donated a part of their income from their first year's practice to their respective schools. In later years this voluntary contribution became a definite obligation to the extent that a definite percentage of the earnings and the form of payment were fixed by imperial decree.

In his training the medical student was required to attend courses in materia medica, based upon textbooks and the study of medicinal herbs and mineral and animal extracts, and in internal medicine, which included physiology The little knowledge of anatomy that was required at the examinations was taught by means of fanciful drawings. The longest period of study was devoted to the pulse. After these subjects had been mastered, the student turned to supervised practical work, to specialized study of children's diseases, and to diseases of the ear and the eye.

The Chinese medical works that had been brought back by Japanese scholars upon their return from their studies in China eventually proved to be insufficient for the number of students in the courses based upon them. In the early tenth century medical teachers began to feel the need for a greater number of textbooks and also for overcoming the difficulties inherent in the use of Chinese textbooks for the instruction of Japanese students. As a consequence, many of the Chinese books were adapted to the Japanese language and new books were compiled from the Chinese sources. The most important of these new works is the ambitious compilation by Yasuyori Tamba, the *Ishinho,* composed in 984 A.D.; it is the oldest Japanese medical work still extant and contains abstracts from more than one hundred Chinese medical works. Since many of these have since been lost, the *Ishinho* is a

valuable aid to the student of Chinese medicine. According to Fujikawa, the Japanese medical historian, the book is divided into fifteen sections dealing with the following subjects: 1. General medicine; 2. Acupuncture; 3. Diseases of the pneuma; 4. Diseases of the intestines; 5. Skin diseases; 6. Diseases of the eye, ear and teeth; 7. Diseases of the hands and feet; 8. Abscesses and tumors; 9. Wounds; 10. Diseases of children; 11. Gynecology and midwifery; 12. Hygiene; 13. Sexual hygiene; 14. Dietetics; 15. Medicines.

The medical concepts and practices of the period under consideration, as they are expressed in the *Ishinho* and other slightly later works on the subject, show clearly that Japanese medicine deviated but a little from its Chinese sources.

Tibetan Medicine

Chinese medicine spread beyond the confines of Japan and also affected the center of Asia and particularly the border territory of Tibet in whose medical systems Chinese as well as Indian and also Arabic influences can be traced.

Lamaist temples traditionally serve as centers of ecclesiastical education as well as of religious services. Since the study and practice of medicine is part of the dogma of Buddhism and is carried out by priests only, medical scrolls, including anatomical charts, are hung on the walls of temples dedicated to Bhaishajyaguru (or Yao-shih-fo), the Buddha of the healing art. Inasmuch as Tibetan temples are generally inaccessible to strangers, these charts are virtually unknown in the Western world.*

The originals of the charts here shown were displayed in Peking in the Temple Hall IV of the Yu-Ho-Kung. They were discovered in 1947 by the late Professor Ferdinand D. Lessing, and the copies made at his behest are now among the manuscript materials at the East Asiatic Library of the University of California.** Like their originals the charts are painted on canvas scrolls, which are mounted on cloth. They measure thirty inches in length and are twenty-four inches wide.

I am deeply grateful to Professor Lessing for having shown me the charts and for his suggestion that I work on their invaluable contents; his crowded schedule, un-

Indra, a god in the Hindu pantheon, who brought medicine to mankind. High-relief in wood.

MUSÉE GUIMET, PARIS

fortunately, did not permit his active collaboration.***

Although it is impossible to date the specific charts shown here, the study of Tibetan and Indian medicine leaves little doubt that the concepts depicted here have been in existence for nearly two millennia. Similar charts

Under the direction of Vishnu, the gods and demons are churning the sea to obtain the elixir of immortality. Vishnu is carried by the physician Dhavantari who emerges from the waves at the end of the churning.

BAS-RELIEF, ANGKOR-VAT, 1113 B.C.

* One similar chart was found in a monastery at Lhasa and described by E.H.C. Walsh in his article on "The Tibetan Anatomical System" in the *Journal of the Royal Asiatic Society*, Great Britain and Ireland, 1910, p. 1215 ff.

** I am indebted to Dr. Elizabeth Huff, Director of the East Asiatic Library, for her kind permission to publish the charts.

*** A full translation of the Tibetan legends was prepared. For this, the author is indebted to the help of Mr. Turrel V. Wylie, Associate Professor, a specialist in Tibetan studies at the Far Eastern Institute of the University of Washington, in Seattle, Washington.

are still in use today for the teaching of medicine in Tibetan temple schools.

Tibetan anatomical and physiological thinking reflect religious and philosophical concepts rather than observation and dissection. Most of these concepts are derived from a combination of classic Hindu medicine, Buddhism, and Yoga practices, all adapted to Tibetan Lamaism which considers the human body a microcosmic image of the macrocosm, and its structure and function designed for the comfort and even distribution of the soul, or spirit of life, rather than for physical ends. For the understanding of the charts the following basic principles should be borne in mind.

The human body is pervaded and activated by four elementary substances: phlegm, bile, wind, and blood. They are conveyed by means of an intricate system of vessels (rtsa), each with its specific function.

The heart is the seat of memory and emotion and to it are ascribed many of the functions which we attribute to the brain. The brain is disregarded as are the lungs, whose relationship with breathing is not recognized.

Breathing, which is of supreme importance in Yoga practices, is held to proceed by means of two channels which spiral around the spine, whereby the (ida) channel originating on the left side serves for inhalation and thus takes in the spiritual essence of life and the right channel (pingalâ) serves for exhalation.

A channel, called the "Cord of Hope" (sushumnâ), leads through the spinal column from its end to the posterior fontanelle. Through this suture, called the "Aperture of Brahma," the soul (altman) leaves the body at the time of death.

In addition to the vessels (rtsa) man contains a number of channels (nâdf) which concretize and localize certain aspects of the soul. Yoga exercises involving certain channels are intended to affect that aspect of the soul that is related to the channel involved.

The Tibetans assume the existence of five states of consciousness. These are housed in five centers, called "Wheels" (chakras), which are located along the "Cord of Hope." The concept of consciousness pertains to the body as well as the psyche and hence the five centers also harbor the five senses, (smell, taste, sight, feeling, and hearing) the five faculties, (locomotion, grasp, excretion, procreation, and speech). Human individuality merges with the universe in the highest center located above the eyes.

In spite of the fact all Far Eastern religious thought — Confucianism, Shintoism and Into-Tibetan Buddhism — frowned on the study of anatomy by dissection of the human body and hence also upon the practice of surgery, the curiosity as to bodily structure existed. It sought outlets in all peoples as well as the desire to perform surgical operations, if conditions arose that made them advisable. Hence we see that the Japanese and Chinese gained a superficial and fanciful idea of human anatomy from chance observations, and furthermore counted among their great doctors one whose surgical exploits became legend and whose skill was said to be more extraordinary than that of any other mortal. He also had the audacity and technique successfully to transplant hearts from one individual to another. The name of this great personality was Hua T'o, whose date of birth is assumed to be A.D. 190. According to legend he received the secret of surgical art from two hermits upon whom he came in the course of his many wanderings.

Hua T'o is also said to have discovered a potent anesthetic, the nature and composition of which have never been ascertained, although it may have been opium.

Hua T'o's surgical feats are recorded in the *Annals of the Late Han Dynasty*; they range from venesection and acupuncture to laparotomy, excision of the spleen, intestines and liver. One of his most celebrated operations he performed without the help of anesthetics. His patient was Kuan Kung, a famous general who was later deified as God of War, and who had been wounded in the arm by a poisoned arrow. The General, who was playing chess at the time of Hua T'o's arrival, declined to be anesthetized and continued his game without flinching as the surgeon with great skill removed the arrow, scraped and cleansed the wound, and sutured the incision. This story and its heroes also became part of the history of Japanese medicine whereby Hua T'o received the Japanese name Kada and General Kuan Kung became known as Kuan Yo or Kanwa (page 280). The Chinese legend holds that Hua T'o was also familiar with the practice of trepanation because it is said that he recommended this operation to a king who suffered from intolerable headache. The King, however, declined the heroic intervention

وتستى الأثمان إلى عمان فاكتفى أبو زيد بالنحلة وأهب للراحة فلم يبح الوالى

بعد تخرية بركته بل أوعز بصمة إلى خزانته وأن يطلق يد في خزانته

وتعرفون ومنهم من يهرب من النور ومنهم من سئل ذلك
ومنهم من نبح مثل الكلاب وبعض من اقترب منه فنصبه
ذلك ايضاً وقد ذكرنا انهم راوا خمراً وانساناً او انسانين عضهما فافلتنا

واز اود موس استلى لهذه الآفه وهسون وان احدهما عض وانسلى

Arabic painting of the Baghdad school, done in 1224 by Abdallahibn al Fadl. We see a man being bitten by a mad dog.

FREER GALLERY OF ART, WASHINGTON

Cauterization of leprosy lesions, after the Turkish translation of a Persian treatise on surgery, "Imperial Surgery," written in Persia c. 1300. The Turkish translator, Sharaf ad-Din ibn el Hadjdj Ilias, called Sapoundji-oghlou, "the soap-merchant's son," worked in Amasia, in Asia Minor.

The manuscript was handwritten by the author and offered to Sultan Mahomet II in 1465. The numerous paintings adorning it are copied from those of the Persian original which in turn were copied from a treatise on surgery written in Baghdad in the twelfth century.

BIBLIOTHÈQUE NATIONALE, PARIS

on the suspicion that such drastic means could only have been suggested to the doctor at the behest of enemies of the King. He displeased another of his royal patients who demanded his constant attendance at Court. Pleading illness in his own family. Hua T'o took leave from his difficult master, planning never again to return to Court. The King, however, had him returned forcibly, arrested and thrown into prison, and later condemned to die. Before his execution. Hua T'o burnt all his manuscripts which presumably contained descriptions of his various operations. A few leaves were rescued from the ashes; they described the method of castration which was the only surgical procedure practiced in China until the introduction of Western medicine into that country.

The initial Japanese aversion towards anatomy and surgery even surpassed that of the Chinese and remained active for many centuries. As in China, so also in Japan there were no surgical writings and one must assume that inevitable restorative surgery, such as the setting of fractures and the treatment of accidental wounds, received perfunctory attention by a clan of manipulators who were not formally a part of the medical profession. It must be remembered that for centuries, Japan was free from internal and external strife and that war injuries did not constitute an incentive for the development of surgery.

In the eleventh century, however, the ancient and peaceful imperial rule was shaken by the newly evolved feudal system which abruptly ended the tranquillity of the earlier period. New developments unsettled the existing social system and considerably depreciated the value of imperial honors. Individual clans had grown in strength and fought each other in an endeavor to acquire supremacy in land and men.

These wars and the resulting social upheaval brought about a deterioration of the medical profession, but the result was not entirely detrimental; for the period of unsettlement eradicated completely the imported and native prejudices which had prevented the development of surgery in Japan. With the decay of the medical schools the Confucian stigma attached to the practice of surgery which had been adopted by the Japanese together with the Chinese medical system, fell into oblivion. The ancient Shinto tenets which considered the inflicting, receiving, and even touching of wounds as equally defiling were greatly modified with the growth of a socially prominent warrior class. Surgery, the study of Anatomy (Fig. 11), and especially battle surgery, became increasingly important during the centuries of internal strife. While the medical history of this period suffers from a lack of great names, the history of surgery is rich with reports of great endeavors. Indeed, some of the most outstanding surgeons were military men who made the transition from warrior to surgeon on the very field of battle.

The Far East and the Middle East

This work was supported by a research grant from the United States Public Health Service, National Institute of Mental Health.

The illustrations are reproduced from holdings of the Oriental Collections from the Libraries of the University of California at Berkeley and the San Francisco Medical Center.
With grateful appreciation of the generous advice and assistance of Mrs. Atsumi Minami.

List of color reproductions

GERRITS VAN BREKELENKAM (1620-1668)
The Consultation

LOUVRE, PARIS

Page 15 The Sorceror of the Grotto of Trois Frères

18 Sorcerer

22 Fetish for Amulet

23 Symbolic depiction of the mother of a large family

35 Mother and Child

47 Philoctetes at Lemnos

57 Adonis wounded

60 Illustration from Kition's "Commentary of Appolonius"

73 The Mask of Nanahuatzin

76 Divinity with Plumed Headpiece

86 The Verbena Illumination, Italy, thirteenth century, after a manuscript (no longer in existence) dating from the fourth century.

87 Childbirth

90 The Vision of Daniel. An illustration from the "Commentaries on the Apocalypse"

91 Miniature illustrating a surgical manuscript of the School of Salerno

97 Hippocrates

100 Visiting of the Sick

109 FRA ANGELICO
Saint Palladius being treated by Saint Cosmas and Saint Damian

112 DOMENICO CURRADO called GHIRLANDAIO
Presumably a portrait of Count Sassetti and his grandson

116 Gathering sage
Miniature on parchment

117 FRANCESCO DI STEFANO called PESELLINO
Saints Cosmas and Damian

121 Delivery of a Baby
From a manuscript, end of the fifteenth century

129 NICOLAS MANUEL DEUTSCH
Detail of an ex-voto

136 QUENTIN METSYS
Portrait of Dr. Paracelsus

141 HIERONYMUS BOSCH
The Ship of Fools

148 PETER BRUEGHEL, THE ELDER
The Parable of the Blind

156 GÉRARD DOU
The Dropsical Woman

160 REMBRANDT VAN RIJN
Doctor Tulp's Anatomy Lesson

165 JAN STEEN
The Sick Girl

170 DAVID TENIERS, THE YOUNGER
The Village Doctor

Page 175 JOSÉ DE RIBERA
The Club-foot

177 NICOLAS POUSSIN
The Philistines stricken with the plague

188 GASPARE TRAVERSI
The Injured Man

193 PIETRO LONGHI
The Apothecary

200 A patient pursued by apothecaries
Tapestry based on a work by ANTOINE WATTEAU

207 WILLIAM HOGARTH
Visit to a Charlatan

214 THÉODORE GÉRICAULT
The Madwoman

220 ANTOINE GROS
The Plague Victims of Jaffa

221 CLAUDE GAUTHEROT
Napoleon wounded at Ratisbon

225 MARGUERITE GÉRARD
Bad News

232 EDGAR DEGAS
Absinthe

239 VINCENT VAN GOGH
Self-portrait with one ear cut off

242 HENRI DE TOULOUSE-LAUTREC
An Examination at the Medical Faculty of the University
of Paris

244 CHAÏM SOUTINE
The Village Idiot

251 CHARLES DUFRESNE
Medicine

254 ROGER DE LA FRESNAYE
The Sick Man

260 PABLO PICASSO
The Sick Child

265 The Lady Pope of the Students

268 Infantile Eruption
Chinese silk-painting, eighteenth century

277 The Charlatan Oculist
Japanese painting on paper, attributed to Mitsunaga or
Yoshimitsu
Beginning of the Kamakura period (thirteenth century)

288 SHAH NAMEH
The Birth of Rustam
The Book of Kings, by Firdusi
Indo-Persian (sixteenth century)

293 The Makomad of Hariri Neshki Mesopotamium, copied
in the year 635 of the Hegira, by the painter Yahya ibn
Mahmud.

HONORÉ DAUMIER (1808-1879)
The Imaginary Invalid

BIBLIOTHÈQUE NATIONALE, PARIS

300

Table of black-and-white reproductions

Page 9 A. R. WAUD
The Country Doctor

10 WINSLOW HOMER
Playing Old Soldier

11 JACK LEVINE
Medicine Show

12 The Venus of Laussel

14 The Venus of Sireuil

16 The Venus of Willendorf

19· Statuette of king sitting on an animal symbolizing a throne

20 Enema

21 Witchdoctor's mask

24 Baoulé Fetish

26 Cup of King Gudea

28 Mother nursing her child

29 Code of Hammurabi

30 The Seal of the male midwife named Urlugadinna

32 Thot, the god of magic and medicinal secrets

34 Imhotep, the god of healing

36 Syrian prince consulting an Egyptian doctor

37 Healing Statue

37 Hunchback wearing a miter

38 The Scales

39 The dwarf Khnoumhotep

40 Injured worker being treated by a physician

42 Achilles bandaging Patroclos

44 Ex-voto dedicated to Aesculapius

45 The Peytel Aryballos

48 Authentic bust of Hippocrates

49 Torso of Aesculapius

50 Amphiaraos treating a patient

51 Bacchic Scene, the so-called "Dying Bacchante"

52 Aesculapius and his daughter Hygieia

53 Sthenelos bandaging the finger of Diomedes

55 Jason the physician examining the liver of a patient

56 Hippocrates

58 Aesculapius and his daughter Hygieia

59 With the aid of an instrument, Japyx the physician removes an arrow from the thigh of Aeneas, the hero of Troy

Page 61 Aesculapius with poppies

63 Roman soldiers treating their wounded comrades
Detail of the Trajan column

64 Roman girl with arm-injury

65 Sick woman

66 Tlazolteotl

68 Maternal Idol

69 Man showing an injury in his right leg

70 Head sculpture

71 Hunchback with tattooed face

74 Human sacrifice
Codex Magliabecchiani

75 Ciuateotl

75 Indian eating mushrooms
Codex Magliabecchiani

77 Ovoid bowl decorated with a female figurine in childbirth
position

77 Doctor treating a patient

78 Hunchback

78 Woman giving birth

79 Doctor and a sick child

79 Blind man

79 Syphilitic woman with her child

80 The Good Samaritan

82 Funeral stele of a woman doctor, found in Metz

83 Three ivory plaques

85 Saint Cosmas and his case of medical instruments, on the
famous mosaic of the apse of the Church of Cosmas and
Damian, Rome

88 Aesculapius discovers the betony plant

89 Hippocrates and Galen

92 Care given to the sick

93 Vomiting man

94 Physician examining a patient

95 Josaphat as a child, meeting a leper and an old cripple at
the gates of Jerusalem

96 GILLES DE DINANT
The Plague in Tournai, 1349

98 Two miniatures from the book "Grande Chirurgie" by
Guy de Chauliac

101 The Anatomy Lesson

Page 102 Capital of Aesculapius

103 The impatience of the sick man

104 DOMENICO DI BARTOLO
Treatment of the sick

105 ANDREA PISANO, after a sketch by GIOTTO
The medicine maker

106 Four wood-cuts from the incunabulum "Hortus Sanitatis" by Joannes de Cuba

108 Wood cut from the "Hortus Sanitatis"

110 JAN VAN EYCK
Detail from *The Madonna of Canon van der Paele*

111 MASTER OF FRANKFURT
Saint Roch

113 Head of a man with facial paralysis

114 Reception of patients in the Hôtel-Dieu

114 Sick ward at the Hôtel-Dieu

115 GIOVANNI DELLA ROBBIA
Examination of the sick

118 Treatment of a fracture

118 Intestinal suture

119 Depiction of treatment for injuries due to dangerous animals

119 GENTILE BELLINI
Examination of the patient

120 Saint Cosmas and Saint Damian examining urine

122 LEONARDO DA VINCI
Depiction of legs

124 HANS HOLBEIN
Allegory of the medical arts

125 ALBRECHT DÜRER
Self-portrait meant for the doctor, the artist asking for a long-distance consultation

126 ALBRECHT DÜRER
Melancholy

128 ALBRECHT DÜRER
Thinness and Obesity

130 LEONARDO DA VINCI
Mona Lisa (study)

131 LEONARDO DA VINCI
Outer and inner muscles of the neck

132 TITIAN
Anatomy

133 MICHELANGELO
Dissection of a corpse

134 ANDREAS VESALIUS
Anatomical plates

Page 138 Agony of King Henry II at the Hôtel des Tournelles

139 Portable pharmacy of the Renaissance

139 Bronze mortar, High Renaissance

140 Jan Sanders van Hemessen
The extraction of the "Stone of madness"

142 Ligier Richier
Death, a statue on the tomb of René de Chalon, Prince of Orange

143 Drawing attributed to Primaticcio

144 Gérard David
The flaying of the corrupt judge

145 Andrea del Sarto
San Matteo Hospital, Florence

146 Raphael Sanzio
The cripple

147 Mattias Grünewald
A man stricken with "St. Anthony's Fire"

150 Four engravings by Hendrik Goltzius
—The physician is a god
—The physician is a man
—The physician is a devil
—The physician is an angel

152 Joan Galle
Preparing and taking a remedy against venereal disease

153 The military surgeon and his assistant

154 The tooth-puller

154 An extract from the "Recueil des pièces facétieuses et bouffonnes"

158 Rembrandt van Rijn
Woman ill in bed

159 Rembrandt van Rijn
Servant at a patient's bedside

161 Rembrandt van Rijn
Doctor Deyman's Anatomy Lesson

162 Gabriel Metsu
The sick child

163 Cornelis Dusart
The Charlatan

164 Adrien van Ostade
A healer praising his wares

166 Thomas de Keyser
The Anatomy Lesson

167 Jan Steen
A patient in bed and her doctor

168 Theodor Rombouts
The tooth-puller

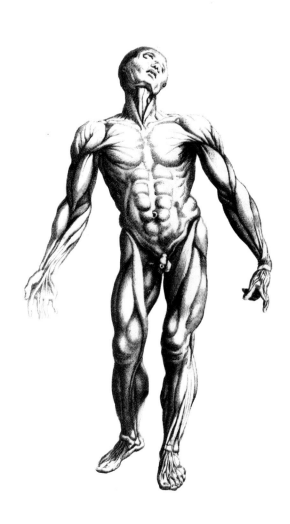

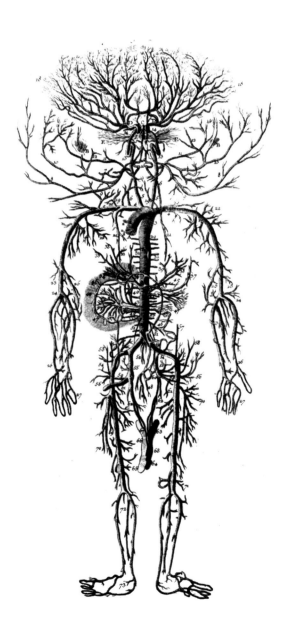

Page 169   DAVID TENIERS, THE YOUNGER
Surgical operation

171   DAVID RYCHAERT III
The surgeon

172   JACOB JORDAENS
The Sisters of Charity of Antwerp

174   DIEGO VELASQUEZ
Presumably a portrait of the dwarf Sebastiano de Morra

176   JACQUES CALLOT
Crippled beggar

178   JACQUES CALLOT
Childbirth in a Gypsy camp

179   ABRAHAM BOSSE
The Blood-letting

180   ABRAHAM BOSSE
Anne of Austria visiting the great hospital ward of La
Charité, c. 1640

181   PHILIPPE DE CHAMPAIGNE
The sick child

182   PIERRE PUGET
The Plague in Marseilles

183   PEDRO GAETANO
The Plague

184   WOLFGANG HEIMBACH
The Sick Man

185   "Fools make themselves known at all times"
From a collection of the best-known proverbs divided into
three illustrated books by Logniet, c. 1675

186   Remedies of all ailments

190   The Surgeon

190   The Surgeon's Wife

190   PIETRO LONGHI
The tooth-puller

191   The Arterial System, an engraving based on Roberg

194   SÉBASTIEN LE CLERC
Dissection experiment

195   JEAN-BAPTISTE OUDRY
Dr. So-much-the-worse and Dr. So-much-the-better

196   GIOVANNI-BATTISTA TIEPOLO
The Charlatan

197   The botanical and mineralogical doctors run over by the
fashionable physicians

198   PIERRE-ANTOINE BAUDOIN
The Young Mother or The Fruit of Secret Love

199   NICOLAS LAVREINCE
The Unseasonable Arrival

199   JEAN-HONORÉ FRAGONARD
The Remedy

306

Page 202 FRANÇOIS BOUCHER
An illustration for *The Imaginary Invalid*

203 DOMINIQUE LELEU
The Sick Child

204 RICHARD SAINT-NON
The Sick Woman

205 WILLIAM HOGARTH
An Anatomy Lesson in the hall of barbers

206 WILLIAM HOGARTH
"Gin Lane" or the Evils of Drunkenness

208 JEAN-ANTOINE HOUDON
Flayed Man

209 JACQUES GAMELIN
"Pray not to be led into temptation"

211 THOMAS ROWLANDSON
Hypochondriac

212 CHARLES BELL
Anatomical plate

216 FRANCISCO GOYA
Portrait of Goya sick

217 FRANCISCO GOYA
The Insane Asylum

218 JACQUES LOUIS DAVID
Episode from an epidemic of the plague that ravaged
Marseilles in 1720

219 JACQUES LOUIS DAVID
Study of the head of a plague-stricken man

219 PIERRE-JEAN DAVID D'ANGERS
Pain

222 BACLER D'ALBE
Françoise, the Canteen-keeper of the 88th, bandaging a
wounded soldier

223 EUGÈNE DELACROIX
The Consultation

226 LOUIS BOILLY
The Patient

227 LOUIS BOILLY
The Vaccination

228 ALFRED JOHANNOT
The Duke of Orleans visiting the cholera victims at the
Hôtel-Dieu in 1832

229 PAUL GAVARNI
A scene from student life

229 HONORÉ DAUMIER
The Anatomy Lesson

230 HONORÉ DAUMIER
The Autopsy

234 CONSTANTIN GUYS
The Hospital of Pera

307

Page 235 ALBERT EDELFELT
Pasteur in his laboratory in 1885

235 JEAN GEOFFROY
Visiting Day in the Hospital

236 THOMAS EAKINS
The Gross Clinic

237 JOHN S. SARGENT
The members of the first medical faculty of Johns Hopkins,
Baltimore, Maryland.

238 VINCENT VAN GOGH
The vestibule of the hospital of Saint Rémy

240 VINCENT VAN GOGH
Portrait of Dr. Gachet in 1890

240 Charcoal portrait of Vincent Van Gogh on his death-bed,
July 29, 1890, in Auvers-sur-Oise. Drawn by Dr. Gachet.

241 HENRI DE TOULOUSE-LAUTREC
Tracheotomy operation by Dr. Péan in 1891

247 ÉDOUARD VUILLARD
Professor Gosset Operating

248 RAOUL DUFY
The Operation

249 EDVARD MUNCH
The Sick Child

250 JULES
The Business Agent

252 GEORGES ROUAULT
Portrait of the Artist

253 OSCAR KOKOSCHKA
Portrait of Herwarth Walden

256 GEORGE GROSZ
The Draft Board

257 PAUL KLEE
The Buffoon

259 HYMAN BLOOM
Autopsy

261 FRANCIS PICABIA
The Ill-smelling Eye

262 SALVADOR DALI
Dream

266 GEORGE W. BELLOWS
Dance in a Mad House

270 The three gods of Chinese medicine

271 OKUBO TODATAKA
Shen Nong, Chinese god of medicine

272 Needle-prcking plate and anatomical scheme, from
"T'ong-jen chen Kieu King" by Wang Wei-tö, 1031 A.D.

273 Chinese illustration in a secret book on needle pricking

308

Page 274 UTSUMU RANKEI
Illustrated herbarium

275 Japanese engraving by Sadahide

276 Figurine

278 Childbirth
Japanese painting, School of Yamato-e (fourteenth century)

280 KUNIYOSHI
Hua T'o operating on General Kouan Kong

281 TOGUDA
Dissection of the body of Matsugoro, twenty-four-year-old criminal, Japan

282 Japanese painting attributed to Mitsunaga or Yoshimitsu
Beginning of the Kamakura period. Thirteenth century

283 TOSA MITSUNGA
The Hunchback

284 HOKUSAI
Blind men fording a river

286 Tibetan painting: anatomical plate

287 Statue from the Khajuraho temple. Central India

290 Bas-relief, Angkor-Vat

291 Indra, a god in the Hindu pantheon, who brought medicine to mankind
High-relief in wood

294 Arabic painting of the Baghdad school, done in 1224 by Abdallah ibn al Fadl

294 Cauterization of leprosy lesions, after the Turkish translation of a Persian treatise on surgery (*Imperial Surgery*)

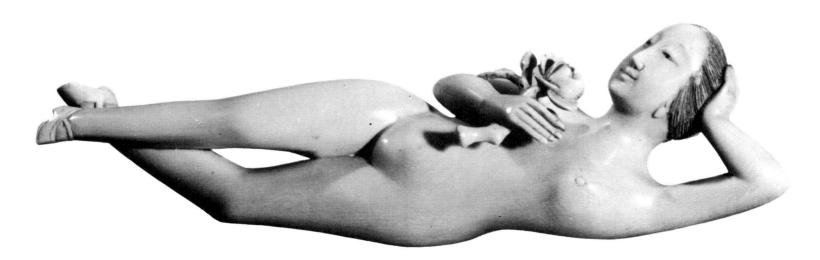

Index

A

Abe no Masanawo	289
Abnormality	201
Absinth, Edgar Degas	*232*, 241
Achilles	46
Achilles Bandaging Patroclos	*42*
Acupuncture	282, 285, 289, 291
Adonis Wounded	**57**
Adulterers, The, Grunewald	155
Aegina and Zeus, Greuze	249
Aesculapius	5, 33, 44, 46, 49, 52, 56, 58,
	61, 62, 65, 74, 84, *102*, 224
Aesculapius and His Daughter Hygeia	*52, 58*
Aesculapius Discovers the Betony Plant	*88*
Aesculapius with Poppies	*61*
Agnew Clinic, Thomas Eakins	10
Agony of King Henry II at the Hôtel des Tournelles	*138*
Ague and Fever, Thomas Rowlandson	208
Akhenaton	34
Albani, Francisco	174
Salmacis and Hermaphrodite	174
Alberti, Leon Battista	111
Albinus, Siegfried	210
Alcmaeon	52
Allegory of the Medical Arts, Holbein	123, *124*
Aloyse	265
The Lady Pope of the Students	*265*
Ambrose, Saint	93
Amenophis I	34
Amenophis IV	34
Amour Médecin, Molière	179
Amulet (*See also* Fetish, Talisman)	19, 20, 21, 22, 30
Amphiarios	50, 62
Amphiarios Treating a Patient	*50*
Amusing Scene	143
Anathomia, Guido of Vigevano	88
Anathomia, Mondino de' Luzzi	108
Anatomical plate, Tibetan painting	*286*
Anatomical plate, Charles Bell	*212*
Anatomical plates, Vesalius	*134*
Anatomy, Titian	*132*
Anatomy Lesson, The, anonymous	101
Anatomy Lesson, De Gheyn	10
Anatomy Lesson, The, Daumier	229, 236
Anatomy Lesson, The, Thomas de Keyser	166
Anatomy Lesson, An, William Hogarth	*205*
Anatomy Lesson, The, John Sloan	10, 263
Anatomy Lesson of Dr. Tulp, Rembrandt	10, 159, *160*
Anatomy lessons	7, 131, 137, 159, 161, 163, 187, 210, 234-235
Anaximander	50
Anaximenes	50
Andrée, Ellen	233, 241
Anemia, Géricault	233
Angelicus, Bartholomaeus	111
Annals of the Late Han Dynasty	292
Anne of Austria	180, 182
Anne of Austria Visiting the Hospital Ward, Bosse	*180*
Annunciation, The, Henry O. Tanner	253
Anschutz, Thomas	10
Anthony, Saint	152, 155, 184
Antonio el Inglés	173
Anubis	**39**
Apollinaire, Guillaume	252, 261

Apollo	58, 84
Apothecary, The, Pietro Longhi	*193,* 198
Archinus	62
Aretaeus	56
Aristotle	55
Arp, Hans	258
Arrieta, Dr.	226
Art of the Insane, The, Marcel Réja	247, 250
Arterial System, The	*191*
Asclepius (*See* Aesculapius)	
Ashurbanipal, Assyrian king	28
Assalini	238
Atlan	264
Audran, Benoît	203
Audran, Gérard	186
Aurelianus, Caelius	65
Autopsy, Hyman Bloom	*259,* 263
Autopsy, Cézanne	241
Autopsy, The, Daumier	*230,* 236
Avicenna	111, 145
Aztec art	68-80

B

Babylonian medicine	28-31
Bacher, Adriaen	164
Bacon, Francis	101, 146, 266
Bad News, Marguerite Gérard	225
Bader, Alfred	264-266
Balbulus, Notker	98
Balzac	219
Baoulé fetish	*24*
Barbola	173
Bary, Marchisedec	179
Basil, Father	84
Bastian, Adolph	16
Baudelaire	128, 231, 240
Baudoin, Pierre-Antoine	198
The Young Mother	*198*
Bayle, Pierre	99
Beccaria, Cesare	189
Beggars of the Brotherhood of Ribaldry, Breughel	45
Bell, Charles	212, 238
Anatomical Plate	*212*
Bellecourt, Veron	229
Bellini, Gentile	96, 119
Examination of the Patient	*119*
Bellini, Giovanni	139
Bellows, George	10, 266
Business Men's Class	*10*
Dance in the Madhouse	*266*
Dempsey and Firpo	*10*
The Drunk	*10*
Benedetto, Alessandro	111
Benevieni, Antonio	111
Berengario da Carpi, Jacopo	137
Berlioz	231
Bernard, Claude	233, 235, 238
Berni, Antonio	266
Bernier, François	178
Bernini, Gianlorenzo	174
The Ecstasy of St. Teresa	*174*
Berruguete, Pedro	152, 153
Bhaishajyaguru	291
Bicker, Andries, portrait of, Bartholomeus van der Helst	167
Biddle, George	10
Bigarelli	155
Birch, William	9
Philadelphia Hospital in Pine Street, Philadelphia	9
Birth (*See* Childbirth)	
Birth of a Child in a Gypsy Camp, The, Jacques Callot 176, *178*	
Birth of Rustam, The, Shah Nameh	*288*
Birth of Tragedy, Nietzsche	246
Blake, William	204, 224, 231
Blancard, Stephen,	187
Bleeding (*See also* Blood-letting)	178, 181, 182
Blind Belisarius Recognized by a Soldier,	
Jacques-Louis David	229
Blind Man	*79*
Blind Men Fording a River, Hokusai	*284*
Blood-letting (*See also* Bleeding) 21, 46, 72, 179, 219, 229-230	
Blood-letting, The, Abraham Bosse	*179*
Bloom, Hyman	259, 263
The Autopsy	*259,* 263
Blooteling, A.	187
Blue Night, Paul Klee	263
Boccaccio	127
Bock, Hans	155
Boileau	178
Boilly, Louis	186, 226, 233
The Patient	226
The Vaccination	227
Bol, Ferdinand	166
Boniface VIII, Pope	146
Bonnard	255
Bonnat	234
Borel, Petrus	231
Bosch, Hieronymus	96, 140, 141, 143, 224, 246
The Ship of Fools	*141,* 143
Bosse, Abraham	179, 180, 182, 229
Anne of Austria Visiting the Hospital Ward	*180*
The Blood-letting	*179*

Bucrotius 187
Buch der Chirurgia, Brunschwig 119
    wood engraving in, *119*
Buddhism 285, 286, 289
Buffet, Bernard 253, 264
Buffon, The, Paul Klee 257
Burckhardt, Jacob 101
Business Agent, The, Jules *250*
Business Men's Class, George Bellows 10
Byron 231

C

Cabanne, Pierre 252
Caesar, Augustus 64
Caesar, Julius 64
Callot, Jacques 174, 176,178, 258
    The Birth of a Child in a Gypsy Camp 176, *178*
    Crippled Beggar *176*
Calvin 124
Canape, Jean 146
Caprices, Goya 224
Caras Sonrientes 71
Caravaggio 159
Carco 255
Card, Laurent 203
Care Given to the Sick *92*
Carolus-Duran 234
Carracci, The 159
Carrying of the Cross, The, Bosch 224
Cassou, Jean 258
Catherine, Saint 186
Cato 64
Cauterization of Leprosy Lesions *294*
César 266
Cézanne 224, 234, 241, 252
    Autopsy 241
Chagall, Marc 263
Chardin, Jean-Baptiste Simeon 192
Charensol, Georges 255
Chariot of Love, The, anonymous artist 149
Charlatan (*See also* Charlatanistic medicine, Quack) 198, 207
Charlatan, The, Cornelis Dusart *163*
Charlatan, The, Miger 197
Charlatan, The, Tiepolo *196*
Charlatan Oculist, The, Mitsunaga or Yoshimitsu 277
Charlatanistic medicine (*See also* Charlatan, Quack) 11
Charles V 224
Charles VIII 149
Charles X 229
Charles Giving Communion to the Sick Struck
    by the Plague, Charles Lebrun 186
Charles, Philarète 231
Chayssac, Gaston 264
Chenier, André 192
Cheops, Pharaoh 33
Cheselden, William 210
Childbirth 21, 71-72, 76, 77, 78, 87, 121, 152, 182, 255, 264, 278, 288, 292
Childbirth *87*
Childbirth, Japanese painting *278*
Children Care, Joseph Hirsch 263

Botticelli 258
Boucher, François 192, 202, 203
    Illustration for the "Imaginary Invalid" *202*
Bouguereau 234
Bouilland 217
Bourgery, Jean-Baptiste Marc 238
Boyen, Gabriel François 201
    Plague of the Epileptics 201
Branles des Fous, Daniel Stoffer 155
Breton, André 246, 264
Broken Pitcher, The Greuze 194
Broussais 229, 230
Brouwer, Adriaen 172
    Surgeon 172
Brueghel, Pieter 5, 140, 143, 144, 148, 176, 246, 258, 284
    Beggars of the Brotherhood of Ribaldry 145
    Parable of the Blind 5, 145, *148*, 284
Brunschwig, Hieronymus 118, 119
    Buch der Chirurgia 119

Chimères, Nerval	246
China	269-285
Chiron	58
Christ (*See also* Jesus)	74, 84, 93, 154, 168, 186, 264
Christ Curing the Blind, Tiepolo	201
Christ Curing the Blind at Jericho, Poussin	186
Christ Curing the Dropsical Man, Charles Vignon	186
Christ of St. John of the Cross, The, Dali	262
Cibolontun	74
Cicero	127
Cimabue	99
Circumcision	41, 152
Civil War	10
Classicism	226-231
Cloquet, Jules	238
Clubfoot, The, Goya	226
Clubfoot, The, Jose Ribera	173, *175*
Cochin, Charles Nicolas	210
Cocteau, Jean	247-248, 250, 265
Code of Hammurabi	28, *29*
Codex Magliabecchiani	*74, 75*
Collection of Methods of the Daido Era	289
Colombo, Realdo	137
Commentary of Apollonius	60
Company of Undertakers, The, Hogarth	208
Confucius	269
Constable, John	204
Constantine of Africa	87
Consultation, The, Delacroix	223, 233
Consultation, The, Gerrits von Brekelenkam	297
Consumption, Gout, and Colic Cured by Punch, Gillray	238
Consumptive, A, Paul Klee	263
Controlled Medicine, William C. Palmer	11
Copernicus	124, 158
Cornil's Experiments on the Consumptives in the Laennec Hospital	236
Corot	233
Corpus Hippocraticum	53, 54. 56, 111
Cortés, Hernan	67
Cosmas, Saint (*See also* Saint Cosmas)	84, 85, 92, 109, 127
Count Sassetti and His Grandson, Ghirlandaio	*112*
Country Doctor, A. R. Waud	*9*
Country Wife, The, Greuze	194
Coup de Lance, Rubens	168
Courbet	233
Cowper, William	210
Coypel, Antoine	194
Esther in the Presence of Ahasuerus	194
Cripple, The, Raphael	*146*
Crippled Beggar, Jacques Callot	*176*
Cromatius	149
Cruikshank, George	238
Indigestion	238
Currado, Domenico, (*See Ghirlandaio*)	
Custod, Dominique	155
Cyrus	30

D

D'Agoty, Jacques Fabien Gautier	210
D'Agrate, Marco	137
D'Albe, Bacler	222
Françoise	222, 236

Dalecluze	228
Dali, Salvador	250, 261-262
The Christ of St. John of the Cross	262
Dream	262
The Last Supper	262
The Three Sphinxes of Bikini	262
Damian, Saint (*See also* Cosmas, Saint Cosmas, Saint Damian)	84, 85, 92, 109, 120, 127
Dance in the Madhouse, Bellows	*266*
Dance in the Mad House, Goya	5, 10, *217*, 224
D'Angers, Pierre-Jean David	219, 230
Pain	219
Dante	102, 127
Daquin	178
Darwin	215
Origin of the Species	215
Da Silva, Vieira	264

Daumier, Honoré   229, 230, 236, 241, 264
   The Anatomy Lesson   229, 236
   The Autopsy   230, 236
   Doctor and Nurse   236
   Imaginary Invalid   300
   Paris Has a Cold   236
David, Gérard   130, 137, 143, 144
   The Flaying of the Corrupt Judge   144
David, Jacques Louis   5, 192, 201, 218, 219, 229, 238
   Blind Belisarius Recognized by a Soldier 229
   The Death of Marat   192, 194
   Episode from an Epidemic   218
   Pain   5
   Study of head   219
David, Joris   139
De Alvarado, Pedro   67
Death, Ligier Richier   142
Death of Marat, The, David   192, 194
Death of a Miner, Ben Shahn   10-11
De Boulogne, Madeleine   182
   Sisters of the Hôtel-Dieu Feeding the Patients, The 182
De Bray, Jan   159
De Châlons, René   137, 142
De Champaigne, Philippe   181, 183
   The Sick Child   181
De Chauliac, Guy   90, 92, 98
   Two miniatures from *Grande Chirurgie* 98
De Chirico, Giorgio   261
De Cuba, Joannes   106
   Hortus Sanitatis   106, 108, 113
De Dinant, Gilles   96
   The Plague in Tournai   96
De Garangeot, Croissant   210
Dégas, Edgar   233, 234, 241, 252
   Absinth   232, 241

De Joncières, Louis   253
   The Doctor's Visit   253
De Ketham, Johannes   139
De Keyser, Thomas   163, 166
   The Anatomy Lesson   166
Delacroix   223, 231, 233, 234
   The Consultation   223, 233
   Tasso in the Madhouse   233
De la Fresnaye, Roger   254
   The Sick Man   254
De Lairesse, Gerard   187
De Larmessin, Nicolas   176
De la Tour, Georges   183, 186
   Joueur de Vieille Aveugle   183
   The Wounded Saint Sebastien   186
De Launay Nicolas   210
De Lavallée, Etienne   210
Delivery Room, Rembrandt   164
Della Croce, Giovanni Andrea   139 - 140
Della Robbia, Andrea   130
Della Robbia, Giovanni   115
   Examination of the Sick   115
Delorme, Charles   183
Del Rincon, Fernando   127
Del Sarto, Andrea   155
   San Matteo Hospital   145
De' Luzzi, Mondino   108, 137
   Anathomia   108, 137
De' Medici, Cosimo   128
De' Medici, Lorenzo   155
De Médicis, Marie   158
De Méricourt, Théroigne   240
Democritus   54, 55
De Morra, Sebastiano   173
   Portrait of, Velasquez   174
Dempsey and Firpo, George Bellows   10
De Muralto, Jean   187
Dentistry (See also Tooth-puller)   83, 146, 147, 198
Depression, United States   10, 11
Derain   255
Desbordes, Constant   233
Desboutin, Marcellin   233, 241
De Serre, François   215
Deslandres, Yvonne   258
D'Estouteville, Cardinal   125
De Troy, Jean François   201
Deutsch, Nicolas Manuel   129, 149
   Ex-voto detail by   129
De Witte, Gaspard   186
Di Bartolo, Domenico   103, 105, 108
Di Cione, Andrea (See Orcagna)
Dickens, Charles   218
Diderot   189, 194, 223, 249
Die Bruecke   255
Diepgen, Paul   16
Diocles of Carystus   55
Disasters of War, Goya   224
Dissection Experiment, Le Clerc   194
Dissection of a Corpse, Michelangelo   133
Dissection of Matsugoro, Toguda   281
Divinity with Plumed Headpiece   76
Doctor, Paul Klee   263
Doctor and Nurse, Daumier   236
Doctor and Sick Child   79
Doctor Curing a Phantasy, The, Mathias Greuter   181

Doctor Deyman's Anatomy Lesson, Rembrandt *161*, 163
Doctor So-Much-the-Worse and Doctor So-Much-the-Better,
   Jean-Baptiste Oudry *195*
Doctor Treating a Patient 77
Doctor Tulp's Anatomy Lesson, Rembrandt 10, 159, *160*
Doctor's Visit, The, Louis de Joncières 253
Doctor's Visit, The, Rowlandson 238
Donatello 128
D'Orvieto, Ferrante 197
Dou, Gérard 5, 157, 164
   The Dropsical Woman 5, *156*, 164
Draft Board, The, George Grosz 256
Dream, Dali 262
Dream, The, Louis Lacombe 253
Droll Pieter (See Pieter Brueghel)
Dropsical Woman, The, Gerard Dou 5, *156*, 164
Drouais, François Hubert 191
Droyn, Jean 149
Drunk, The, George Bellows 10
Dubucet 264
Dubuffet, Jean 253, 264, 267
Duchamp, Marcel 252, 258, 259
   Nude Descending a Staircase 259
Dufresne, Charles 250
   Medicine 251
Dufy, Raoul 248, 255
   The Operation *248*, 255
Duke of Orleans Visiting the Cholera Victims, The,
   Tony Johannot *228*, 233
Dupuytren 229, 238
Dürer, Albrecht 125, 127, 128, 130, 132-133, 250
   Martyrdom of St. Catherine 250
   Melancholy *127*
   Self-Portrait *125*
   Thinness and Obesity *128*
Dusart, Cornelis 163, 172, 181
   The Charlatan *163*
Dwarf 39, 40, 45, 140, 173, 198, 201, 241
Dwarf, The, Paul Klee 263
Dwarf Khnoumhotep, The *39*
"Dying Bacchante" *51*

E

Eakins, Thomas 10, 235, 236, 253
   Gross Clinic 10, 11, 235, *236*
   Agnew Clinic 10
Eastman, Seth 9
   Medicine Man 9
Ecstasy of St. Teresa, Bernini 174
Edelfelt, Albert 235
   Pasteur in his Laboratory *235*
Egyptian art and medicine 33-41
Eight, The 10, 11, 263
Einstein, Albert 250
Eliade, Mircea 263
Eluard, Paul 246
Emetic, The, Gillray 238
Empedocles 52
Empress Eugenie's Visit to the Cholera Patients 236
Enema 20, 21, 24, 139, 140, 166,
   182, 199, 202, 203, 204,
   211, 213, 233, 236
Ensor, James 255

Erasistratus 55, 108
Erasmus 124
Ernst, Max 250, 261
  A Week of Goodness 261
Esquirol 217, 240
Esther in the Presence of Ahasuerus, Coypel 194
Estienne, Charles 137
Everything as a Precaution, Guerard 181
Evils of Drunkenness, The, Hogarth 206
Examination at the Medical Faculty of the University
  of Paris, Toulouse-Lautrec 242
Examination of the Sick, Giovanni della Robbia 115

F

Fabre, François 241
Fagon 178, 182
Faivre, Abel 267
Faker (See also Charlatan) 11
Falca, Pietro 198
Fallopius 128
Faure, Élie 123
Faust II, Johann Wolfgang von Goethe 30
Fautrier 264
Fauvet, Jean 158
Fecundity, Jordaens 169
Federal Art Project 11
Felix, Cassius 65
Fetish 17, 19, 20, 21, 22
  for amulet 22
  baoulé 24

Firdusi 288
Flayed Man, Jean-Antoine Houdon 208
Flayed Ox, Soutine 249
Flaying of the Corrupt Judge, The, Gerard David 144
Flaying of the Unjust Judge, Luca Signorelli 137
Flemish school 168-172
Fleury, Robert 235
Flinck, Govaert 166
Forain, Jean-Louis 266
Forneret, Xavier 231
Four Stages of Cruelty, Hogarth 204, 205, 208
Fra Angelico 109
  Saint Palladius 109
Fracastoro, Girolamo 149, 184
Fragonard, Honoré 192, 203
  The Remedy 199, 203
Francastel, Pierre 252
Francis I 149
Françoise, Bacler d'Albe 222, 236
Frankfurt, Master of 111
  Saint Roch 111
Frederick II 90
Freud, Sigmund 246, 250, 262
  The Science of Dreams 250
Frieze of Life, The, Munch 257
Fruits of Secret Love, François Voyez 194
Fu-Hsi 269
Fujikawa 291
Functions of a Hospital, William Palmer 11
Funeral Stele of a Woman Doctor 82

G

Gachet, Dr. 240
  Portrait of, 240
  Charcoal portrait of Van Gogh 240
Gaetano, Pedro 183, 185
  The Plague 183
Galen 52, 53, 54, 55, 56, 58, 81,
  94, 108, 111, 128, 145, 158
  Hippocrates and, 89
Galle, Jean 149, 152
  Preparing and Taking a Remedy against
  Venereal Disease 152
Gamelin, Jacques 197, 209, 210
  "Pray not be be led into temptation" 209
Gathering sage, miniature 116
Gauguin, Paul 252
Gautherot, Claude 221
  Napoleon Wounded at Ratisbon 221
Gautier, M. 210
Gavarni, Paul 229, 236
  Scene from student life 229
Genre painting 192-199
Geoffroy, Jean 235-236
  Visiting Day in the Hospital 235
Gérard, Baron 228, 230
  La Pasta 230
Gérard, Marguerite 225
  Bad News 225
Gerhardt, Nicholas 155
Géricault 215, 233
  Anemia 233

The Mad Child-Snatcher	*233*
The Madwoman	*214*
Raft of the Medusa	*233*
Tasso in the Madhouse	*233*
Gérôme	10
Gersaint	222
Gervex	235
Ghirlandaio	102, 113
Portrait of Count Sassetti and his Grandson	*112*
Ghisi, Giorgio	149
Venus Wounded by Thorns	*149*
Ghost of Hunger, The, Paul Klee	*263*
Gillray	238
The Emetic	*238*
Consumption, Gout, and Colic Cured by Punch	*238*
The Purge	*238*
"Gin Lane", Hogarth	206
Giotto	90, 99, 128
Giuochi, Giuliano (*See* Pesellino)	
Giuteotl	72
Glass of Absinth, The, Picasso	*258*
Goethe, Johann Wolfgang von	30, 258
Goltzius, Hendrik	147, 150-151
The Physician is a God	*150*
The Physician is a Man	*150*
The Physician is a Devil	*151*
The Physician is an Angel	*151*
Good Samaritan, The	*80*
Gorgiullo	184
Gosse	233
Gourmelon, Etienne	146
Goya, Francisco de	5, 10, 147, 154, 176, 210, 216, 223, 224, 226, 238, 258
Caprices	*224*
The Carrying of the Cross	*224*
The Clubfoot	*226*
Disasters of War	*224*
The Hunt for Teeth	*226*
The Insane Asylum	*5, 10, 217, 224*
The Old Woman	*224*
The Pilgrimage to San Isidro	*224*
Portrait of Goya Sick	*216*
Gravelot, Henry	210
Greet art and medicine	43-66
Greuter, Mathias	181
The Doctor Curing a Phantasy	*181*
Greuze, Jean Baptiste	192, 194, 197, 223, 224, 233, 246, 249
Aegina and Zeus	*249*
The Broken Pitcher	*194*
The Country Wife	*194*
The Paralytic Visited by a Charitable Lady	*197*
Paternal Curse	*194*
The Young Girl and the Dead Bird	*194*
Gros, Antoine	220
The Plague Victims of Jaffa	*220*
Gros, Baron	228
Napoleon on the Battlefield of Eylan	*228*
Gross Clinic, The, Thomas Eakins	10, 11, 235, *236*
Gross, Samuel D.	236
Grosz, George	256, 267
The Draft Board	*256*
Grünewald, Matthias,	147, 155
The Adulterers	*155*
A Man Stricken with "St. Anthony's Fire"	*147*

Grunpeck	149
Tractatus de Scorra	*149*
Guardi, Francisco	191
Gudea of Lagash	26, 28, 62
cup of,	*26, 28*
Guerard	181
Everything as a Precaution	*181*
Guercino	174
Guérin	228
Guernica, Picasso	*258*
Guidi, Guido	138
Guido of Vigevano	88, 94
Anathomia	*88, 94*
Guizot	218
Gunther, Johannes	133
Guys, Constantin	234, 235
The Hospital of Pera	*234*

H

Hals, Frans	164, 222
Malle Bobbe	*164*
Halsted, William Steward	235
Hamann, Johann Georg	13
Hammurabi	28, 29
Harlot's Progress, A, Hogarth	204
Hartung	253
Harvey, Gideon	183
Harvey, William	158, 178
Hauptmann, Gerhard	13
Healer Praising His Wares, A, Van Ostade	*164*
Heckel	255

Heijo, Emperor 289
Heimbach, Wolfgang 184
    The Sick Man *184*
Heister, Lorenz 210
Hemorrhaging 82
Henri IV 181
Henry II 152
Heraclitus 51-52
Herbarium, Illustrated, Utsumu Rankei *273*
Hernandez, Miguel *264*
Herodotus 31, 36
Herophilus 55, 108
Hersant 233
    The Remedy *233*
Herwarth Walden, Oscar Kokoschka *253*
Hesiodus 58
Hippocrates 45, *48*, 53, 54, 55, *56*, 58, 89, 96, *97*, 125, 210
"Hippocratic Oath" 53, 271
Hirsch, Joseph 11, *263*
    Children Care *263*

Hoffmann, Friedrich 191
Hogarth, William 7, 182, 204, 206, 207, 208, 236
    Anatomy Lesson, or *The Reward of Cruelty* *205*
    The Company of Undertakers *208*
    Four Stages of Cruelty 204, *205*, 208
    "Gin Lane" or *The Evils of Drunkenness* *206*
    A Harlot's Progress 204
    Marriage-à-la Mode 204
    A Rake's Progress 204
    Visit to a Charlatan *207*
    Visit to the Doctor 204
Hokusai 284
    Blind Men Fording a River *284*
Holbein, Hans 123, 140
    Allegory of the Medical Arts 123, *124*
Homer, Winslow 9-10
    Playing Old Soldier *10*
    Sick Children 10
    Surgeon at Work During an Engagement 10
    Surgeon's Story 10
Hortus Sanitatis, Joannes de Cuba *106, 108,* 113
Hospital of Pera, The, Constantin Guys *234*
Hospital Ward, The, Lucien Simon *253*
Hôtel-Dieu Sick Ward *114*
Houdon, Jean-Antoine 208
    Flayed Man *208*
Huff, Elizabeth 291
Hua T'o 292, 295
Hua T'o Operating on General Kuan Kong, Kuniyoshi *280*
Huang Ti 269
Huet, G. 204
Hugo, Victor 217, 218, 231
Huguet 127
Hume, David 189
Hunchback *37, 71,* 75, *78,* 283
Hunefer 37, *38*
Hunter, John 191
Hygeia, daughter of Aesculapius 52, 58, 62, 65, 84
    Aesculapius and, *52, 58*
Hypochondriac, Thomas Rowlandson 210, *211*

I

Ibsen 246
Idzumo no Hirosada 289
Ill-Smelling Eye, The, Picabia *261*
Illumination *80,* 81, *86, 87, 90, 91, 94, 95, 98, 113, 116, 118, 119, 121, 272, 273, 274*
Illustrated medical books 187, 210, 238, 241
Imaginary Invalid, The, Daumier *300*
Imaginary Invalid, The, Molière 202, 203
    illustration for, Boucher *202*
Imhotep 33, *34,* 37
Impatience of the Sick Man, The *103*
Incan art 68-80
Indigestion, George Cruikshank 238
Indra, high relief in wood *291*
Infantile Eruption, Chinese silk painting *268*
Ingres, J. A. D. 223, 229, 231
    Stratonice, or *The Illness of Antiochus* 229
Injured Man, The, Gaspare Traversi *188*

Inoculation, or *The Triumph of Vaccine,* anonymous 201
Insane Asylum, Goya 5, *217,* 224
Insufflation *24*
Interior, Vuillard 255
Intestinal Suture, in Brunschwig's *Die ist das Buch der Chiurgia* *118*
Isabella del Porcel de Cobos 224
Ishinho, Yasuyori Tamba 289-291
Ixchel 74

J

Jackson 233
Japan 285-291
Japyx and Aeneas *59, 65*
Jarry, Alfred 250
Jason 52, *55*
Jeaurat, Etienne 197
   The Quack 197
   The Orvietan Merchant 197
Jefferson Medical College 10
Jenner, Edward 201
Jesuits 189
Jesus (*See also* Christ) 84, 152, 154, 155, 186
Johannot 233
   The Duke of Orleans Visiting the Cholera Victims *228,* 233
John, Saint 154
Jordaens, Jacob 169, 172
   Fecundity 169
   Peasant and the Satyr 169
   Saint Martin Healing the Possessed 169
   The Sisters of Charity of Antwerp *172*
Josaphat *95*
Joueur de Vielle Aveugle, Georges de la Tour 183
Joulain, Francois 202
Jourdain, Francis 257
Jouve, Pierre-Jean 246
Jules 250
   The Business Agent *250*
Julius II, Pope 124
Jung 262

K

Kada 292
Kafka 266
Kandinsky, Wassily 250, 263
Kant 189
Kelly, Howard Attwood 235
Khajuraho, statue from *287*
Khnoumhotep *39*
Kimnei, Emperor 286
Kirchner, Ernst Ludwig 255, 257
Klee, Paul 257, 261, 263, 264
   Blue Night 263
   The Buffon 257
   A Consumptive 263
   Doctor 263
   The Dwarf 263

   The Ghost of Hunger 263
   The Loved One 263
Knight-Errant, The, Kokoschka 257
Kokoschka, Oscar 255, 257
   The Knight-Errant 257
Ko-otsu-kiyo, Huang-fu Mi 289
Korea 285-291
Kung, Kuan 292
Kuniyoshi 280
   Hua T'o Operating on General Kuan Kong *280*

L

Lacombe, Louis 253
   The Dream 253-254
Lady Pope of the Students, The, Aloyse *265*
Laennec 217
Lagniet, Jacques 181-182
Lamarck 215
La Pasta, Gerard 230
Larrey 238

321

Las Meninas, Velásquez   5, 173
Last Communion of St. Francis, Rubens   169
Last Supper, The, Dali   262
Laurens, André   187
Lavreince, Nicolas   199
    The Unseasonable Arrival   199
Lebenstein   266
Lebrun, Charles   186
    The Plague of Aegina   186
    Charles Giving Communion to the Sick Struck
    by the Plague   186
Le Clerc, Sébastien   194
    Dissection Experiment   194
Leczinski, Stanislas   201
Leeuwenhoek   157
Léger   252
Leibniz, Gottfried Wilhelm   189, 191
Leleu, Dominique   203
    The Sick Child   203
Lombardo, Tullio   152
Leonardo da Vinci   5, 123, 124, 125, 131, 132,
          133, 146, 155, 250
    Depiction of the Legs   122
    drawing of a fetus   155
    Mona Lisa (study)   130
    St. Anne   250
    study of muscles   131
Leprosy   95, 159, 294

Les Demoiselles D'Avignon, Picasso   250
Lessing, Ferdinand D.   291
Leucippus   51
Levine, Jack   10, 11
    Medicine Show   11
Levy-Bruhl, Lucien   17
Liénard   176
Lister, Joseph   233
Locke, John   189
Longhi, Pietro   190, 192, 198
    The Apothecary   193, 198
    The Tooth-puller   190
Louis IX   140
Louis XII   140
Louis XIII   158, 178, 179, 183
Louis XIV   174, 178, 179
Louis XV   191
Louis XVI   181
Loved One, The, Paul Klee   263
Loyola, Ignatius   124
Luther, Martin   124

M

Mad Child-Snatcher, The, Géricault   233
Madwoman, The, Géricault   214
Makomad of Hairiri Neshki, The   293
Malevitch, Kasimir   252, 263
Malgaigne   238
Malle, Bobbe, Frans Hals   164
Malpighi, Marcello   158
Malraux, André   246, 247, 249
Man with the Hoe, Millet   234
Manet   234, 241, 252
Mantegna   159
Mapp, M. Sally   208
Marey   233
Marie-Amélie, Queen   233
Marin, John   263
Marquet   255
Marriage-à-la-Mode, William Hogarth   204
Martial   204
Martin, Guillaume   210
Martyrdom of St. Catherine, Dürer   250
Mascagni   238
Mask of Nanahuatzin, The   73
Massys, Quentin   152, 153
Maternal Idol   68
Matisse   255
Matsugoro   281
Matta   262
Matthieu, Georges   264
Mauvilain   176
Maximilian   149
Mayan art   68-80
Medici (*See* De' Medici)
Medicine, Charles Dufresne   251
Medicine Maker, The, Andrea Pisano   105
Medicine man (*See also* Charlatan, Quack)   19, 20, 21
Medicine Man Curing a Patient, Seth Eastmen   9
Medicine Show, Jack Levine   11
Mei-do-kiyo   289
Melampus   62

Melancholy, Albrecht Dürer   127
Memling, Hans   143
Menelaus   45
Methodicalists   56
Metsu, Gabriel   163
    The Sick Child   *162,* 164
Metsys, Quentin   137
    Doctor Paracelsus   *137*
Meynier   228
Mi, Huang-Fu   289
    Ko-otsu-kiyo   289
Michaux, Henri   258
Michelangelo   124, 125, 132, 133, 159, 224
    Dissection of a Corpse   *133*
Michelet, Jules   99
Mictlantecuhtli   71
Middle Ages, art of   81-98
Miger, Simon Charles   197
    The Charlatan   197
Mignard, Nicolas   185
Military Surgeon and his Assistant, woodcut   *153*
Miller, Henry   256, 264, 267
Millet   234
    Man with the Hoe   234
Miracles   183-186, 201
Miró, Joan   261
Misaubin, Doctor   203
Mitsunaga, Tosa   277, 283
    The Hunchback   *283*
    Untitled painting, attributed to   *282*
Miya-ku-kiyo, Wang Shu-ho   289
Modigliani, Amedeo   257-258
Molière   174, 176, 178, 179, 202, 203, 236
    illustration for *The Imaginary Invalid,* Boucher   *202*
Mona Lisa, Leonardo da Vinci   130, 246
    study for   *130*
Mondrian, Piet   252, 263
Monet   5, 234, 241, 252
Monnet, Charles   210
Montagne, Michel de la   199
Moreau, Hégésippe   230
Moro, Antonis   140
Mother and Child   *35*
Mother Nursing Her Child   *28*
Moxibustion   282, 285
Mueller   255
Müller, Fritz   215
Munch, Edvard   255
    The Frieze of Life   257
    Portrait of the Painter with Cigarette   255
    The Next Morning   257
    The Sick Child   *249,* 255
    The Sick Girl   255
Muntaner, Gregory   90
    The Vision of Daniel   *90*
Murer, Christoph   138
Murillo, Bartolomé Estéban   173
Musa, Antonius   64, 65

N

Napoleon   218, 220, 221, 226, 228, 229
Napoleon on the Battlefield of Eylau, Gros   228
Napoleon Wounded at Ratisbon, Gautherot   *221*

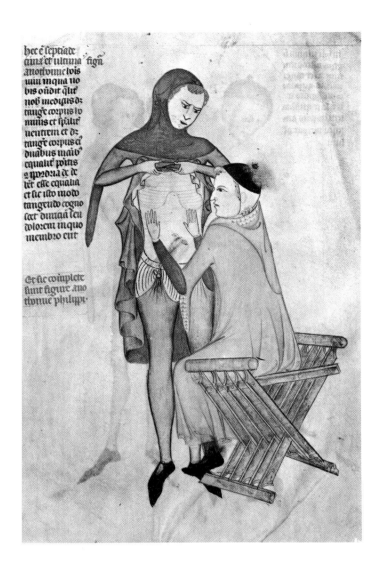

Nattier, Jean Marc   192
Nebamon, Doctor   *36, 37*
Nefertiti   34
Nerval   246
    Chimères   246
Next Morning, The, Munch   257
Nicholas of Cusa   102
Nietzsche   246
    Birth of Tragedy   246
Nolde, Emil   255, 257
Nude Descending a Staircase, Marcel Duchamp   259
Nurioda, Nasotsu   286
Nursing   *28,* 29

O

Odyssey, The   36
Ogé   267
Old Woman, The, Goya   224
Onamuchi   289
Operation, The, Raoul Dufy   *248,* 255
Operation for Cataract, Rembrandt   164

Oppenheimer	246
Orcagna	98
Origin of the Species, Darwin	215
Orvietan Merchant, The, Jeaurat	197
Osler, William	235
Ossian	231
Otto III, gospel book of	*80*
Oudry, Jean-Baptiste	195
Dr. So-Much-the-Worse and Dr. So-Much-the-Better	*195*

P

Paaw, Pieter	187
Paeon	58
Pain, David	5
Pain, Pierre-Jean David D'Anger	219
Palmer, William C.	11
Controlled Medicine	11
Functions of a Hospital	11
Panakeia	84
Parable of the Blind, Brueghel	5, 145, *148*, 284
Paracelsus	124, 125, 145, 146, 154
portrait of, by Quentin Metsys	*137*
Paralytic Visited by a Charitable Lady, The, Greuze	197
Paré, Ambrose	124, 125, 138, 145, 146, 154, 158, 187
Parival	166
Paris Has a Cold, Daumier	236
Parmenides	55
Pascal	6
Passarotti, Bartolomeo	137
Pasteur, Louis	215, 217, 233, 235
Pasteur in his Laboratory, Albert Edelfelt	235
Paternal Curse, Greuze	194
Patient Pursued by Apothecaries, Watteau	*200*

Patin, Guy	178, 179
Patroclos	42, 45, 46
Paul, Hermann	267
Peasant and the Satyr, Jordaens	169
Pechstein	255
Penrose	258
Permeke	255
Pesellino, Francesco	117, 127
Saints Cosmas and Damian	*117*
Petrarch	102, 127
Peytal Aryballos, The	*45*
Phèdre, Racine	246
Philadelphia Hospital in Pine Street, Birch	9
Philatros (*See* Jean Canape)	
Phillip II	133
Phillip IV	173
Philistines Stricken with the Plague, The, Poussin	*177*
Philoctetes at Lemnos	*47*
Philosophie Zoologique, Lamarck	215
Phrygian Plague, The, Raphael	152
Physician Examining a Patient	*94*
Physician is a God, The, Hendrik Goltzius	*150*
Physician is a Man, The, Hendrik Goltzius	*150*
Physician is a Devil, The, Hendrik Goltzius	*151*
Physician is an Angel, The, Hendrik Goltzius	*151*
Picabia	258-259, 261
The Ill-Smelling Eye	*261*
Picasso	250, 258
The Glass of Absinth	258
Guernica	258
Les Demoiselles d'Avignon	250
The Sick Child	260
Pilgrimage to San Isidro, The	224
Pilon, Germain	155
The Putrified Body	155
Pinel	217, 235, 240
Pisano, Andrea	90, 105
The Medicine Maker	*105*
Pisano, Nicola	127
Pissarro	252
Pizarro	68
Plague	83, 94, 96, 149, 152, 174, 181, 182, 183-186, 199, 201, 218, 219, 220, 228, 231
Plague, The, Pedro Gaetano	*183*
Plague in Marseilles, The, Pierre Puget	*182*
Plague in Tournai, Gilles de Dinant	*96*
Plague of Aegina, The, Charles Lebrun	186
Plague of the Epileptics, Boyen	201
Plague Victims of Jaffa, The, Gros	220
Plato	55
Playing Old Soldier, Winslow Hommer	*10*
Pollock, Jackson	263-264
Polybius	27
Portable Pharmacy	*139*
Portrait of the Painter with Cigarettes, Munch	255
Pouchet	217
Poussin, Nicolas	177, 185, 186
Christ Curing the Blind at Jericho	186
The Philistines Stricken with the Plague	*177*
"Pray not to be led into Temptation", Gamelin	*209*
Pregnancy (*See also* Childbirth)	20, 41, 68, 154, 236
Prehistoric art	13-26
Primaticcio, Francesco	127, *143*
Professor Gosset Operating, Vuillard	247, 255
Professor Tulp's Anatomy Lesson, Rembrandt	10, 159, *160*

Protagoras   51
Prud'hon   224
Psychiatric Ward, Robert Riggs   263
Psychology   240, 246, 250
Psychostasia   38
Ptah   33
Puget, Pierre   182, 185
    The Plague in Marseilles   182
Purge, The, Gillray   238
Putrified Body, The, Germain Pilon   155
Pythagoras   50, 51

Q

Quack (*See also* Charlatan, Medicine Man)
            75, 143, 146, 172, 179-180, 197, 199, 204, 208
Quack, The, Jeaurat   197
Quart Livre, Rabelais   146
Quetzalcoatl   69

R

Rabelais   124, 125, 146
    Quart Livre   146
Rabelais, Anatomist et Physiologiste, De Bouble   146
Racine   246
    Phèdre   246
Raft of the Medusa, Géricault   233
Ragon, Michel   263, 266
Rake's Progress, A, William Hogarth   204
Ramses II   34
Rankei, Utsumu   273
    Illustrated herbarium   274
Raphael   132, 133, 139, 146, 152, 153, 154, 159
    The Cripple   146
    The Phrygian Plague   152
    Visitation   154
Raulin, Joseph   210
Realism   233-236
Rectal syringe (*See* Enema)
Rédon, Odilon   241
Réja, Marcel   247
    The Art of the Insane   247, 250
Rei-su   289
Rembrandt   5, 10, 158, 159, 160, 161, 163,
                                    164, 166, 168, 224
    Delivery Room   164
    Doctor Deyman's Anatomy Lesson   161, 163
    Operation for Cataract   164
    Professor Tulp's Anatomy Lesson   10, 159, 160
    Saskia   164
    Servant at a Patient's Bedside   159
    A Sick Person Kneeling by a Cavalier in Armor   164
    Woman Ill in Bed   158
Remedies of All Ailments   186
Remedy, The, Jean-Honoré Fragonard   199, 203
Remedy, The, Hersant   233
Renaissance   131-155
Reni, Guido   159
Renoir   5, 234, 241
Reward of Cruelty, The, Hogarth   204, 205, 208
Reynolds   224
Ribera, José de   173, 175
    The Clubfoot   173, 175
Richier, Ligier   137, 142, 154
    Death   142
Riemenschneider, Tillman   152
Riggs, Robert   263
    Psychiatric Ward   263
Riolon, Jean   158
Roch, Saint   83, 111, 149
Roberts, Thomas   235
Roentgen   233
Roesslin, Eucharius   152
Roger II of Sicily   90
Rombouts, Theodor   168, 172
    The Tooth-Puller   168
Roman art and medicine   43-66
Romano, Giulio   139
Romanticism   231-233
Rops, Felicien   267
Rouault, Georges   252, 255, 267
    Portrait of the Artist   252
Rousseau, Jean-Jacques   14, 189
Rowlandson, Thomas   208, 210, 211, 238
    Ague and Fever   208
    The Doctor's Visit   238
    Hypochondriac   210, 211
Rubens, Peter Paul   168, 169, 184, 186
    Coup de Lance   168
    Last Communion of St. Francis   169
    St. Francis Triumphs Over Satan   186
    St. Ignatius Healing the Possessed   169
    St. Martin Healing the Possessed   169

Rüdlinger   257
Ruysch, Fredrick   164
Ryckaert III, David   171
   The Surgeon   *171*

S

Sadahide   *275, 276*
Saint Anne, Leonardo da Vinci   205
Saint Cosmos   *85*
Saint Francis Triumphing Over Satan, Rubens   186
Saint Ignatius Healing the Possessed, Rubens   169
Saint Martin Healing the Possessed, Rubens   169
Saint-Non, Richard   194, 204
   The Sick Woman   *194, 204*
Saint Roch, Master of Frankfurt   111
Saints Cosmas and Damian, Francesco Pesellino   *117*

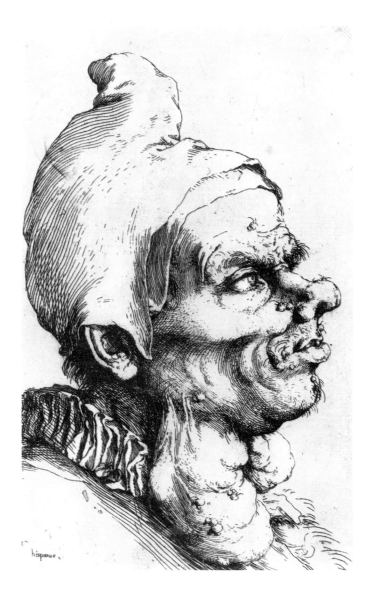

Saints Cosmas and Damian Examining Urine   *120*
Salmacis and Hermaphrodite, Albani   *174*
Sargent, John S.   235, 237
   Medical Faculty of Johns Hopkins   *237*
Saskia, Rembrandt   164
Sauvage, Norbert   201
Schelling, Friedrich Wilhelm   13
Schmidt, Georg   264-265
Schuppach, Michel   199
Schwitters, Kurt   258, 259
Science of Dreams, The, Freud   250
Scotus, Duns   101
Sculet, Jean   187
Sebastian, Saint   149
Secrets of Life, The, Harry Sternberg   267
Self-Portrait with one ear cut off, Van Gogh   *239*
Servant at a Patient's Bedside, Rembrandt   *159*
Sesostris II   34
Sesostris III   34
Set, Prince of Evil   33
Shahn, Ben   10-11
   Death of a Miner   10-11
Shakespeare, William   246
   The Tempest   246
Shen-Nung   269
   picture of, by Todataka   *271*
Shintoism   286, 292
Ship of Fools, The, Bosch   *141, 143*
Sho-hin-kiyo   289
Sigerist, Henry E.   30
Signorelli, Luca   137
   The Flaying of the Unjust Judge   137
Sick Child, The, Philippe de Champaigne   *181*
Sick Child, The, Gabriel Metsu   162, 164
Sick Child, The, Dominique Leleu   *203*
Sick Child, The, Munch   255
Sick Child, The, Picasso   260
Sick Children, Winslow Homer   10
Sick Girl, The, Munch   255
Sick Girl, The, Jan Steen   *165*
Sick Man, The, Roger de la Fresnaye   *254*
Sick Man, The, Wolfgang Heimbach   *184*
Sick Person Kneeling by a Cavalier in Armor, Rembrandt 164
Sick Woman   *65*
Sick Woman, The, Louis Boilly   *226*
Sick Woman, The, Richard Saint-Non   194, *204*
Simon, Lucien   253
   The Hospital Ward   253
Simpson   233
Sisley   252
Sisters of Charity of Antwerp, The, Jordaens   *172*
Sisters of the Hôtel-Dieu Feeding the Patients, The,
   de Boulogne   182
Sloan, John   10, 263
   The Anatomy Lesson   10, 263
Smallpox   201
Smithson, Harriet   231
Socrates   54
So-mon   289
Somrotidas of Megara Hybla   52
Sorcerer rock painting   *18*
Sorcerer of the Grotto of Trois Frères   *15*
Sosias, potter   42, 65
Soulage   253

Soutine, Chaim   245, 249, 255, 267
   Flayed Ox   249
   The Village Idiot   244
Soyer brothers   10
Spieghel   187
Stahl, Georg Ernst   191
Steen, Jan   164, 166, 167
   The Sick Girl   165
Steher, Berth   149
   A Mala Franczos   149
Sternberg, Harry   267
   The Secrets of Life   267
Sthenelos Bandaging Diomedes' Index Finger   53
Stoffer, Daniel   155
   Branle des Fous   155
Stratonice, or The Illness of Antiochus, Ingres   229
Sue, Eugene   218
Sugai   264
Sukonahikona   289
Sultana Commissioning Work from the Odalisques, Van Loo   197
Sumerian medicine   27-28
Surgeon, The   190
Surgeon, Brouwer   172
Surgeon, The, David Ryckaert III   171
Surgeon at Work During an Engagement, Winslow Homer   10
Surgeon's Story, Winslow Homer   10
Surgeon's Wife, The   190
Surgical Operation, Teniers   169
Sutherland   264
Sydenham, Thomas   158
Syphilis   79, 149, 198, 231
Syphilitic Woman with Her Child   79

T

Taboo   21
Tai-so-kiyo   289
Talisman (*See also* Fetish, Amulet)   19, 20
Tamba, Yasuyori   289
   Ishinho   289-291
Tanguy, Yves   261
Tanner, Henry O.   253
   The Annunciation   253
Tao   271, 272, 273, 276, 279
Tardieu, Ambroise   240
Tasso in the Madhouse, Géricault   233
Tattooing   21, 71
Taylor, Chevalier   208
Teilhard de Chardin, Pierre   13
Tempest, The, Shakespeare   246
Teniers the Younger, David   5, 168, 169, 170, 172
   Surgical Operation   169
   Village Doctor   5, 170
Terborch, Gerard   164
Testelin, Louis   140
Thales of Miletus   48
Thinness and Obesity, Albrecht Dürer   128
Thomas, Saint   153
Thot   32, 33
Three Sphinxes of Bikini, The, Dali   262
Thucydides   94
Tibet   291-295

Tiepolo, Giovanni-Battista   191, 196, 198, 201, 224
   The Charlatan   196
   Christ Curing the Blind   201
Tinti, Giovanni Battista   127
Titian   132, 152
Anatomy   132
Tlaelquani   75
Tlaloc   72
Tlazolteotl   66, 72, 74, 78
Tobey   264
Todataka, Okubo   271
   Shen-Nung   271
Toguda   281
   Dissection of Body of Matsugoro   281
Tonatiuh   72
Tooth-extractor (*See also* Dentist, Tooth-puller)   172
Tooth-puller (*See also* Dentist, Tooth-extractor)   181
Tooth-puller, The   154
Tooth-puller, The, Pietro Longhi   190

Tooth-puller, The, Theodor Rombouts 168
Torpor 267
Tortelli, Giovanni 102
Toulouse-Lautrec 241, 242
   Examination at the Medical Faculty of the
     University of Paris 242
   Tracheotomy Operation by Dr. Péan in 1891 ...... 241, 242
Touzé, Jean 197
Tracheotomy Operation by Dr. Péan in 1891,
   Toulouse-Lautrec 241, 242
Trajan's Column 62
Traversi, Gaspare 188, 198
   The Injured Man 188
   The Wounded Man 198
Treatment of a Fracture, in Brunschwig's Dis ist
   das Buch der Chirurgia 118
Trepanation 77, 78-79, 187, 190, 292
Trois Frères Grotto 15, 19
Tulp, Professor (See also Rembrandt) 160, 163
Turner, J. M. W. 204
Tzara, Tristan 258

U

Unseasonable Arrival, The, Nicolas Lavreince 199
Urinalysis (See also Uroscopy) 89-90, 139, 154, 157, 164,
                              166, 170, 199
Urlugaledinna, male midwife, seal of 30
Uroscopy (See also Urinalysis) 105
Utrillo, Maurice 257-258

V

Vaccination, The, Boilly 227
Vallot 178
Van Brekelenkam, Gerrits 297
   The Consultation 297
Van Calcar, Jan Stephan 10, 111, 137
Van der Helst, Bartholomeus 167
   Portrait of Andries Bicker 167
Van der Paele 102
Van Dyck 169
Van Eyck, Jan 102, 110, 253
   Detail from the Madonna of Canon van der Paele ... 110
Van Gogh, Vincent 234, 238, 240, 241, 246, 247
                       249, 252, 255, 259, 266
   Portrait of Dr. Gachet 240
   Self-Portrait with one Ear Cut Off 239
   The Vestibule of the Hospital of Saint-Rémy 238
Van Hemessen, Jan Sanders 143
   Extraction of the "Stone of Madness" 140
Van Loo, Charles Amédée 197
   The Sultana Commissioning Work from the Odalisques 197
Van Neck, Jan 163
Van Orley, Barend 139
   Job's Friends 139
Van Ostade, Adriaen 164, 166, 167, 181
   A Healer Praising His Wares 164
Van Rijn, Rembrandt (See Rembrandt)
Vasari, Giorgio 99, 155
Vauxcelles, Louis 255
Velásquez, Diego 5, 140, 173, 174, 224
   Las Meninas 5, 173
   Portrait of Sebastiano de Morra 174
   Venus of Laussel, The 12, 13, 16
Venus of Sireuil, The 14
Venus of Willendorf, The 16
Venus Wounded by Thorns, Giorgio Vasari 149
Vermeer, Jan 192
Verspronck 222
Vesalius, Andreas 10, 111, 124, 125, 133, 134, 137, 158
   Anatomical plates 134
Vestibule of the Hospital of Saint-Rémy, The, Van Gogh 238
Victory of Samothrace 246
Vignon, Charles 186
   Christ Curing the Dropsical Man 186
Village Doctor, Teniers 5, 170
Vindician 65
Virgil 127
Vision of Daniel, The, Gregory Muntaner 90
Visit to a Charlatan, William Hogarth 207
Visit to the Doctor, The, William Hogarth 204
Visiting Day in the Hospital, Geoffroy 235
Visiting the Sick 100
Vlaminck 249, 255
Voltaire 99, 189
Vomiting Man 93
Von der Straet, Jan 149
Von Gersdorff, Hans 138
Von Hohenheim, Philip (See Paracelsus)
Von Hutten, Ulrich 121
Von Soest, Konrad 103
Voyez, François 194
   Fruits of Secret Love 194

Vuillard, Edouard   247, 255
    Interior   255
    Professor Gosset Operating   247, 255

W

Walberg, Patrick   261
Walsh, E. H. C.   291
Wang Ping   270
Wang Shu-ho   289
Ward, Spot   208
Watteau, Antoine   199, 200, 202, 203, 222, 224
    A Patient Pursued by Apothecaries   200
Waud, A. R.   9
    Country Doctor   *9*
Week of Goodness, A, Max Ernst   261
Weenix, Jan   201
Weiditz, Hans   149
Welch, William Henry   235
Willette, Adolphe   266
William of Ockham   101
Willis, Thomas   90
Wilson, Scottie   264
Witchdoctor's Mask   *21*
Wols, Wolfgang   263
Woman Ill in Bed, Rembrandt   *158*
Wounded Man, The, Gaspare Traversi   198
Wounded Saint Sebastien Tended by Holy Women, The,
    de la Tour   186
World War I   257, 258
World War II   11, 252, 257, 261, 263
World's Three Snares, The, anonymous   182
Wylie, Turrel V.   291

X

Xipetotec   *72*
Xolotl-Nanahuatzin   *72*

Y

Yang   271, 272, 273, 276, 279, 283
Yellow Emperor (*See* Huang Ti)
Yellow Emperor's Classic, The   269-273, 276
Yin   271, 272, 273, 276, 279, 283
Yoshimitsu   277
Young Girl and the Dead Bird, The, Greuze   194
Young Mother, The, Pierre-Antoine Baudoin   198

Z

Zamna   *74*
Zweig, Stefan   235

MVNIFICENTIA. PII. SEXTI. P·M

Acknowledgments

The authors and publishers are grateful for the cooperation given by the staffs of the following museums and libraries:

MUSÉE DU LOUVRE — MUSÉE MUNICIPAL D'ART MODERNE, PARIS — MUSÉE DU JEU DE PAUME, PARIS — MUSÉE DU PETIT PALAIS, PARIS — MUSÉE DE L'HOMME, PARIS — MUSÉE CONDÉ, CHANTILLY — MUSÉE DE VERSAILLES — MUSÉE CARNAVALET, PARIS — MUSÉE DE L'ASSISTANCE PUBLIQUE, PARIS — MUSÉE DES BEAUX-ARTS, MARSEILLE — MUSÉE DES BEAUX-ARTS, BESANÇON — MUSÉE DES BEAUX-ARTS, VALENCIENNES — MUSÉE DE COLMAR — MUSÉE D'ALBI — MUSÉE DE L'ŒUVRE NOTRE-DAME, STRASBOURG — MUSÉE DE METZ — MUSÉE DES BEAUX-ARTS, ANGERS — MUSÉE PRÉHISTORIQUE DES EYZIES, DORDOGNE — MUSÉE CROZATIER, LE PUY-EN-VELAY — THE NATIONAL GALLERY, LONDON — THE BRITISH MUSEUM, LONDON — KUNST-HISTORISCHES MUSEUM, VIENNA — MUSEO NACIONAL DEL PRADO, MADRID — ACADEMIA SAN FERNANDO, MADRID — RIJKSMUSEUM, AMSTERDAM — MAURITSHUIS, THE HAGUE — GALLERIA DEGLI UFFIZI, FLORENCE — MUSEUM OF NAPLES — PINACOTECA DI BRERA, MILAN — VATICAN MUSEUMS — GALLERIE DELL'ACCADEMIA, VENICE — PALAZZO PAPADOPOLI, VENICE — STAATLICHE MUSEUM, BERLIN — MUSEUM FÜR VÖLKERKUNDE, BERLIN — WALLRAF-RICHARTZ MUSEUM, COLOGNE — KUNSTHALLE, BREMEN — KUNSTHALLE, HAMBURG — NATIONAL GALLERY OF ART, WASHINGTON — MUSEUM OF MODERN ART, NEW YORK — WHITNEY MUSEUM, NEW YORK — WADSWORTH ATHENEUM, HARTFORD — PHILADELPHIA MUSEUM — MUSÉE ROYAL, BRUSSELS — MUSÉE DES BEAUX-ARTS, BRUGES — KUNSTMUSEUM, BASEL — NATIONAL ARCHAEO-LOGICAL MUSEUM, ATHENS — ARCHAEOLOGICAL MUSEUM, PIRAEUS — ARCHAEOLOGICAL MUSEUM, ANKARA — CAIRO MUSEUM — MUSEO NACIONAL, MEXICO CITY — PALACE OF RECTORS, DUBROVNIK

as well as:

BIBLIOTHÈQUE NATIONALE, PARIS — BIBLIOTECA MEDICEA LAURENZIANA, FLORENCE — ACADEMY OF MEDECINE, DÜSSELDORF — NATIONALBIBLIOTHEK, VIENNA — ROYAL LIBRARY, WINDSOR CASTLE — OXFORD UNIVERSITY — BIBLIOTHÈQUE DES ARTS DÉCORATIFS, PARIS — L'ÉCOLE DES BEAUX-ARTS, PARIS — BIBLIOTHÈQUE DE LA FACULTÉ DE MÉDECINE DE PARIS — COURTAULD INSTITUTE, LONDON — SAN FRANCISCO MEDICAL CENTER — SERVICES DE DOCUMENTATION ARTISTIQUE DES LABORATOIRES CIBA.

We also wish to thank the following for their welcome assistance:

MAURICE RATTON COLLECTION, PARIS — RASMUSSEN COLLECTION, PARIS — R. W. BLISS COLLECTION, WASHING-TON — LE CORNEUR ROUDILLON COLLECTION, PARIS — "REINE MARGOT" COLLECTION, PARIS — DR. DEBAT COLLECTION, PARIS — SELIGMANN COLLECTION, PARIS — THE COLLECTION OF THE COUNT DU BOURG DE BOZAS — MOINEVILLE COLLECTION, PARIS — ALCIDE BOULANGER COLLECTION — COLLECTION OF JEFFERSON MEDICAL COL-LEGE, PHILADELPHIA — NATHAN CUMMINGS COLLECTION, CHICAGO — JOHNS HOPKINS UNIVERSITY, BALTIMORE — PAUL GACHET COLLECTION — STERLING AND FRANCINE CLARK INSTITUTE OF ART, WILLIAMSTOWN — GOSSET COLLECTION, PARIS — DR. A. BADER — DR. PIERRE VALLERY-RADOT — DR. ALBERT C. SANTY.

ARCHIVES PHOTOGRAPHIQUES
Pages 12, 65, 83, 176, 184, 219, 235 (left).

JOSSE-LALANCE
Pages 14, 35, 36, 37, 39, 40, 45, 68, 69, 90, 94, 97, 98, 99, 103, 106, 107, 108, 112, 114, 116, 117, 118, 119 (above), 121, 121, 124, 128, 132, 134, 135, 136, 138, 141, 143, 153, 154, 156, 163, 164, 175, 177, 185, 186, 190 (the two people), 191, 194, 197, 199, 200, 205, 206, 209, 211, 212, 214, 221, 223, 225, 226, 229, 232, 242, 247, 248, 276.

J. DOMINIQUE LAJOUX
Pages 15, 18.

GIRAUDON
Pages 16, 17, 26, 29, 30, 42, 50, 52, 56, 59, 61, 63, 64, 78, 79, 93, 95, 96, 104, 105, 115, 130, 142, 146, 152, 169, 171, 174, 178, 180, 195, 198, 199 (left), 203, 204, 208, 216, 218, 220, 239, 240 (above), 244, 254, 288.

SMI
Pages 19, 22, 23, 24, 76.

RENÉ PASQUINO
Page 20.

ROGER-VIOLLET
Pages 44, 49, 58, 101, 110, 133, 179, 196, 230, 235, 252, 253, 257, 261.

MAURICE CHUZEVILLE
Page 47.

CIBA
Pages 48, 51, 85, 87, 129, 266.

BRITISH MUSEUM
Pages 55, 91.

MUSEUM OF NAPLES
Pages 57, 148.

BIBLIOTECA MEDICEA LAURENZIANA (FLORENCE)
Page 60.

GISÈLE FREUND
Pages 66, 71, 73.

UNIVERSITY OF DUSSELDORF
Pages 74, 75, 89.

E. IRVING BLOMSTRAND
Page 77.

MUSÉE DE L'HOMME (PARIS)
Page 78.

D. RISCHMANN
Page 79.

MUSÉE DE METZ
Page 82.

NATIONALBIBLIOTHEK, VIENNA
Page 86.

MUSÉE CROZATIER (LE PUY)
Page 92.

CHIESA DI SAN MARTINO (FLORENCE)
Page 100.

SCALA
Page 109.

RHEINISCHES BILDARCHIV
Pages 111, 126.

ALBERT HUCK
Page 113.

PHILADELPHIA MUSEUM
Pages 119, 150, 151, 202, 237, 249.

ROYAL LIBRARY OF WINDSOR
Pages 122, 131.

KUNSTHALLE (BRÊME)
Page 125.

MUSEO DEL PRADO
Page 140.

A. C. L.
Pages 144, 170.

MUSÉE DE COLMAR
Page 147.

BULLOZ
Pages 158, 222, 227, 228.

SCHLOSSMUSEUM WEIMAR
Page 159.

MAURITSHUIS
Pages 160, 165.

RIJKSMUSEUM
Page 161.

FOTOCOMMISSIE
Pages 162, 166.

A. DINGJAM
Page 167.

MUSEO DEL PRADO
Page 168

MUSÉE ROYAL DES BEAUX-ARTS, ANTWERP
Page 172.

MUSÉE DES BEAUX-ARTS, BESANÇON
Page 181.

L. BOREL
Page 182.

GALLERIE DELL'ACCADEMIA, VENICE
Pages 188, 193.

PRINTED BY
AMILCARE PIZZI S.p.A. - MILAN
SEPTEMBER 1967